BRAIN DAMAGE IN CHILDREN

the biological and social aspects

BRAIN DAMAGE IN CHILDREN
the biological and social aspects

edited by
Herbert G. Birch, M.D., Ph.D.

THE WILLIAMS & WILKINS COMPANY

Library of Congress
Catalog Card Number: 64-15243

Fourth Printing

PREFACE

The increasing concern with brain injury in children, as well as the growing controversy concerning the characteristics of children with damaged brains, have for some time indicated that an assessment of the current status of our knowledge and the delineation of new and, hopefully, fruitful lines of inquiry would be of considerable value both to investigators and to clinicians in their efforts to serve this variety of handicapped child and his family. As part of its program for the support of research on the causes and consequences of handicap in children, the Association for the Aid of Crippled Children therefore decided to sponsor a conference on the social and biological problems of childhood brain damage. The present volume is an outgrowth of this conference, which was held at the Children's Hospital of Philadelphia on November 15 and 16, 1962.

In the planning of the conference it was agreed that problems arising from brain damage in children were not the province of any single discipline, and that effective consideration required both multidisciplinary and interdisciplinary interchange. Contributors and discussants were therefore selected from pediatrics, psychiatry, epidemiology, experimental, clinical, and social psychology, neurology, sociology, and biochemistry. The chapters and discussions of the book include presentations from all the disciplines except biochemistry, since, despite the interesting general nature of the biochemical contributions, their contents were insufficiently related to the central theme of the conference.

In preparing the manuscript for publication, it was decided that real advantage attached to summarizing the discussions instead of presenting them verbatim. In preparing these summaries, the editor sought faithfully to reflect both the content and tone of the meeting and resisted the occasionally considerable temptation to extend and interconnect aspects of the discussion. Because the discussions retain their original provocative and open-ended character, it is hoped that the readers of this volume will receive from it at least some of the insight and stimulation that were gained by those who were able to participate in the conference itself.

The conference, in both its formal and informal aspects, made it clear that a vast body of literature exists on brain damage in children and that one problem in interdisciplinary communication stems from the difficulty of identifying this literature. It was therefore decided to append to this volume an annotated bibliography which would introduce the reader to selected aspects of the published literature. We are grateful to Dr. Leonard Diller for having accepted principal responsibility for preparing the bibliography.

Responsibility for the structure of the meeting was assigned to a committee composed of Dr. Herbert G. Birch, Dr. Leon Eisenberg, Dr. Charles Kennedy, and Dr. Stephen A. Richardson. Although the instigation and support of the conference derived from the Association for the Aid of Crippled Children, the Childrens' Hospital of Philadelphia and the Department of Pediatrics and Neurology of the University of Pennsylvania School of Medicine agreed to serve as hosts. Our thanks are due to all of the foregoing organizations and individuals for making possible both the conference and this book.

Herbert G. Birch, M.D., Ph.D.
Albert Einstein College of Medicine

New York, N.Y.
Sept. 20, 1963

CONTENTS

A Selective Bibliography on Brain-damaged Children

BRAIN DAMAGE IN CHILDREN—THE BIOLOGICAL AND SOCIAL ASPECTS

The Problem of "Brain Damage" in Children

HERBERT G. BIRCH, M.D., PH.D.
Albert Einstein College of Medicine

THE EFFECTIVE SOCIAL and educational management of children who have problems in learning and behavior depends largely upon the identification of the underlying pattern of psychological functioning. Such identification makes it possible to anticipate the child's developmental course, to determine the sources for his malfunctioning, and to establish curricular and other educational opportunities which will result in optimal progress. Among the various diagnostic subcategories to which educationally difficult children have been assigned, the diagnosis "brain damage" has come to occupy an increasingly important place. In part the increase in the population designated as "brain damaged" reflects improvements in diagnostic skill. It is probable, too, however, that increasing numbers of children with brain damage are to be found in the general population as one unintended consequence of medical progress.

In view of these considerations it is not surprising that pediatricians, psychologists, educators, other professionals, and parents have become increasingly concerned with the problem of brain damage in children. Awareness has led to efforts directed toward improved accuracy in diagnosis, to increased recognition of the need for longitudinal and follow-up studies as a basis for prognosis, and to both experimental and epidemiologic studies of etiology as the prerequisites for primary prevention. In addition to provoking these inquiries, whose results have immediate practical significance, the concern with the problem of brain damage in children has provided both opportunities and impetus for the study of basic problems in the neurophysiology and the neuropsychology of development.

It must be noted at this point, however, that the *fact* of brain damage in children and the *concept* "the brain-damaged child" are quite different matters. As a *fact,* brain damage refers to any anatomic or physiologic alteration of a pathologic kind present in the nerve tissues of the brain. Obviously the functional consequences of such anatomic or physiologic change are most diverse and may range from an entire lack of discernible functional alteration to complete paralysis, amentia, and death. Thus children with cerebral palsy, hemiplegia, mental deficiency deriving from hydrocephalus, epilepsy as a result of cortical scarring, and those who are normally functioning but who have porencephalic cysts are all individuals who *in fact* have brain damage. The *concept* "the brain-damaged child" does not necessarily apply to all of these children but is, rather, a term that has been used to designate a certain pattern or set of patterns of behavioral disturbance. An understanding of the term and the behavioral patterns that it encompasses requires some historical perspective.

The past 25 years have seen a marked acceleration in the effort to define specific entities of disordered functioning and thus refine the differential diagnosis of children who come to clinical notice because of significant aberrations in developmental or educational course. As a consequence of these efforts, a large body of children previously grossly defined as "defective" has come to be subdivided and categorized as schizophrenic, autistic, culturally deprived, simply retarded, and brain damaged. This last category for classifying aberrantly functioning children was developed by Strauss and Werner,[1] who sought to account for divergent patterns of functioning in a population of mentally defective children by diagnosing extrinsic damage to the nervous system from the background histories of the children. Other children, who could be identified as not having such background history, were categorized as individuals without brain damage. Basing their classification on necessarily incomplete and often fragmentary evidence, they divided defective children into two groups: an *endogenous* group for whom there was no history of perinatal or later childhood nervous system damage and an *exogenous* group for whom a history of such risk of insult was available. Comparison of the cognitive and emotional behaviors of the two groups revealed that, despite considerable overlap, the exogenous group contained a larger proportion than the endogenous group of children who were hyperactive, emotionally labile, perceptually disordered, impulsive, distractible, and abnormally rigid and perseverative. It was to the children with these peculiar patternings of behavioral organization that the term "brain damaged" or "brain injured" came to be applied, and with it came the concept of "the brain-damaged child."

Considerable confusion has resulted from the use of this term, since from its first application until the present two problems have persisted: (1) evidence that children exhibiting the behavioral pattern described do in fact have damage to the brain is poor, and (2) many children with known and independently verified brain damage (*i.e.,* nonbehavioral neurologic or anatomic evidence) do not exhibit the patterns of behavior presumably characteristic of "brain damage." At the risk of provoking a useless semantic storm, it must be noted that attaching the adjective "minimal" to the term "brain damage," as Pasamanick and Knobloch have done,[2] does not increase the descriptive accuracy of the term or add to either its scientific validity or its usefulness. Regardless of any adjectives, we have the overriding obligation to demonstrate, in terms of replicable, valid, and clearly defined criteria, that the multiplicity of aberrant behaviors we now attribute to "minimal brain damage" are, in fact, the result of damage to the brain.

In large part our difficulties derive from the fact that a considerable proportion of the children who now come to our attention have rather subtle disturbances of the nervous system. Many of them do not exhibit the gross motor disturbances and alterations of normal reflex patterns that have classically been correlated with damage to the central nervous system. Instead, they present varied pictures of developmental lag, of behavioral disturbance, of transient or persistent motor awkwardness, of minor perceptual disturbance, of distractibility, of limitation of attention span, of thought disturbance, and of educational and emotional difficulties. There has been a tendency to separate such children from the more classical cases of neurologic injury by a change in nomenclature and to term them "minimally" or "diffusely" brain damaged. Whether or not the damage they may have sustained is minimal, or whether they are brain damaged at all, is entirely presumptive and can be entertained as an etiologic diagnosis only if one *assumes* that, in the absence of reflex changes and of demonstrable motor deficit, behavioral disturbances occurring in association with antecedent difficulty during pregnancy, at delivery, or in infancy must derive from minimal damage to the nervous system. With equal justification, the damage (if damage there is) could be identified as diffuse or nonfocal. The fact is that we lack sufficient knowledge about the nature of the central nervous system damage that may have been sustained by the children to whom the label "brain damaged" has been applied. As a consequence, all of our designations of nervous system damage, whether they be described as minimal, as diffuse, or as nonfocal, remain presumptive in the absence of well-established data demonstrating the nature of the damage to the underlying structure itself.

Our first problem, then, is to determine how we know that the children whom we describe as minimally brain damaged have indeed sustained damage to the brain. In many of the existing studies, the methodological fallacy can perhaps best be illustrated by the old story about the artillery sergeant and the clockmaker.

Many years ago a visitor to a small garrison town was impressed by the fact that each evening, at the stroke of five, the artillery sergeant lowered the colors and ordered his squad to fire a cannon. Amazed at such punctuality, the visitor inquired of the sergeant as to how he determined when it was precisely five o'clock. The sergeant replied that the town was famous not only for the excellence of its garrison but because one of its inhabitants was perhaps the best clockmaker in the world. "Each morning," he said, "as I walk past the clockmaker's shop I reset my own watch and therefore know that when I fire the cannon it is precisely five o'clock."

Only partially satisfied by this answer, the visitor went into town and addressed himself to the clockmaker, saying, "Sir, could you please tell me how you achieved your reputation for having clocks that are always precisely on time?" The clockmaker replied: "Well, living in this town I have a special advantage. You see, every evening precisely at five o'clock the garrison gun goes off, and I reset all my clocks at that time."

It is, I believe, apparent to all of us that many studies in which the medical examination bases itself upon the presumption of minimal brain damage as determined by the psychological test, or in which the psychological test indicates that certain of its signs are indicative of minimal brain damage on the basis of prior assumptive medical findings, are very similar to the situation that pertained in this small garrison town. Although it is certainly true that interdisciplinary cooperation is desirable, it is extremely unwise for disciplines each of whose findings are markedly contaminated by the findings of the others to use one another as the essential independent proof of the soundness and validity of its inferences. One of our problems, therefore, is the interrelation of independently obtained and verified data. This kind of interrelation would permit different fixes on the question in a manner that would permit sound identification of the fact of lesion.

One major obstacle to knowledge has been the tendency to consider the problem of the "minimally brain-damaged" child as a problem in the singular. The essential inadequacy of the term "brain damage" for purposes of classification derives from the contradiction between its singular form and the plurality of content which it seeks to embrace. As Birch and Demb,[3] Laufer and Denhoff,[4] and Wortis [5] have pointed out, brain damage may vary with respect to etiology, extent, type of lesion, locus, duration of damage, rate at which damage has been sustained, time of life and developmental stage at which the injury has occurred, and the syndromes of dysfunction that may result. In point of fact there is not *a* minimally brain-damaged child but rather many varieties of brain-damaged children.

In the course of time it has become increasingly clear that the syndrome described as the "brain-damaged child" by Strauss and Werner [1] or described as the hyperkinetic child by Laufer and Denhoff,[4] Bradley,[6] and their associates represents but one variety of behavioral consequence that may attend damage to the central nervous system. In addition to those children who are identified by pathologic patterns of behavior and whose functioning is characterized by difficulties in figure-ground perception, abnormal distractibility, perseverative tendencies, conceptual rigidity, emotional lability, hyperactivity, and motor awkwardness, there are several other varieties of behavioral disturbances that may accompany damage to the central nervous system. These patterns may range from relatively simple subtractive dysfunctions manifested in over-all mental deficiency to patterns of personality disturbance arising from difficulties in impulse control or from disturbances in the development of body boundaries that in certain instances result in the development of patterns of dysfunction that in a clinical setting are phenomenally identical with the childhood psychoses.

The failure to examine this multiplicity of syndromes and the concentration instead upon what can, in effect, be called a stereotype of brain damage has served to prevent us from understanding the richness of the possibilities for behavioral alteration that may occur as the consequence of brain damage, minimal or otherwise. At least in part, the stereotype of brain damage derives from a confusion between the concept of organicity in dysfunction and organic brain damage. The first concept, *organicity*, is not a neurophysiologic but a behavioral one. It involves the idea that certain patternings of behavior and psychological functions exist as the result of damage to the cerebral hemispheres. The fact of "organicity" cannot be denied. Further, it is clear that the behaviors described under the concept almost never occur in the absence of cerebral damage. However, there is no good reason for assuming that the converse of this proposition is true: namely, that cerebral damage never occurs without the consequent production of "organicity" in behavior. Rather, the evidence suggests that organicity in behavior is the consequence of *some* kinds of cerebral damage and not the consequence of other kinds of cerebral damage. On the basis of investigations of Birch and Diller [7] and others,[8] it may be stated that organicity in behavioral functioning is the characteristic manifested by individuals with certain kinds of brain damage and should in no sense be mistaken as the prototype of disturbance which may accompany all instances of injury to the brain. In point of fact, as Pavlov suggested many years ago,[9] there is no specific prototype, for brain damage must be considered in connection with such particular features as (1) locus of the injury, (2) extent and distribution of the lesion that has occurred, (3) the character of the lesion, whether it is subtractive or active in its functioning, and (4) the developmental stage in the life history of the individual at which the damage has been sustained. In the absence of this type of detailed consideration, brain damage as such has neither anatomic nor physiologic reality. Productive analytic thinking about the relation of behavioral changes to the character of brain damage in children has been inhibited by the view that injury to the brain may be viewed as a *mere fact* which has similar and recognizable consequences independent of its specifiable properties.

The "simplistic" view in its extreme form appears in the work of Strauss and Lehtinen, who have stated that "all brain lesions, wherever localized, are followed by a similar kind of disordered behavior." [10] This position bears some superficial resemblance to the equipotentiality concept of Lashley [11] and to the general function concept of Goldstein.[12] Unfortunately, this type of general theory, first implemented by Franz and Lashley [13] and rather uncritically accepted in clinical circles, was never based upon firm experimental findings. It should be noted that the task used by Lashley was a maze and that the learning of this maze and the retention of the learned patterns was in general influenced only by the extent of brain lesion. However, the learning of a maze is a multisensory task and, as a consequence, an animal could function equally appropriately in a maze if it used vision, olfaction, kinesthetic cues, or a variety of auditory or other input systems around which to organize its behavior. Using such multiply-determined and multiply-directed behavior as an indicator of the effects of brain injury, Lashley found no differences that were dependent upon locus of lesion. But when these studies were repeated [14] in circumstances in which performance required the utilization of visual information, of auditory information, of olfactory information, etc. (*i.e.,* when specific environmental aspects had to be selected and used to organize behavior), the laws of mass action disappeared and much more specificity in the consequence of damage to the nervous system resulted.

Although it may be true that lesions of a given extent have some common consequences as a function of the mass of tissue that has been destroyed, the independence of the effects from the locus of injury has at no point received substantial support in experimental evidence. On the contrary, much evidence exists for the specificity of the effects of localized brain lesions even at the level of cerebral cortex,[15] and a considerable body of evidence [16] demonstrates that differences in consequence attend subcortical damage in accordance with locus of injury. Moreover, even when one attempts to select a relatively homogeneous population of patients with brain damage (*e.g.*, persons with damage to the right cerebral hemisphere resulting in a left hemiplegia), decided differences in behavioral dysfunction occur as the result of the irritative or nonirritative character of the residual lesions, of the extent of the lesion, and of premorbid personality, among other variables.

Clearly, then, the problem of minimal brain damage in children is not a region for simple thought. For greater understanding, in view of the complexity of the problem, it is necessary to analyze the entire grouping of behavioral consequences that have been attributed to "brain damage" and from such an analysis develop hypotheses as to the nature of changes in the underlying system which may have been capable of producing the aberrations that are observed to occur.

It is essential that we recognize that the disturbed behavior seen in the clinic is not "due to" brain damage as such. We never see an individual whose disturbed behavior is a direct consequence of his brain damage. Instead, we see individuals with damage to the nervous system, which may have resulted in some primary disorganization, who have developed patterns of behavior in the course of atypical relations with the developmental environment, including its interpersonal, objective, and social features. The behavioral disturbances of children who come to our notice are developmental products and not merely manifestations of a damaged portion of the brain.

Despite the fact that "brain damage" is an unfortunate diagnostic label in that it implies both the existence of etiologic knowledge where none exists and a stereotyped view of the consequences of cerebral injury, there is little doubt that the children designated by it constitute an important clinical grouping. It is therefore essential that the baby not be thrown out with the bath water and the problem represented by the label ignored or minimized because of semantic or diagnostic unclarity. The issue may for practical purposes be resolved if it is agreed that the entity with which we are concerned is not a neurologic designation but a behavior pattern. Thus, as has been indicated in an earlier publication,[3] the category is entirely behavioral and implies that any of a number of kinds of cerebral damage will result in a common pattern of behavioral disturbance. Locus of injury, nature of the lesion, and the temporal course of the illness are usually not considered in the designation, and the nonbehavioral, neurologic confirmation of the fact of anatomic insult has been conspicuous by its absence. These considerations make it clear that the term "brain damage" refers to a behavior syndrome and not to the fact of brain damage as such.

Our task is to try to make more explicit the mechanisms of a disordered kind which may underlie such patterns of behavioral disturbance. We are led to a consideration of intervening mechanisms at a number of levels. At one level the general environmental forces affecting the birth of the child prior to its birth, including considerations of genetics, and factors in the biochemical development and environment of the fetus and young child, must be assessed. At another level we must consider problems related to the neuroanatomic and neuropathologic processes which may underlie some of the observed behavior disturbances. At yet another point the social and familial consequences of primary, neurologically induced disturbances of function must be analyzed in relation to the development of the individual child. If these paths are taken we may perhaps begin to explain some features of disordered behavior in children, or at least to examine a heuristic scheme within which we may begin productively and usefully to investigate disordered behavior. We may further be able to deal with problems of social incompetence and the conditions which contribute to the development of such incompetence or competence. We may be able to deal at some point with some of the mechanisms underlying variabilities of behavioral manifestation of insults to the central nervous system, including those that are intrinsic to the system as well as those that are the product of the interaction between this system and the developmental environment.

The characteristics that have been used as the basis for the differential diagnostic assignment of children to the "brain damage" category have varied with the specific clinical setting. However, certain features of functioning have been used with sufficient frequency to constitute a set of diagnostic criteria. The features contributing to the syndrome may be considered systematically under the headings of presenting complaints, history of behavioral development, neurologic findings, psychologic findings, and special studies.

The reasons for bringing a given child to attention vary with age and, in general, the younger the child the more likely it is that restlessness and overactivity will be a prominent feature of the complaint. In the child of school age the referral may be based upon all or any patterning of the following symptoms:

Disordered behavior. The child will often be described as overactive. But on closer questioning the amount of motor behavior may be found to be no greater than that found in a normal child of the same age. It is troublesome to parent or teacher because it is activity without clear direction, focus, or object. Its direction shifts from instant to instant and the actions may best be described as irrelevant and repeatedly tangential.

Short attention span. As in gross motor behavior, so too in perception and thinking the child's engagement is often fleeting and his concern shifts apparently at random from one aspect of the environment to another. He is easily distracted, and weak extraneous stimuli can readily divert him from ongoing concerns. Yet on other occasions the same child may be perseverative and persist in his own direction of activity despite concerted efforts made by teacher, parent, or peer to effect a change. Attention may best be characterized as capricious—now will-o'-the-wisp and again fixed with gluelike intensity upon socially irrelevant and educationally impertinent aspects of the environment.

Emotional lability. Conduct is "dramatically unpredictable" [17] and is characterized by rapid shiftings of mood and affective expression. Tantrum behavior characteristic of much younger age levels is not uncommon, and relatively minor changes in routine or moderate demands can provoke marked outbursts of rage, grief, and aggressiveness.

Social incompetence. Frequently the child is described as functioning at a social level which is significantly below his age and often far lower than his estimated intelligence. In play with other children his level of fine motor coordination is below that of his age mates and in ordinary children's games he is awkward, clumsy, and inept. Social failure may produce aggressive behavior, tears, withdrawal, or all of these either in sequence or pattern. Other children call the child "queer" and actively avoid his company.

Defective work habits. Effort is often described as markedly varying in its quality. Some tasks are pursued *ad nauseum* while others receive only intermittent and unevenly energized notice. Direction of effort appears unrelated to what the teacher seeks to stimulate and often seems to be determined by egocentric caprice or by negativistic reaction to instruction.

Impulsiveness and meddlesomeness. The child is apparently unable to refrain from touching, moving, and handling objects, especially in a new environment. Meddling may extend to rougher handling and, when overstimulated, the child may be destructive. Lack of inhibition may extend to all aspects of social functioning and be reflected in unacceptable sexual displays, unprovoked aggressions, and verbal outbursts.

Specific learning disorders. Reading at a competence that is below age level, marked discrepancy between skill in oral reading and the comprehension of what is being read, difficulty in grouping concepts and in mastering arithmetic, general incapacity in dealing with abstractions, or poor transfer of learning from one context to another may each constitute the basis for referral.

In summary, the child confronts the community with what one extraordinary parent has described as:

> . . . not a nice handicap. Such technical descriptions as catastrophic behavior, perceptual impairment, perseveration, disinhibition, mimism, short attention span, exogenous behavior contagion, learning disability, Strauss syndrome, neurological impairment, and hyperactivity are translated by the outside world as spoiled, bratty, bad-mannered, ill-behaved, badly brought up, undisciplined, obnoxious, and by the other children as queer.[18]

Given the complex matrix of behavioral disturbance which children designated as "brain damaged" present, it is clear that no single scientific discipline and no simple research strategy can possibly provide knowledge that will result in adequate understanding or effective planning for the children with whom we are concerned. To approach the problems meaningfully requires the pooled resources, skills, and techniques of, at the very least, such disciplines as neurology, psychology, physiology, psychiatry, education, epidemiology, sociology, pediatrics, and obstetrics. Working together, these disciplines can approach the questions of etiology, pathology, pathogenesis, and developmental interaction which emerge in any serious consideration of children with brain injury.

The first step in achieving a common focus among the separate disciplines is the exploration of mutual interests. It is to be hoped that the present conference in which we will address ourselves to the problems of "brain-damaged" children and their parents will help us to pool our knowledge, develop common understanding, and identify significant areas for investigation. If it serves to facilitate communication among the professions represented, the conference cannot help but contribute to our understanding of brain damage in children.

REFERENCES

1. Werner, H., and Strauss, A. A.: Pathology of figure-background relation in the child, *J. Abnorm. Soc. Psychol.,* *36*:236–248, 1941.
2. Pasamanick, B., and Knobloch, H.: Syndrome of minimal cerebral damage in infancy, *J.A.M.A.,* *170*:1384–1387.

3. Birch, H. G., and Demb, H.: The formation and extinction of conditioned reflexes in "brain-damaged" and mongoloid children, *J. Nerv. Ment. Dis.*, *129*:162–169, 1959.
4. Laufer, M. W., and Denhoff, E.: Hyperkinetic behavior syndrome in children, *J. Pediat.*, *50*:463–474, 1957.
5. Wortis, J.: A note on the concept of the "brain-injured child," *Amer. J. Ment. Defic.*, *61*:204–206, 1956.
6. Bradley, C.: Characteristics and management of children with behavior problems associated with brain damage, *Pediat. Clin. N. Amer.*, pp. 1049–1060, 1957.
7. Birch, H. G., and Diller, L.: Rorschach signs of "organicity": a physiological basis for perceptual disturbances, *J. Project. Techn.*, *23*:184–197, 1959.
8. Klebanoff, S. G., Singer, J. L., and Wilensky, H.: Psychological consequences of brain lesions and ablations, *Psychol. Bull.*, *51*:1–41, 1954.
9. Pavlov, I. P.: *Conditioned Reflexes*, ed. G. Anrep. Oxford University Press, 1927.
10. Strauss, A. A., and Lehtinen, L.: *Psychopathology and Education of the Brain-Injured Child.* Grune & Stratton, 1947.
11. Lashley, K. S.: *Brain Mechanisms and Intelligence.* University of Chicago Press, 1929.
12. Goldstein, K.: The modification of behavior consequent to cerebral lesions, *Psychiat. Quart.*, *10*:586–610, 1936.
13. Franz, S. I., and Lashley, K. S.: The effects of cerebral destruction upon habit formation and retention in the albino rat, *Psychobiology*, *1*:71–140, 1917.
14. Rollin, A. R.: Mass action effects in learning, *J. Psychol.*, *39*:301–319, 1955.
15. Jeffress, L. A., ed.: *Cerebral Mechanisms in Behavior: The Hixon Symposium.* John Wiley & Sons, 1951.
16. Baldwin, M., and Bailey, P., eds.: *Temporal Lobe Epilepsy.* Charles C. Thomas, 1958.
17. Doll, E. A.: Neurophrenia, *Amer. J. Psychiat.*, *108*:50–53, 1951.
18. *The Child with Brain Damage*, Association for the Aid of Crippled Children, New York, 1959.

Brain Damage as a Cause of Behavior Disturbance in Children

CHARLES KENNEDY, M.D. LOURDES S. RAMIREZ, M.D.
University of Pennsylvania Medical School and Children's Hospital of Philadelphia

THE ROLE OF A CLINICAL neurologist in the field of behavior aberrations is occasionally tangential, but it often involves critical judgment and considerable responsibility. He may be called upon as the final authority to confirm what may have been very obvious to educators, yet not faced squarely by parents—namely, that a child's behavior and mentation may be outside the realm of normal, not because of failure of training, guidance, or upbringing but rather because of abnormal brain function. His acumen is somewhat more severely taxed in another circumstance—*i.e.,* when counseling, special education, or psychiatric care has failed to alter a child's deviant behavior and the onus of responsibility needs to be shifted; the symptoms previously considered to be environmental in origin may now more properly be placed on the child himself. In a third capacity he joins with the psychiatrist or pediatrician, jointly analyzes the data at hand, and aids in arriving at a conclusion that this or that facet of the problem represents organic brain damage whereas another facet requires environmental or attitudinal manipulation. Let us look for a moment at the tools of study by which the important conclusions are reached.

HISTORICAL DATA

Firstly, historical data may be all-important. Knowing that a child was hospitalized and was critically ill with meningitis, following which a discontinuous change in behavior was present, may be unequivocal evidence that his present deviant function could be attributed to brain injury from that illness. How does this fact carry such weight? It is well known that early in this course of acute bacterial meningitis the inflammatory process goes beyond the meninges to involve the adjacent brain. After the first few hours of onset, the illness may more accurately be labeled "meningo-encephalitis," in which the changes on the surface of the cortex result in irreversible destruction of cerebral tissue. This is seen so consistently that the clinician feels safe in extrapolating from autopsy findings: whenever he is involved in the care of a child with meningitis he can picture, early in its course, rapid destruction of precious cortical neurons.

But how often does he have the opportunity of making such an examination in the child who is treated early and adequately and recovers without sequelae? Certainly there are instances in which the disease process is arrested so early that complete recovery takes place. A history of meningitis, therefore, is not in itself evidence of brain damage. However, if, associated with the meningitis, there is a sudden change in consciousness or behavior, this may reasonably be attributed to the disease process and its reversibility would be determined by the nature of the recovery. If, after many weeks of gradually returning motor and sensory function, the child is a different person—*i.e.,* less responsive to people, distractible, hyperactive, manneristic—we say also, with conviction, that this is the end result of irreversible changes in brain tissue.

But what can we say if the personality change is more subtle in a child whose meningitis was successfully treated very early in its course? What if a two-year-old recovers and goes home, perhaps ceases talking, or displays restlessness and repeated panic over trivia? Before saying "brain damage" we must take into account what we know happens to a greater or lesser degree to all children when they are suddenly taken from a familiar environment, separated from familiar people, and surrounded by the alarming strangeness of a hospital and its peculiarly dressed personnel who restrain, cause pain, and go about their business as though nothing very unusual were happening. Therefore, the interpretation of a change in personality following recovery from acute meningitis calls for a judgment to be made by the historian, who may be biased by his own upbringing and professional training. Such a judgment will also be subject to errors of parents' recollections of the child's behavior before and after the illness. Especially if the meningitis occurs in early infancy, how can one say "personality change" when the patient is in a most labile and amorphous state of growth?

Even when a known threatening event is a matter of document, therefore, historical data may not provide conclusive evidence that the deviant behavior is "organic." How frequently is the error compounded by less well-defined historical events! Was the infant's drowsiness and unwillingness to feed for two days at the time of measles really a manifestation of mild encephalitis? Was the fall from the bathinette at six months, when the sound of the head striking the floor resounded through the house, the origin of hemorrhage or contusion which altered normal neuronal growth in spite of the reassurance given by the pediatrician at the time? Is the history of neonatal cyanosis, listlessness, and poor sucking evidence of birth injury?

NEUROLOGIC EXAMINATION

The findings on neurologic examination form additional evidence for determining the basis for abnormal behavior. An honest review of items tested in a specific or all-or-none fashion indicates that although detailed information can usually be gathered with respect to the integrity of the spinal cord, cerebellum, cranial nerves, basal ganglia, pyramidal system, and a variety of sensory and special sensory functions, the complex neural apparatus concerned with behavior, attention, and mental state as a whole is looked at rather casually and judged by highly nonspecific end points.

We tend to assign great significance to associated positive findings such as bilateral up-going toes on plantar stimulation, marked hyperreflexia, obvious ataxia, or impairment in rapid alternating movements as we form opinions on the causes of behavioral deviation. We draw upon the teachings passed on to us that injuries to the brain tend to be diffuse and that if the apparatus necessary to emotional expression and behavior has been injured, most certainly the noxious agent will have wrought havoc elsewhere in the brain. But is not such an opinion one of guilt by association? Are we not forgetting the variety of diffuse brain injuries in which the derangement is confined to the motor system? In acanthocytosis, the cerebellar ataxia is disabling but the mental state, sense of humor, social responsiveness are all quite normal. Likewise, the peculiar predilection of bilirubin to brain stem and basal ganglia leaves the kernicteric child an ingenious, aware, and often charming personality in spite of a severe motor incapacity. The basilar arachnoditis of older times caused extensive pyramidal-tract and cranial-nerve signs but spared cortical function and left behavior unaltered. It is clear, therefore, that findings on the neurologic examination (although perhaps indicating "brain injury" to the systems tested) cannot be considered as unequivocal evidence that such injury extended to the neural apparatus of behavioral function.

ELECTROENCEPHALOGRAPHY AND PNEUMOENCEPHALOGRAPHY

Acknowledging the limitations of information to be derived from the history and physical findings, one turns to an independent assessment of neural function with electroencephalography. Occasionally one is rewarded by the disclosure of electrical abnormalities localized to a given region indicating cerebral injury not detectable by any other technique. This was the case in an irritable 3-year-old girl with headache who was found to have a large abscess in the frontal region. In general, however, the correlation of electrical with structural abnormalities of the brain is disappointing, as is illustrated by the cases of mongoloid children whose cortex is grossly malformed yet whose EEG tracings are within normal limits. Adding to the unreliability of this procedure in assessing the presence of brain damage is the wide variability in the character of tracings with respect to background rhythm, frequency, response to hyperventilation, and changes occurring in light and deep sleep. Depending on one's definition of normal, "abnormalities" have been found in 15 to 40 percent of normal children.[1-3]

Finally one considers the use of roentgenograms of the skull or pneumoencephalography as a means of determining the presence of injury or defect. Calcifications, suture configuration, and evidence of pressure and displacement of bony structures are occasionally found and may lead to highly specific diagnoses, but in the vast majority of cases the question of the presence of cerebral defect is left unanswered.

Were it not for the fact that special conditions are necessary for its safe and proper execution, pneumoencephalography would be routinely helpful because a positive finding may indicate not only the presence of defect but also its location and extent. However, in the absence of a variety of other findings not to be reviewed here, alterations in the pneumoencephalogram are seen in relatively few instances and, indeed, in a significant number of severe organic disorders—*e.g.*, kernicterus, Wilson's disease, diffuse sclerosis —both the ventricular configuration and the external surface markings of the brain are quite normal.

DEVELOPMENTAL HISTORY

If we leave aside a few other rather specialized procedures, it is clear that a medical evaluation may or may not determine whether previous injury to the brain took place, not to mention the cause or extent of such injury. What are the biologic circumstances that leave us so defeated? In an attempt to answer this question, I should like to describe the manner in which the growing human brain responds to a variety of disease processes, illustrating this with observations on children seen during the past ten years at the Children's Hospital of Philadelphia.

The asymptomatic nature of a large cortical lesion is illustrated in the case of R.Mc., who was first seen at the age of five years because of the sudden onset of generalized, afebrile seizures. Gestation had been uncomplicated, but labor was arrested in the second stage for a prolonged period. The baby was normal at birth and in the first week of life, but at home he began vomiting. In the third week of life vomiting was projectile, requiring hospitalization. Several right-sided convulsive seizures were noted while he was in the hospital, but he was discharged without additional studies, with a diagnosis of "improper feeding." His subsequent developmental course was quite normal. His experienced mother noted nothing unusual in the rate of achieving milestones of motor and social behavior, and the onset of seizures at five came as a complete surprise in the light of his previously robust health.

In the course of his being studied at the Children's Hospital, a pneumoencephalogram indicated the presence of a large porencephalic cyst in the left parietal region, a finding consistent with the great difficulty he had had in learning to write. It seems reasonable to speculate that the right-sided seizures and vomiting in the neonatal period were the result of a vascular lesion produced by the stress of delivery, resulting in the porencephalic cyst. The noteworthy feature of this case is that the lesion itself was not epileptogenic until the age of five years and signs relative to the absence of a large portion of the left parietal lobe were virtually nil until the boy was mature enough to make feasible a test of cortical sensation. Thus injury to the brain may be extensive early in the neonatal period but, for reasons poorly understood, it may become a seizure focus only years later.

A second characteristic of certain types of "brain damage" is the physiologic peculiarity of the damaged region. In certain circumstances, damage is not manifested simply as an absence of function but as an irritating lesion, capable not only of causing seizures but of influencing behavior in an adverse way. This is illustrated in the following case.

S.S. was eight years old at the time of his admission to the Children's Hospital in 1957 for evaluation of uncontrolled petit mal seizures and a severe behavior problem. He was the product of a normal pregnancy and delivery, and he was well till the age of five weeks, when he developed severe diarrhea complicated by electrolyte imbalance and cardiac arrest for five minutes, from which he was revived by intracardiac injection of adrenalin. In the course of his two-month hospitalization, he recovered remarkably, but persistent poor sucking and hyperactivity were noted.

At the age of nine months he had a right-sided seizure associated with hyperpyrexia and pharyngitis and subsequently developed frequent staring spells that persisted in spite of anticonvulsant drugs. At two years he was noted to drag his right leg in walking.

Development milestones were essentially normal, the child standing alone at eight months and walking alone at fourteen months. At the time of admission to the Children's Hospital at eight years he was a third-grade pupil in a private school and was said to be bright. However, since his serious illness in infancy he had been a very difficult child to manage. As he grew older, he became demanding, aggressive, irrational, and destructive. He would smash dishes at meals and scream, etc. without provocation and he threatened the well-being and safety of a younger sister who was consistently innocent of provoking his irrational rage.

Following pneumoencephalography, which demonstrated left cerebral atrophy with considerable dilatation of the left ventricle, a hemispherectomy was done. The postoperative course was stormy but on recovery there was a marked change in behavior; he cooperated well with examinations and procedures, was cheerful, and, when he was discharged from the hospital on the 23d postoperative day, he expressed happiness at going home. This changed behavior continued; on rehospitalization last year for fever of unknown cause, he was no problem on the ward with respect to behavior. The observation of this change was borne out in the description of the boy at home by very grateful parents. In addition, he has remained seizure-free with no anticonvulsant medication since the hemispherectomy.

The history of this child's illness again illustrates the changing manifestations of a fixed neurologic deficit and also confirms observations elsewhere reported—namely, that absence of tissue may be quite different in its physiological effects from malfunctioning tissue. The difference with respect to emotional and behavioral states is most striking here.

To what extent is normal mentation dependent upon the presence of both cerebral hemispheres? That one hemisphere can be sacrificed without serious consequences is seen in the case of M.H., who was born with a vast hemangioma covering her entire right cerebral hemisphere (Sturge-Weber syndrome). The entire structure was removed at the age of 11 months after hemiparesis and seizures developed. Only the basal ganglia, thalamus, and middle portions of the visceral brain remained on the involved side, yet the child recovered and has gone on to school, remaining in the appropriate grade for her age. Seen recently at the age of eight, she was an attractive, responsive schoolgirl, able to walk and having some voluntary control over proximal muscles controlling the left arm and leg. A homonymous visual field cut was present, as would be expected. Her IQ had been judged 132 by a psychologist.

Normal reactivity and behavioral state may also be preserved under circumstances of severe distortion of the brain, as is seen in the case of C.W., a seven-year-old boy who was the second of unsuspected twins and who was so unresponsive and cyanotic at birth that the parents were told he would not live. Development progressed normally except for delayed walking, which was achieved at two and one-half years, the delay being accounted for by spasticity of the lower extremities. He was a very intelligent, well-behaved child with an excellent school record (IQ 137) and was capable of normal physical activity in spite of mild pyramidal tract signs and tremulousness and a large head that measured 60 cm. at the age of seven.

Pneumoencephalography done at seven years disclosed marked dilatation of all ventricles and basal cisterns, leaving only a centimeter of brain tissue at the periphery of the lateral ventricles.

In summary, the histories of these children show (1) that the brain of the newborn, because of its immature state, may suffer extensive injury which may go unrecognized for a period of years, when it may become a seizure focus or may impair skills of higher learning and behavior; (2) that the brain may suffer partial injury in such a way that it becomes a focus of dysfunctioning tissue, affecting behavioral function adversely; (3) that mentation and behavior are not seriously curtailed when one hemisphere is removed provided the remaining structure is normal; and (4) that there may be severe distortions of the normal brain configuration, as in extreme hydrocephalus, without functional impairment.

ONE ETIOLOGY

Let us now move to one specific and common mechanism which is known to injure the developing brain—namely, viral encephalitis. There appear to be certain characteristics of this disease which, together with the phenomena outlined above, may indicate lines of study for a better understanding of behavioral aberrations due to brain injury.

Although pathologic studies of children who have died from viral encephalitis have recorded varying degrees of involvement in different structures of the brain, there is only rarely good clinical pathologic correlation with symptoms or signs. Rather uniformly the illness has been characterized by a few descriptive terms: convulsions, disturbances of consciousness, involuntary movements, deepening coma, and failure of vital signs. These have so dominated the clinical course that the tendency to local involvement of particular structures is not appreciated. The history and findings in the following children are noteworthy in this regard.

R.W., a nine-month-old boy, who was well until three weeks prior to admission, developed a mild respiratory infection with a fever of 101°. During this time he was irritable and would cling to his mother and want to be held continuously. He was otherwise well until a week later, when the mother noticed that his left eye began to "roll around" in a bizarre fashion. The following day this was seen in the other eye. His irritability continued, but he remained alert, fed and slept well, and at times was playful. Although he had some jerking movements of the body, these were not prominent and in spite of them he was able to sit in his crib, hold his bottle, and handle a rattle. There was no indication that his vision was impaired.

The history of the pregnancy, delivery, and neonatal period was quite unremarkable, and growth and development had been normal until the present illness.

On examination, there was a nasal discharge, but all other findings were related to the nervous system. Continuous tremulous movements of the extremities could be seen when the infant was sitting erect, at which time a trunkal ataxia was also apparent. Rapid spontaneous conjugate eye movements in all directions were noted, together with appropriate alterations in the associated movements of the lids and face. In spite of this, he was able to see and recognize objects and people, but opticokinetic nystagmus and reflex movements of the eyes with change in head position could not be elicited.

The laboratory findings were: Hemoglobin 11.4 gm.; WBC 12,000, with a normal differential. The cerebrospinal fluid pressure was normal and the protein content was 32 mg.%. A culture from the nose and throat revealed a mixture of pneumococcus, paracolon bacillus, and aerobacter bacillus, and attempts to isolate a virus from the nose, throat, and spinal fluid failed. An electroencephalogram was within normal limits.

During the two-week period of hospitalization the violence of the bizarre eye movements varied, being extreme during periods of excitement and rage but minimal during sleep. Sedatives and anticonvulsant medications were ineffective. He remained afebrile, the associated respiratory infection subsided, and he was discharged to out-patient care, where during a three-month period there was little change and then gradual improvement took place. The child's walking was delayed until after two years of age and, when he was examined at three years of age, no residua were noted except for a very rapid, fine intermittent pendular nystagmus in the left eye. He had not learned to talk, the significance of which was uncertain, but he was alert and playful and showed no gross evidence of a defective mental state.

In a comparable illness which progressed to coma and death in a 61-year-old woman, pathologic changes consisted of foci of perivascular infiltration and spotty disappearance of nerve cells, many being shrunken and distorted. These were most marked in the thalamus and hypothalamus and extended into the upper brain stem and pons. Sections of the cerebral cortex failed to show any sign of inflammatory change.

Another illustration of local destruction secondary to encephalitis is the case history of a three-year-old girl repeatedly subject to fever of unknown cause. She had been well until the age of one year, when she suddenly became drowsy and had a temperature of 105°. The physician noted a tonsillitis and began treatment with antibiotics at home. On the third day after onset she became stuporous and unresponsive and was hospitalized, where tests were all said to be "negative." Recovery was gradual, and over the subsequent two weeks she seemed well again and was discharged.

Three months later fever recurred and extensive study, at this time in a major medical center, failed to reveal the cause. Curiously, in spite of temperatures which ranged regularly between 102° and 104°, she acted well, had a normal appetite, and gave no indication of being ill. The unexplained fever recurred during the next six months and two other major centers were involved in an attempt to account for it, but an exhaustive search for infection, blood dyscrasia, malignancy, granulomata, etc. was unrewarding.

One year after her acute illness she had a first generalized convulsion with several recurrences in spite of anticonvulsant medication. Now, at the age of three and one-half years, this seizure-prone, recurrently febrile child is beginning to show a hyperactivity out of proportion to what might be accounted for by the emotional trauma of repeated hospitalization. In retrospect, it becomes increasingly clear that this child's original acute illness was an encephalitis from which she emerged with her hypothalamic temperature control apparatus injured and some additional "damage" resulting in seizures which became manifest one year later. We submit that this interval represents the "silent" period between the time of injury and the evolution of a seizure focus. We would defer, for the moment, any comment regarding her "hyperactivity" and its relation to the locus of "brain damage."

Another instance of highly local injury is illustrated in the case of a 14-year-old high school freshman with a brilliant academic record. He has had 15 admissions to the Children's Hospital of Philadelphia since the age of nine because of prolonged periods of irresistible sleep occasionally accompanied by generalized or focal motor seizures. His illness dates back to the age of 18 months, when he was found to be unresponsive following his usual nap time. He was covered with a nearly confluent macular rash and had a fever of 105°. He was unable to take oral feeding and was taken to a local hospital, where, with supportive measures, he gradually became more alert. The physician in charge felt that he might have had "spotted fever" but lacked any laboratory evidence to support the impression.

He recovered and was sent home, only to have recurrent periods of unexplained drowsiness every four to six weeks but otherwise did well and showed a normal pattern of motor and social development. The drowsiness continued intermittently and, at the age of seven, seizures occasionally accompanied his attacks of prolonged sleep. On anticonvulsant medication he had a four-year period of relief from both abnormal sleep and seizures, but at the age of 12 both recurred.

Pneumoencephalography has repeatedly been normal, and no neurologic signs have developed other than nystagmus, impairment in upward gaze, and some degree of ataxia, these appearing only with the onset or immediately following the period of prolonged sleep. Repeated electroencephalograms have shown only normal patterns in wakefulness, drowsiness, and sleep.

This boy's illness certainly is the end result of injury to deep midline structures, probably involving brain stem and hypothalamus, having its beginning with an acute exanthematous illness and associated encephalopathy, presumably an encephalitis.

In another instance, selective injury to the hypothalamus may be presumed to have occurred, resulting in orthostatic hypotension. This was in a young adult who developed classical signs of mumps, the late course of which was marked by headache, confusion, and delirium. On convalescence he was unable to stand or even sit in the erect position without having profound hypotension, which caused him to faint.

In each of the foregoing cases, actual pathologic change in the brain, or "brain damage," is presumed to have occurred. The report of Lipsett *et al.*[4] describes the evolution of a hypothalamic syndrome in a six-year-old boy leading to hyperthermia, hyperphagia, and secondary hypothyroidism which resulted in death. The histologic changes in the hypothalamus, particularly in the region of the supraoptic nuclei and tuber cinereum, consisted of areas of gliosis and lymphocytic infiltration, and comparable changes were found in no other structures. Thus, in this patient, local damage in the expected structures was actually found to have taken place.

These cases illustrate the manner in which encephalitis may cause permanent deficits in neural function when such structures as the hypothalamus and midbrain are involved. That local changes affect other structures also, even when the severity of the process results in death, has been clearly shown by pathologic studies.[5]

As previously emphasized, the neurologist's classic examination is specific for relatively few cerebral functions and, should encephalitis produce scattered focal lesions in the temporal or frontal regions, it would not be surprising if his examination were "negative" even if mental function were impaired. Our increasing knowledge of the limbic system allows us to hypothesize further that lesions in the hippocampus, fornix, and parts of the hypothalamus may selectively impair behavior as it is modified by motivation and emotions without having any effect on intellective function. Although such separation of cerebration into compartments may be specious, we can appreciate more and more clearly the extreme variability of sequelae of brain injury, both from encephalitis with its predisposition to be focal and from a variety of other disease processes which are selective in their locus of injury.

It is clear that the tools for the recognition of previous brain injury are grossly inadequate and that the cause for behavioral aberrations in many instances must go undiscovered. There is reason to believe that even if the brain of the individual in question were available for pathologic examination, the answer would not be conclusively forthcoming because of changes in histology which occur over time. More probably the answer lies in improving research techniques by which injury to the brain may be recognized with respect to extent and location at the time of the insult, which then may be correlated with deficits of brain function evolving later in life.

REFERENCES

1. Secunda, L., and Finley, K. H.: Electroencephalographic studies in children presenting behavior disorders, *New Eng. J. Med., 226*:850, 1942.
2. Rapin, I., Goldensohn, E. S., Baruch, R., and Hoefer, P.: "The Quantitative Measurement in Hyperventilation in Adults and Children." Unpublished paper.
3. Gibbs, F. A., Gibbs, E. L., and Lennox, W. G.: Electroencephalographic classification of epileptic patients and control subjects, *Arch. Neurol. Psychiat., 50*: 111, 1943.
4. Lipsett, M. B., Dreifuss, F. E., and Thomas, L. B.: Hypothalamic syndrome following varicella, *Amer. J. Med., 32*:471, 1962.
5. Haymaker, W., *et al.:* "Pathology of

Viral Disease in Man Characterized by Intranuclear Inclusions," in *Viral Encephalitis,* eds. W. Fields and R. J. Blattner. Fifth Annual Scientific Meeting of the Houston Neurological Society. Charles C. Thomas, 1958.

DISCUSSION

The longitudinal approach embodied in this paper focused discussion on the natural history of brain damage in children. It was generally agreed that there is little clear relationship between the fact of an anatomic lesion in the brain and the development of the behavioral disturbances and other signs or symptoms that would bring the child to clinical notice. One view was that the development of symptoms in cases of brain injury in children may be due less to the fact of a brain lesion than to the possibility that the lesion disorganizes the physiology of the remaining intact brain. It was indicated that some of the recent work on the experimental induction of epilepsy in animals suggests an approach to the problem of the time course of the development of symptoms in the case of porencephalic cyst presented in the paper. In this case a massive lesion remained silent, or relatively silent, in a child until approximately the fifth year of age, at which time his first presenting problem was convulsive seizure.

In animal preparations, one of the findings has been that massive dendritic growth occurs at the borders of the cystic formation. Such marginal growth is slow and, as the dendrites extend into the margins of the cyst, the absence of normal neurologic tissue results in masses of dendrites of poor organization developing in relatively unpatterned ways. Apparently this abnormal structural pattern results in a disorganization of synchrony in the firing of the neural elements. Symptoms appear only when this abnormal growth reaches a stage of maturity, at which disruption of normal firing patterns is induced. It may well be that this phenomenon of abnormal and atypical growth at the margins of the existing lesion is one of the reasons why an initially silent lesion comes to be clinically manifest. Thus, the absence or subtraction of the tissue appears to be less disruptive than the presence of abnormally functioning tissue.

The view that the disruptive behavioral consequences of damage to nervous system tissue stem less from the fact of the brain lesion than from its interfering effect upon the remaining intact nervous system gained support from the evidence reported for hemispherectomy. When damage appears to be restricted to one hemisphere and the resultant disorganization of behavior is not amenable to medical or environmental control, removal of the damaged hemisphere has in some cases resulted in improvement in behavior. Since the removal of the hemisphere involves the excision of additional intact neural tissue as well as the removal of the damaged areas, the child has a smaller amount of intact neural tissue available after hemispherectomy than before. However, in spite of the reduction in the total mass of normal, undamaged tissue, the result is a more effective and functional total organization of the remaining structure.

At this point in the discussion, Dr. Kennedy cautioned that hemispherectomy should be considered only as a last resort and never as a preferred mode of treatment. However, after all other available forms of management have been attempted without success, it may be considered in the hope that the child's life may be made livable. He indicated that different reasons for the procedure underlay each case in the two that he had reported in his presentation. Vascular anomalies, once started, often run a progressive course and eventually result in a persistent state of extremely severe mental deficiency. Thus the rationale for hemispherectomy in the case of the child with Sturge-Weber syndrome was, "Let's spare her this."

It should be noted, however, that the case reported was the only one of eight similar cases in which such operation had been performed in which the result was good. In all of the other cases, removal of the hemisphere did not result in a functionally effective child. In the second case reported—that of a child with severe behavior disorder complicated by uncontrolled seizures and hemiparesis—Dr. Kennedy indicated that he had initially been opposed to hemispherectomy. In this case, however, the results were remarkably good following surgery. It was clear, therefore, that at present no generally agreed upon criteria for undertaking hemispherectomy exist and, although the findings are of great value from the point of view of our ability to conceptualize certain ways in which brain lesions may affect behavior, sound criteria for deciding to perform such an operation and good prognostic indicators as to the nature of the functioning of the child after hemispherectomy are lacking.

A second phase of the discussion concerned itself with the problem of the age-specificity with which symptoms of behavioral disturbance manifest themselves in children with cerebral damage. In particular, concern was expressed in relation to the so-called hyperkinetic syndrome. There has been widespread belief flowing from clinical experience that this behavior pattern, reported so frequently in young children with brain damage, often begins to decline at the age of eight or nine years and may frequently disappear altogether in adolescence. The published literature contains an inadequate body of information on the longitudinal course of hyperkinesis and, in the absence of such information, it is most difficult to assess the value of a variety of methods of treatment and management for hyperkinetic children. It could well be that many of the so-called effective measures for the management of the syndrome of behavioral disturbance owe their reported effectiveness to the time of life at which they are introduced. Thus, if, beginning with the eighth or ninth year, the manifestations of kinetic disturbance begin spontaneously to subside and, in most instances, are either markedly modified or absent in adolescence, the reported successes in modifying hyperkinesis by various educational and other therapeutic approaches in these age periods may well have been artifacts of spontaneous change in kinetic disturbance itself. Since only fragmentary information exists on this problem, it was urged that detailed follow-up studies be instituted on the development of children with brain damage.

One of the difficulties attending such longitudinal study is the problem of adequate diagnosis and hence the identification of the group to be studied. Children who are identified as having brain damage represent, in the main, individuals who have come to notice because they have functional disturbances. This necessarily means that we can study the natural history of only a fraction of the individuals who have in fact damage to the brain—namely, those who have both brain damage and symptoms or signs of such disturbance. Further, the diagnosis of brain damage is often made on behavioral and not on neurologic evidence. One way to surmount these obstacles is to identify the study population in advance of the development of any symptoms. In part, this may be done by studying not children with brain damage but children who have been subjected to perinatal or postnatal circumstances of such a nature that they risk the development of this disorder. The possibility for pursuing such study, it was pointed out, exists in the National Collaborative Study for the Study of Cerebral Palsy (NIH). However, the children being followed in this study population are still too young to provide useful information on the natural history of the disturbance.

It was emphasized that being at risk and being damaged are by no means the same thing. In studies of the nervous system of monkeys and other lower animals who had been subjected to asphyxia early in life, it has been found that some of the animals had no detectable damage to the brain. In others, nonspecific evidence of hemorrhage existed, whereas in still others, small amounts of sclerosis were found. When such animals, all of whom had been subjected to the same objective condition of risk, were permitted to develop, the patterns of symptoms manifested were at least as varied as the anatomic findings upon pathologic examination of the brain. Functional disturbance ranged from no manifestations of disorder in learning ability, behavior, or motor coordination to massive disturbance in intellectual and motor functioning.

Recognition of the need for longitudinal studies of children with brain damage naturally led to a consideration of techniques and methods for the early identification of such individuals. There was consensus that our current techniques for early identification are inadequate, that too little is known about the normal neurologic integration of neonates and young infants, and that our understanding of the electrophysiologic organization of such individuals is insufficient for the development of good diagnosis. Similar diagnostic difficulties exist at other age levels.

It was pointed out that electroencephalographic studies of the brain do not always give us an answer that corresponds to the pathologic condition of the brain itself. This inadequacy is particularly true in cases where the deeper cortical or subcortical structures are involved. If we conclude that the brain is normal because we have obtained a normal EEG, we may often be seriously misled. It was noted, too, that the time course of electroencephalographic events, even in children who have clear-cut clinical evidence of brain damage, poses real difficulties. Thus, in children with encephalitis, the initial electroencephalographic response is the development of slow waves, or slow wave foci. This state of affairs may last for a week or two and then disappear, leaving no apparent abnormal electroencephalographic residua. However, six months or more after this set of events, the child may show spike foci and epileptogenic lesions as well as the convulsive seizures characteristic of clinical epilepsy. It was argued that among the more important EEG studies that may be pursued is the longitudinal analysis of electroencephalographic disturbance, and that the earlier such study is begun and the longer it is continued, the fuller will be our understanding of the time course of change in neurologic abnormalities.

The final phase of the discussion concerned itself with the need for knowing more about the neuropathology that underlies the disturbed functional states noted in children with cerebral damage. It was agreed that our neuropathologic information is sparse and that the tendency to speak of diffuse cerebral damage in circumstances in which we have no localizing evidence of a focal lesion is more a poetic than a scientific statement of the underlying pathologic state. It was emphasized that we have reports of pathologic examinations that relate massive lesions to lack of clinical signs or symptoms and focal lesions to large ones, that both diffuse brain pathology and focal abnormality appear to contribute to the development of abnormal function. It was pointed out that the method for the pathologic examination of the human brain and the usual course of pathologic inquiry are crude. Very small samples of brain tissue are studied, and the techniques by which they are studied are insufficiently sensitive for the identification of many types of disorder. Detailed pathologic investigation of brains in children with syndromes associated with brain damage have been done only rarely, mainly because it is so expensive. The cost for working up a single brain, most recently done in the collaborative studies of cerebral palsy, is approximately $2000. Despite the expense, however, it was considered essential that a more comprehensive investigation on the relationships between neuroanatomic alteration and behavioral disturbance be encouraged as one way to obtain greater understanding of the relationship between damage to the nervous system and disturbance in function.

Psychological Evaluation of Children with Cerebral Damage

LEONARD DILLER, PH.D.
Institute of Physical Medicine and Rehabilitation
New York University Medical Center

HERBERT G. BIRCH, M.D., PH.D.
Albert Einstein College of Medicine

ACCURATE APPRAISAL of the child with cerebral damage is beset with many difficulties. One problem stems from confusion in the concept: the term "brain-damaged child" may refer to several subsyndromes including the cerebral-palsied child, the epileptic, the nonfamilial mental defective, and the hyperkinetic.[1,2] Secondly, behavioral characteristics attributed to children with brain injuries overlap other diagnostic entities—the schizophrenic,[3,4] the aphasic,[5,6] and the mentally retarded child.[7] Thirdly, in the interpretation of behavior, there is often a confusion between a symptom and its underlying cause, and hence it is difficult to separate the child's defect from his adaptation to it—*e.g.*, does anxiety cause the behavior disturbance or is it a product of the disturbance?

A fourth problem is presented by the existence of independent factors whose effects on behavior cannot be immediately determined: age at time of damage, duration of damage, age of child at time of examination, and locus, type, and amount of damage. A fifth problem stems from the fact that, in the main, psychological tests are not developmentally oriented and the information they supply is discontinuous from age to age. Their interpretation is further complicated by the fact that they consist of contrived situations which are purposely removed from real life problems. Hence prediction from a given behavior in a test situation to one outside the test situation may involve a complex chain of inferences. Each link in the chain may weaken confidence in the validity of the interpretation.

Having enumerated these difficulties—and one can point to many more —it must be added that they are placed at the beginning of the paper, as a caveat, rather than at its conclusion, as a summary of the status quo. For progress has been made in the psychological assessment of brain-damaged children. A systematic approach to these issues, gaps in our knowledge, and research needs are clearly delineated in the recent reviews of Graham [8] and Benton.[5,9] However, before we accumulate more data, let us reappraise our existing knowledge and the basis for its accumulation. Until recently, relatively little was done. Indeed, an authoritative review written a decade ago [10] on psychological testing of the brain damaged during the 1940's and early 50's devotes less than five pages and fewer than 10 percent of the 300-odd references to children. But, spurred on by public interest and by grants, research has increased rapidly, and an examination of its general direction seems to be in order.

Perhaps the best vehicle for considering the current status of psychological evaluation is perception. "The most extensive and definitive studies of brain-injured children have been in the area of perception." [10] As Allen has put it,[11] for the psychologist, "The role of perception in the functioning of the cerebral-palsied person is almost the entire story of cerebral palsy as a condition." In a series of studies stretching over the past 20 years, perceptual problems have been implicated in traumatic and postencephalitic brain damage in children.[12–14] For many psychologists, the term "perceptual disturbance" has become almost synonymous with brain damage—to the point where such disturbance is regarded as a primary behavioral criterion for the existence of brain damage. Now it is unfortunately true that once a perceptual disturbance is uncovered in the test findings, the psychologist feels absolved of a responsibility to account for it or deal with it. He has explained it—and he dismisses it by invoking the concept of brain damage. But exactly what is a perceptual disturbance? How did it come to be associated with brain damage? Does describing the behavioral problems of the brain-damaged child as "perceptual" increase our understanding or does it merely substitute one label for another?

Let us, for simplicity's sake, consider perception as the interpretation of a stimulus. The problem then can be restated: Are there any systematic ways in which brain-damaged children misinterpret a stimulus? Heinz Werner, whose ingenious work in the late 1930's and early 1940's did so much to help establish a basis for distinguishing endogenous from exogenous mentally defective children, suggested that one of the basic difficulties of the brain-damaged children he studied was an inability to form figure-ground relationships.[15] He selected this dimension of perception because (*a*) in Gestalt psychology it was thought to be one of the fundamental and most primitive activities of the organism,[16] and (*b*) in his work with brain-damaged adults, Goldstein [17] had extended figure-ground relationships beyond perception into a basic principle of neural organization, so that what held true for perception held true also for thinking and memory.

Figure-ground relations offer one fundamental answer to the question of why the individual selects some stimuli to respond to and ignores others. The difficulties the brain-damaged child experiences in copying a design from a marble board, therefore, reflects a disturbance in figure-ground relationships and, hence, more fundamentally, a disturbance in neural organization. In addition, Werner called attention to the stimulus characteristics of the test situation in a way that had been largely ignored in the straightforward psychometric approaches of American psychologists. The stimulus situation posed by Werner permitted the response style of the brain-damaged children fuller expression. The erratic, jumpy, forced quality in responding to a task involving a sequence of acts could be observed. Distractibility as well as fixation, isolation of function as well as diffuse spread, perseveration and lability—all represent disturbances in the "figure-ground syndrome." [15]

The wide variety of stimulus situations which could elicit these characteristics may be seen in the following list.[18–29]

1. Rorschach test.
2. Marble board: (*a*) copying marble pattern from model and (*b*) drawing the model.
3. Tachistoscopic exposure of embedded figures.
4. Tactual motor task: (*a*) thumbtacks and (*b*) raised wooden surfaces.
5. Repeating tone patterns.
6. Recalling pictures.
7. Reproducing dot patterns.
8. Picture object test.
9. Repeating rhythms.
10. Sorting objects.
11. Critical flicker frequency.

The influence of these studies carried out on a small sample of boys at the Wayne County Training School is still apparent. The techniques have been applied to cerebral-palsied populations as well as non-physically handicapped brain-damaged children of normal and retarded intelligence.[30–35] They have become incorporated into current thinking despite the fact (*a*) that criticisms have been made against Werner's statistical design; [36] (*b*) that the tasks are of limited use in clinical interpretation because they are difficult to quantify; [32] (*c*) that Werner failed to pair off systematically one task against another—*e.g.*, what is the relationship of sorting behavior (thinking) to the marble-board performance (perception)? (*d*) that the difficulties of the brain-damaged children may be due to task complexity rather than figure-ground problems.

Why, then, despite its obvious weaknesses, does interest persist in this work? First, because there is continuing clinical evidence that many brain-damaged children tend to show perceptual problems, and, second, there is a clinical impression that the child's inability to respond to a seemingly trivial task reflects a more fundamental disturbance which influences or "causes" the many behavioral aberrations associated with brain damage. There is evidence, for example, that reading disability is related to perceptual disturbance in brain-damaged children but not in emotionally disturbed children.[1,37] One also suspects that interest in perception stemming from interest in projective techniques as one gateway to understanding personality dynamics was also influential. Suggesting that the hyperactive child got that way because he has perceptual problems permits us to have a ready explanation for his behavior and, as translated in the works of Strauss and associates,[35,38] offers us handy suggestions for educational intervention.

Now that this idea has been incorporated into our clinical work, it may be worth while to examine it more carefully. Although Werner demonstrated perceptual disturbances in a wide variety of situations, in clinical practice it has become associated with those tasks involving the recognition, manipulation, or copying of visual stimuli or objects in space. Thus, Stephenson [39] found that a group of cerebral-palsied children performed less well than a carefully matched control group in spatial tasks, although they appeared equal to the controls in language measures. Furthermore, the difference could not be explained on the basis of the difficulty, novelty, or abstraction of the spatial tasks, for the differences persisted even when these factors were controlled.

To know that a brain-damaged child is inferior on spatial tasks may be useful, but it raises several other questions. Why is he inferior? Does he fail to organize the task properly because of a perceptual difficulty? Does he fail to receive all the stimuli in a clear way because of difficulty in sensation? Or does he fail to execute properly what he sees? What accounts for some of the strange phenomena—*e.g.*, rotation—associated with the brain damage? If the field is to become more sophisticated and clinical practice is to be improved, one must not only point out the perceptual deviations but also try to understand them. Let us turn, for the moment, then, from the problems of identifying and classifying brain-damaged children and address ourselves to observing and understanding some of the phenomena commonly associated with brain damage.

SENSORY VS. PERCEPTUAL INTACTNESS AND FIGURE-GROUND PROBLEMS

Werner, Strauss, Lehtinen, and others state that deviant perceptual performances of brain-damaged children occurred in the absence of noticeable defects in sensation. This notion fits in with the classical ideas of Gestalt psychologists, who argue that the nervous system parallels the patterned organization of stimuli and does not represent a collection of isolated sensory elements. Damage to the brain should, therefore, disrupt the organization of stimuli. Teuber,[40] working with brain-damaged adults, demonstrated that injuries in any area of the cortex may cause a disruption of figure-ground relationships. However, he made the further point that disturbances of figure-ground relationships in a given modality vary with the locus of the lesion. When a brain-damaged person performs poorly on spatial tasks we cannot, therefore, be sure whether or not a defect in primary sensation exists.

Is there evidence for disturbances in sensation in brain-damaged children? In the case of the cerebral palsied, 50 to 86 percent are reported to have visual problems.[41,42] Hemianopsia is associated with somesthetic defect and undergrowth in the arm and leg on the affected side in a spastic hemiplegic.[43] Hearing difficulties are present in 11 to 41 percent of the cases.[42] Disturbances in sensation also occur in brain-damaged children who show no motor problems. Solomons [44] has reported the presence of sensory defects, including form, weight, and texture discrimination, in non-motor-handicapped brain-damaged children as well as in cerebral-palsied. Denhoff and Robinault noted an increase in defects in sensation with age,[42] but this finding may be a function of testing techniques.

The difficulties of separating disturbances in primary sensation from disturbances in perception have been reviewed recently by Battersby.[45] There have been few attempts to match varieties of brain-damaged children on batteries of tests of sensation and perception. Aside from this seemingly straightforward approach, a number of alternate paths of investigation seem promising.

The Effects of Intrasensory Variation on Behavior

Studies of adult hemiplegic patients show that a brain-damaged individual who has difficulty in adjusting a luminous line to a vertical position in a dark room will have no trouble in a room that is well lighted.[46,47] Furthermore, when a luminous frame is introduced to provide a background for the luminous line, brain-damaged individuals are *less* disorganized by the background than non-brain-damaged individuals. A paradox may be observed: Under some conditions of intrasensory variation, the non-brain-damaged will perform less well than the brain-damaged.[48]

When cerebral-palsied children are asked to adjust a luminous line to a vertical position in a dark room, they are strongly influenced by starting position effects, resembling in their performance younger children rather than those of their own age group.[49] Similar findings are noted when cerebral-palsied children are required to find hidden faces in a picture puzzle; [50] they have a great deal of difficulty in separating a figure from its masking context. Because in both studies the degree of difficulty appears to be related to the severity of the motor handicap, the investigators conclude that the more brain damage, the greater the difficulty in perceptual tasks.

These studies raise an interesting question: How does perception based on organization within the same sensory field develop in normal children? Nelson and Bartley [51] found a differential utilization of intrasensory cues with age. Normal children, up to the age of 7, judge figures on the basis of shape. Thus, the two-year-old can fit the shape appropriately into the form-board although he cannot draw the shape. Children aged 7 to 11 use the contour or edge rather than the shape in making judgments. (Perhaps this explains the increasing frequency of profile drawings in this age range.) These findings suggest that cerebral-palsied children may have difficulty in unscrambling hidden figures or separating figures from masking contexts because they are using an inferior set of cues to solve the problem.

The Effects of Intersensory Variation on Behavior

A recent series of investigations of agnosias—the failure to recognize objects—in some brain-damaged adults [52–54] explores their use of different sensory modalities for solving problems, *e.g.,* visual cues vs. tactile cues. The approach suggests two avenues of exploration in brain-damaged children: (*a*) correlating performance on complex perceptual tasks with performance on tasks tapping different sensory modalities and (*b*) studying individuals with different known deficits in sensory modalities on a variety of complex perceptual tasks.

There is some evidence that the normal child becomes increasingly dependent on vision rather than tactile discrimination.[40] Schachtel [55] has traced the change from reliance on the proximal senses—taste, smell, touch—to the distal senses—hearing and vision—in the growing child, and he has outlined the effects of the dependence of the schemata of perception and memory on the sensory preferences. This observation is in marked contrast to what is noted in a cerebral-palsied child: "Indeed, one is often made aware that to some of these children sound conveys so much more meaning than vision that visual stimuli are partially ignored." [56]

The Dimensions of Sensation

There is a tendency among psychologists to reduce sensation to a passive discrimination between stimuli, but, as Gibson has pointed out,[57] this is an oversimplification. The act of touching, for example, is purposive, information-seeking. There is a difference between touching and being touched. Although touch and vision, for example, may have little in common when they are conceived as channels for meaningless sense data, they may have a great deal in common when they are conceived as channels for information-gathering. "In some respects they seem to register the same information and to yield the same phenomenal experiences." Most studies of defective sensation in brain-damaged children are concerned with passive sensation rather than active sensing. There has been little attempt to apply some of the newer models of brain functioning—as an active system that controls its inputs instead of a passive receiver of sensory information—to brain-damaged children.

WHY CAN'T THE CHILD COPY CORRECTLY?

Holden [1] suggests that failure of a child with a mental age of 7 or 8 to draw a diamond is indicative of a visuomotor problem and, hence, of brain damage. Berko [58] offers evidence. Comparing cerebral palsied with a control group matched for mental and chronological age, he found that 18 of the 20 cerebral palsied failed to complete the diamond correctly on the first attempt, whereas only 2 of the 20 controls failed. There is a good deal of similar evidence to indicate difficulties in visuomotor tasks. But a basic question remains: Is the difficulty of the brain damaged visuoperceptual or visuomotor?

Opposing views have been presented. The classical view is that the problem is perceptual on a number of grounds: (1) Difficulties of the brain damaged are related to perceptual rather than motor disturbances.[59] (2) If a child has enough motor control to draw a square, he should be able to draw a diamond; hence, if he fails on the diamond, it is because he does not see it.[51] (3) In normal children, copying ability seems to be more closely related to form perception than to motor skills.[60]

Ball [61] presents further evidence for the primacy of visuoperceptual over visuomotor factors. Dividing normal and retarded children into several groups according to the degree of success with which they could copy a diamond, he subjected the groups to a phi phenomenon situation. In this task the subjects were to indicate when two identical squares merged into one and when a paired square and diamond merged. The group that severely distorted copying the diamond (although it could copy the square) did not show differences in phi thresholds between the two squares and the square–diamond. On the other hand, the group that copied the diamond did show differences in the thresholds between the two tasks. The former group apparently does not see the stimuli as different, whereas the latter does. Ball therefore concludes that there appears to be a parallelism between visuoperception and visuomotor functions. He interprets his findings as contradicting such developmental psychologists as Piaget and Inhelder,[62] who argue that motor phenomena precede the sensory in the child's learning about the world, and as supporting Kephart's [38] assumption that visuoperceptual learning can mediate visuomotor learning.

But the matter is more complex than this. Cassel [63] compared 25 exogenous mentally defective children with 25 endogenous retarded children reasonably equated for CA and MA on their ability to reproduce geometric designs. The endogenous group performed significantly better. Cassel then asked the subjects to identify the same designs seen in another context. The brain-damaged children were able to identify the designs with almost perfect success. Hence, Cassel concluded that the relatively low reproduction scores of brain-damaged children are attributable not to poor memory but to some other factor which limits the ability of the child to express what he has apprehended.

Bortner and Birch have demonstrated a similar effect in adult hemiplegics [64] and in cerebral-palsied children.[65] They found that their brain-damaged subjects made many more errors than the controls did in copying block designs. However, in the vast majority of instances the brain-damaged subjects were able to select the correct design (over their own reproductions and a standard incorrect copy) when the task was presented in multiple-choice version. Hence the investigators conclude that the difficulty of the brain damaged lies not in the perceptual system but in the perceptual-action system. They postulate the existence of functionally autonomous systems—a recognition-discrimination system that develops earlier and a perceptual-motor system, or more complex integrative system, that develops later. Furthermore, these systems are differentially affected by brain damage, the latter system tending to be more easily upset than the former.

The resolution of these opposing conclusions is not easy. Although the differences may be due to varieties of the brain damage or of the specific tasks being utilized, it is possible that other factors enter. In presenting an individual with a diamond or a block design, we usually assume that he is responding to this as an abstract design. However, it is possible—and, indeed, likely, as seen in the case of younger children—that people who have difficulties in dealing with abstract spatial symbols will view the design as a concrete object. Hence, the child draws the object he sees, which is not an abstract symbol of "diamondness" but of something else. Nelson and Bartley,[51] for example, argue that the child who uses loops to join the "east" and "west" corners of a diamond is drawing a compromise between a diamond and a kite. What may therefore be involved in the Birch-Bortner studies is not a difference between recognition discrimination and perceptual-motor actions but a difference between levels of perceptual maturity. The child interprets the stimulus at an inferior level, and hence his production is wrong. When the correct design is available, however, he can recognize it.

The question of perceptual vs. motor defects can be restated in a number of alternate ways. One possibility is that they are inseparably linked and should be considered as one. Indeed, this is the most popular current view in clinical circles. It is part of the theoretical basis of the Bender Visual Motor Gestalt test.[66] In her original monograph describing the test, Bender considers visuomotor patterns as interdependent. However, because she fails to specify the nature and conditions of this interdependency, her theory may actually obscure a number of factors which become marked in neurologically impaired persons. Another possibility is that perceptual functioning is dependent on motor feedback—the theory of reafferent stimulation. This theory has been used to explain findings in a number of experimental situations; for example, when individuals are fitted with lenses that invert everything seen through them, an individual who ambulates while wearing the lenses adapts much more rapidly than an individual who is pushed in a wheelchair.[67,68] It is possible that some types of brain damage, particularly cerebral palsy, involve defective feedback. This might account for the fact that recognition appears to be superior to execution, as in the Bortner-Birch studies,[64,65] and also for the fact that defects in purely perceptual tasks are greatest in individuals with the largest amount of motor impairment.[50]

The Problem of Rotation

One of the classical perceptual-motor signs associated with brain damage is rotation—that is, reorientation of the major axis of a figure when it is reproduced. Although not exclusive to brain damage—for example, it is characteristic of the drawings of preliterates [66]—it is generally accepted as one of the most common signs of organicity.[69,70] Some tests [8] are even based on the fact that there is a relationship between the neurophysical fact of a cortical lesion and the production of figure rotations when the figure is presented tachistoscopically (5 seconds). Bender [66] and Fabian [71] have ascribed rotation to the level of maturation of perceptual-motor patterns. They report such phenomena as normal below the age of 8 years.

Let us examine some of the evidence. Hanvik [72] reported that of a group of 20 children who produced rotations on the Bender Visual Motor Gestalt test in a psychiatric clinic, 18 had abnormal EEG's. In another study, Hanvik [73] reported that in a group of 44 brain-damaged adults, 59 percent had one or more rotations.

Chorost, Spivack, and Levine [74] found that of those children who showed rotations ($N=51$), 69 percent had abnormal EEG's, whereas of those children who did not show rotations ($N=17$), only 47 percent had abnormal EEG's. The difference is significant at the 5-percent level although authors qualify the import of the findings by pointing out that in their population of adolescent children 63 percent show abnormal EEG's.

Quast [75] compared 50 children suspected of brain damage with 50 emotionally disturbed children in a psychiatric setting. In his group ranging from 10 to 12 years, 16 of the brain damaged and only one of the emotionally disturbed showed rotation. In trying to account for the higher incidence of rotations in the brain damaged, Quast suggests conservation of energy as the main reason, although his basis for this explanation is not clear.

Cruikshank and Bice [76] find evidence of rotations in cerebral-palsied children. Koppitz [77] finds rotations one of the significant differential signs of brain damage in non-motor-handicapped children with learning problems.

Table I

Studies Demonstrating Rotation Effects in Other Than Brain-damaged Children

Author	Patient Population and Method	Results	Comment
Shapiro [78-80]	Adult brain-damaged and controls. (Different *N*'s in different studies.) Copy block design: (*a*) With and without blinders. (*b*) Square vs. diamond figure. (*c*) Square vs. diamond ground.	Rotation follows definite laws according to orientation of stimulus, paper on which it appears, and figure reproduced. Brain-damaged show tendencies to rotate. Normals with blinders to reduce visual cues act like brain-damaged.	Space perception is a plural act, orienting first to stimulus then to reproducing it. Excitation in one part of the brain inhibits other parts. Brain-damaged show exaggerated inhibition and therefore peripheral inattention.
Yates [83]	20 brain-damaged adults, 25 psychiatric patients, 20 controls. Similar to Shapiro but required drawing of block design instead of copying it.	Same as Shapiro. Brain-damaged rotate block (ground) shape, draw inner content of block in a twisted way without orientation to figure they just reproduced.	Same theory as Shapiro. Drawing different from copying block design but principles are the same.
Williams *et al.* [81,82]	Brain-damaged adults, controls, retarded. (Different *N*'s in different studies.) Task similar to Shapiro.	Results similar to Shapiro. Instructions to pay attention helped controls, not brain-damaged. Rotation also related to retardation.	Brain-damaged do not suffer from peripheral inattention but are actively confused by periphery.
Hannah [87]	State hospital consecutive admissions. Group I (N=36) received Bender Gestalt standard way. Group II (N=36) Bender Gestalt cards vertically to match.	Group I: 64 rotations. Group II: 22 rotations. (p=.05)	Rotations increase when cards are oriented horizontally, paper vertically.

Griffith and Taylor [85]	1000 veteran mental patients, including brain damage, mental retardation, schizophrenia, neurosis, character disorder, other. Traditional Bender Gestalt.	Brain-damaged rotate 40%; retarded, 55%; other, 18–20%.	Rotation is greater among brain-damaged and retardates than other groups.
Griffith and Taylor [86]	Replicates Hannah procedure. Administered normally (N=157) vs. tablet turned to match axis of card (N=56) to neuropsychiatric veterans.	Under normal administration, 29% rotation; when turned, 12% showed rotation. (p=.05)	Stimulus factors influence rotation; corroborates Hannah.
Fuller and Chagnon [84]	90 disturbed, 90 schizophrenic, and 90 normal children. Special cards varying orientations of (ground) card and (figures) stimuli. 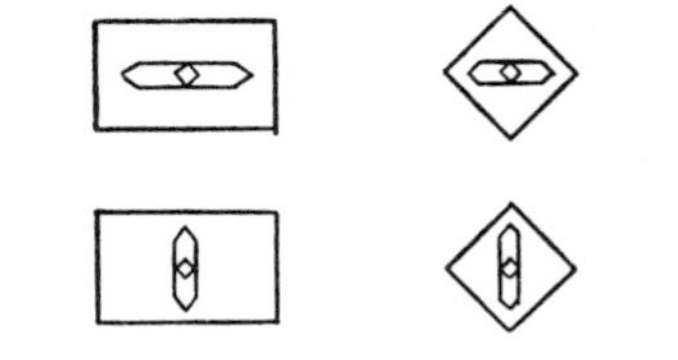	Diamond ground showed more rotation. Incongruous figure-ground orientation increases rotation. Different figures increase rotations. Disturbed children rotate more than controls.	Invokes information theory. Under certain conditions of figure-ground situations and levels of anxiety, rotation occurs.
Hovey [88]	Group I: Abnormal EEG with episodic disturbance (N=82). Group II: Abnormal EEG with no episodic disturbance. All S's were veterans in neurology service. Graham Kendall Memory for Designs test.	Group I rotations (.33) more than Group II (.08). (p=.001)	Rotation due to transient physiologic disturbances. Subject may see design correctly but may be unable to hold it in mind.
Diller [89]	42 hemiplegic adults, divided into right and left hemiplegia. Bender Gestalt rotations and perception of vertical and horizontal planes.	Rotation correlated with distortion in perception of vertical and horizontal planes.	Rotation related to ability to differentiate between self and object. Subject to sensory tonic influences.

A number of studies carried out on a variety of populations other than brain-damaged children helps us pinpoint some of the factors involved. (See Table I.) These findings indicate that rotations in brain-damaged people are enhanced by the distractions of peripheral stimuli,[78-83] by certain figure-ground properties of the stimulus,[84] and by the orientation of the stimulus in relation to the medium (the paper) used for the response.[85-87] Moreover, within a brain-damaged population, rotations occur more often in those showing episodic disturbance on the EEG [88] than in those merely showing abnormalities on the EEG, suggesting that neurophysiologic mechanisms may be implicated. The alternative hypotheses—spatial inattention,[78] spatial confusion,[82] difficulties in separating figure from ground,[9] disruption in memory,[88] difficulties in separating self from object [89]—all appear to be tapping a fundamental description of some brain-damaged people. Here we see an attempt to track down the meaning of a single empirical sign of the presence of brain damage through (*a*) manipulating the conditions which enhance its occurrence and nonoccurrence; (*b*) identifying the clinical populations who manifest it to a greater or lesser degree; and (*c*) examining some of its neurologic correlates in a search for insights into the relationships between disturbed behavior and brain damage.

What can we learn from this? A systematic examination of the variables involved should enable us to construct a clinical instrument that can identify some brain-damaged children. In addition to pointing to the possibilities of an empirically grounded test, it points in the direction of a rationally grounded test—that is, we can hope to describe not only what the brain-damaged child does but why he does it. Closer examination of the individual reports reveals an interesting difference between brain-damaged adults and brain-damaged children. In adults the presence of a pathologic sign such as rotation indicates the presence of brain damage,[90] but the absence of the sign does not indicate that brain damage is absent—*e.g.,* it will be recalled that Hovey's brain-damaged patients with EEG's that were abnormal but not indicative of episodic disturbance showed few rotations. In children, the differential implications of positive and negative signs of brain damage are less clear cut. Many of the pathognomic signs, including rotation, are age specific, so that their presence indicates a perceptual lag which may or may not be due to brain damage.[77,91]

Hovey's findings point in another direction. He suggests that it is the disruptive effects of the brain damage on the neurophysiological milieu rather than the mere presence of the brain damage that is responsible for perceptual disturbance. This inference is similar to that of Birch and Diller,[90] who have argued that perceptual dysfunctions of brain-damaged people have usually been associated with additive or disruptive lesions in the brain in which the normal neurophysiologic functioning is disturbed. However, brain-damaged people who do not show perceptual disturbances may demonstrate subtractive or nondisruptive lesions in which the neurophysiologic functioning of the brain is essentially undisturbed. The implications of this hypothesis for the brain-damaged child have yet to be explored.

OVERVIEW

We have presented a number of questions in search of an answer. Our attempt to explore possible answers has yielded us facts that are difficult to piece together to form an integrated picture. In retrospect, it is remarkable that a perceptual task should be sensitive to the presence of brain damage in view of the fact that we lack an adequate neurophysiologic theory of perception and an adequate picture of how perception evolves in the course of normal development. Some of the facts we have described may fit into theories, such as psychological differentiation, which attempt to account for perceptual development.

How do the questions we have posed and the avenues we have explored fit into clinical practice? From the standpoint of clinical practice, a brain-damaged child is usually evaluated in order to (1) help determine whether in fact he is brain damaged, (2) help identify behavioral disturbances and restrictions and their reasons, and (3) help plan programs of therapy and education. At the beginning of this paper, we pointed out some of the problems involved in using psychological evaluations to identify brain damage and/or the presence of behavioral disturbances. The problems of relating psychological evaluations to treatment are no less complex. We have tried to bypass both ends of this bottleneck—the diagnostic and the therapeutic—by trying to understand the behaviors which brain-damaged children show. An attempt to understand the mechanisms behind the response may be the most fruitful approach to filling gaps in our knowledge and may, in the end, provide the best answers to problems posed in clinical practice.

REFERENCES

1. Denhoff, E., Laufer, M. W., and Holden, R. H.: The syndromes of cerebral dysfunction, *J. Okla. Med. Ass.*, *52*:360–366, 1959.
2. Pond, D. A.: Psychiatric aspects of epileptic and brain damaged children, *Brit. Med. J.*, *2*:1378–1382; 1454–1459, 1961.
3. Baer, P.: Problems in differential diagnosis of brain damage and childhood schizophrenia, *Amer. J. Orthopsychiat.*, *31*:728–738, 1961.
4. Pollock, M., and Kreiger, H.: Oculomotor and postural patterns in schizophrenic children, *Arch. Neurol. Psychiat.*, *79*:720–726, 1958.
5. Benton, A. L.: Behavioral indices of brain injury in school children, *Child Develop.*, *33*:199–208, 1962.
6. Eisenson, J.: When and what is aphasia? *Monogr. Soc. Res. Child Develop.*, *25*:3, Serial No. 77, 1960, pp. 90–95.
7. Sarason, S. B., and Gladwin, T.: Psy-

chological and cultural problems in mental subnormality; a review of research, *Genet. Psychol. Monogr., 57*: 1: entire issue, 1958.

8. Graham, F. M., and Berman, P. W.: Current states of behavior tests for brain damage in infants and preschool children, *Amer. J. Orthopsychiat., 31*: 713–728, 1961.
9. Benton, A. L.: "The Revised Visual Retention Test: Clinical and Experimental Applications," The Psychological Corporation, New York, 1955.
10. Klebanoff, S. G., Singer, J. L., and Wilensky, H.: Psychological consequences of brain lesions and oblations, *Psychol. Bull., 51*:1–42, 1954.
11. Allen, R.: "Cerebral Palsy," in *Psychological Practices with the Physically Handicapped,* eds. J. F. Garrett and E. S. Levine. Columbia University Press, 1962.
12. Byers, R. K., and Lord, E. E.: Late effects of lead poisoning on mental development, *Amer. J. Dis. Child., 66*:471–494, 1943.
13. Lord, E. E., and Wood, L.: Diagnostic values in a visuo-motor test, *Amer. J. Orthopsychiat., 12*:414–428, 1942.
14. Meyer, E., and Byers, R. K.: Measles encephalitis: a follow-up study of sixteen patients, *Amer. J. Dis. Child., 84*:543–570, 1952.
15. Werner, H., and Weir, A.: The figure-ground syndrome in the brain injured child, *Int. Rec. Med., 169*:362–367, 1956.
16. Solley, C., and Murphy, G.: *Development of the Perceptual World.* Basic Books, 1960.
17. Goldstein, K.: *The Organism.* American Book Co., 1939.
18. Strauss, A. A., and Werner, H.: Experimental analysis of the clinical symptom "perseveration" in mentally retarded children, *Amer. J. Ment. Defic., 47*:185–192, 1942.
19. Strauss, A. A., and Werner, H.: Disorders of conceptual thinking in the brain injured child, *J. Nerv. Ment. Dis., 96*:153–172, 1942.
20. Strauss, A. A., and Werner, H.: Comparative psychopathology of the brain injured child and the traumatic brain injured adult, *Amer. J. Psychiat., 99*: 835–840, 1943.
21. Werner, H., and Strauss, A. A.: Causal factors in low test performances, *Amer. J. Ment. Defic., 45*:213–218, 1940.
22. Werner, H., and Bowers, B.: Auditory motor organization in a clinical type of mentally deficient children, *J. Genet. Psychol., 59*:85–99, 1941.
23. Werner, H., and Strauss, A. A.: Pathology of figure background relations in the child, *J. Abnorm. Soc. Psychol., 36*:236–248, 1941.
24. Werner, H., and Thuma, B. D.: A deficiency in the perception of apparent motion in children with brain injury, *Amer. J. Ment. Defic., 55*:58–65, 1942.
25. Werner, H., and Thuma, B. D.: Critical flicker frequency in children with brain injury, *Amer. J. Psychol., 55*: 394–406, 1942.
26. Werner, H., and Carrison, D.: Animistic thinking in brain injured mentally retarded children, *J. Abnorm. Soc. Psychol., 39*:43–62, 1944.
27. Werner, H.: Development of visual motor performance on the marble board test in mentally retarded children, *J. Genet. Psychol., 64*:269–278, 1944.
28. Werner, H.: Abnormal and subnormal rigidity, *J. Abnorm. Soc. Psychol., 41*: 15–24, 1946.
29. Werner, H.: Perceptual behavior of brain injured mentally defective children; an experimental study by means of the Rorschach technique, *Genet. Psychol. Monogr., 31*:51–110, 1945.
30. Dolphin, J. E., and Cruickshank, W. N.: The figure-ground relationship in children with cerebral palsy, *J. Clin. Psychol., 7*:228–231, 1951.
31. Dolphin, J. E., and Cruickshank, W. N.: Tactual motor perception of children with cerebral palsy, *J. Personality, 20*: 466–471, 1952.

32. Goldenberg, S.: "Psychological Evaluation," in *Psychopathology and Education of the Brain Injured Child.* Vol. II, by A. A. Strauss and N. C. Kephart. Grune & Stratton, 1955.
33. Marks, H. J., and Pasamanick, B.: Asynchronism and apparent movement thresholds in brain injured children, *J. Consult. Psychol., 22*:173–177, 1958.
34. *A Five-Year Study of Brain Damaged Children,* The Mental Health Center, Springfield, Ill., 1962, p. 43.
35. Strauss, A. A., and Lehtinen, L.: *Psychopathology and Education of the Brain Injured Child.* Grune & Stratton, 1947.
36. Cronbach, L. J.: Statistical methods as applied to Rorschach scores, *Psychol. Bull., 46*:393–433, 1949.
37. Rabinovitch, R. D., Drew, A. L., DeJong, R., Ingram, W., and Withey, L.: "A Research Approach to Reading Retardation," in *Neurology and Psychiatry in Childhood,* eds. R. McIntosh and C. Hare. Williams & Wilkins, Baltimore, 1956, pp. 363–396.
38. Kephart, N. C.: *The Slow Learner in the Classroom.* Charles E. Merrill Books, Columbus, O., 1960.
39. Stephenson, G. R.: "Form Perception, Abstract Thinking, and Intelligence Test Validity in Cerebral Palsy." Doctoral dissertation, Teacher's College, Columbia University, 1957.
40. Teuber, H. L.: "Perception," in *Handbook of Physiology,* Vol. 3, ed. J. Field. American Physiological Society, Washington, 1959–1960.
41. Breakey, A. S.: Ocular findings in cerebral palsy, *Arch. Ophthal., 53*: 852–856, 1955.
42. Denhoff, E., and Robinault, I.: *Cerebral Palsy and Related Disorders.* McGraw-Hill, 1961.
43. Tizard, J. P., Paine, R. S., and Crothers, B.: Disturbances of sensation in children with hemiplegia, *J.A.M.A., 155*:628–632, 1954.
44. Solomons, H. C.: "A Developmental Study of Tactual Perception in Normal and Brain Damaged Children." Doctoral (education) dissertation, Boston University, 1957.
45. Battersby, W. S.· "Neuropsychology," in *Progress in Clinical Psychology,* eds. L. Abt and D. Brower. Grune & Stratton, 1958.
46. Birch, H. G., Proctor, F., Bortner, M., and Lowenthal, M.: Perception in hemiplegia: I. Judgment of vertical and horizontal by hemiplegic patients, *Arch. Phys. Med. Rehab., 14*:19–25, 1960.
47. Birch, H. G., Proctor, F., Bortner, M., and Lowenthal, M.: Perception in hemiplegia: II. Judgment of the median plane, *Arch. Phys. Med. Rehab., 14*:71–75, 1960.
48. Birch, H. G., Belmont, I., Reilly, T., and Belmont, L.: Visual verticality in hemiplegia, *Arch. Neurol., 5*:444–453, 1961.
49. Teuber, H. L., and Rudel, R. G.: Behavior after cerebral lesions in children and adults, *Develop. Med. Child Neurol., 4*:3–20, 1962.
50. Cobrinik, L.: The performance of brain injured children on a variety of hidden figure tasks, *Amer. J. Psychol., 72*:566–571, 1959.
51. Nelson, T. M., and Bartley, S. H.: Various factors playing a role in children's responses to flat copy, *J. Genet. Psychol., 100*:289–308, 1962.
52. Battersby, W. S., Krieger, H. D., and Bender, M. B.: Visual and tactile discriminative learning in patients with cerebral tumors, *Amer. J. Psychol., 68*:562–574, 1955.
53. Semmes, J., Weinstein, S., Ghent, L., and Teuber, H. L.: Performance on complex tactical tasks after brain injury in man: analysis by locus of lesion, *Amer. J. Psychol., 67*:220–247, 1954.
54. Semmes, J., Weinstein, S., Ghent, L., and Teuber, H. L.: Spatial orientation in man after cerebral injury: analysis by locus of lesion, *J. Psychol., 39*: 227–244, 1955.
55. Shachtel, E. G.: "On Memory and Childhood Amnesia," in *A Study of*

Interpersonal Relations, ed. P. Mullahy. Grove Press, 1957.

56. Ram, M. J.: Some educational aspects of the visuospatial handicap in cerebral palsied children, *Spastics Quart., 11*:13–25, 1962 (p. 13).
57. Gibson, J. J.: Observations on active touch, *Psychol. Rev., 69*:477–482, 1962.
58. Berko, M. J.: Some factors in the perceptual deviation of cerebral palsied children, *Cereb. Palsy Rev., 15*:3–4, 1954.
59. Goldstein, K., and Scheerer, M.: Abstract and concrete behavior: an experimental study with special tests, *Psychol. Monogr., 83*:239: entire issue, 1959.
60. Townsend, E. A.: A study of copying ability in children, *Genet. Psychol. Monogr., 43*:1–43, 1951.
61. Ball, T. S.: Reproductions and phi thresholds as indices of form perception, *J. Consult. Psychol., 26*:455–461, 1962.
62. Piaget, J., and Inhelder, B.: *The Child's Conception of Space.* Rantledge & Paul, London, 1956.
63. Cassel, R. H.: Relation of design reproduction to the etiology of mental deficiency, *J. Consult. Psychol., 13*: 421–428, 1949.
64. Bortner, M., and Birch, H. G.: Perceptual and perceptual motor dissociations in brain damaged patients, *J. Nerv. Ment. Dis., 130*:49–53, 1961.
65. Bortner, M., and Birch, H. G.: "Perceptual and Perceptual Motor Dissociations in Cerebral Palsied Children." Paper presented at the American Psychological Association meeting, New York, 1961.
66. Bender, L. A.: *Visual Motor Gestalt Test and its Clinical Use,* American Orthopsychiatric Association, New York, 1938.
67. Bossom, J.: "Complete Recovery of Accurate Egocentric Localization during Prolonged Wearing of Prisms." Paper presented at the American Psychological Association meeting, Cincinnati, O., 1959.
68. Bossom, J., and Held, R.: "Shifts in Egocentric Localization Following Prolonged Displacement of the Retinal Image." Paper presented at the American Psychological Association meeting, New York, 1957.
69. Clawson, A.: *The Bender Visual Motor Gestalt Test for Children,* Western Psychological Services, Beverly Hills, Calif., 1962.
70. Hutt, M., and Briskin, G. J.: *The Clinical Use of the Revised Bender Gestalt Test.* Grune & Stratton, 1960, p. 166.
71. Fabian, A. A.: Rotations in drawings of children, *J. Educ. Psychol., 36*: 129–154, 1945.
72. Hanvik, L.: A note on rotation of the Bender gestalt test as predictors of EEG abnormalities in children, *J. Clin. Psychol., 9*:399, 1954.
73. Hanvik, L., and Anderson, A. J.: The effect of focal brain lesions on recall on the productions of rotations in Bender gestalt figures, *J. Consult. Psychol., 14*:197–198, 1950.
74. Chorost, S. B., Spivack, A., and Levine, M.: Bender gestalt rotations and EEG abnormalities in children, *J. Consult. Psychol., 23*:559, 1959.
75. Quast, W.: The Bender gestalt; a clinical study of children's records, *J. Consult. Psychol., 25*:155–162, 1961.
76. Cruickshank, W. M., and Bice, H.: *Perception in Cerebral Palsy.* Syracuse University Press, 1957.
77. Koppitz, E. M.: Diagnosing brain damage in young children with the Bender gestalt test, *J. Consult. Psychol., 26*:541–546, 1962.
78. Shapiro, M. B.: Experimental studies of a perceptual anomaly: I. Initial experiments, *J. Ment. Sci.. 97*:90–110, 1951.
79. Shapiro, M. B.: Experimental studies of a perceptual anomaly: II. Confirmatory and explanatory experiments, *J. Ment. Sci., 98*:605–617, 1952.
80. Shapiro, M. B.: Experimental studies of a perceptual anomaly: III. The testing of an explanatory theory, *J. Ment. Sci., 99*:394–409, 1953.

81. Williams, H., Lubin, A., Gieseking, C., and Rubenstein, I.: The relations of brain injury and visual perception to block design rotation, *J. Consult. Psychol.*, *20*:275–280, 1956.
82. Williams, H., Gieseking, C., and Lubin, A.: Interaction of brain injury with peripheral vision and set, *J. Consult. Psychol.*, *25*:543–548, 1961.
83. Yates, A. J.: The rotation of drawings by brain damaged patients, *J. Abnorm. Soc. Psychol.*, *53*:178–182, 1956.
84. Fuller, J. B., and Chagnon, G.: Factors influencing rotation in the Bender gestalt performance of children, *J. Project. Techn.*, *26*:36–47, 1962.
85. Griffith, R. M., and Taylor, V.: The incidence of Bender gestalt rotations, *J. Consult. Psychol.*, *24*:189–190, 1960.
86. Griffith, R. M., and Taylor, V.: Bender gestalt rotations: a stimulus factor, *J. Consult. Psychol.*, *25*:89–90, 1961.
87. Hannah, L. D.: Causative factors in the production of rotation on the Bender-gestalt design, *J. Consult. Psychol.*, *22*:398–399, 1958.
88. Hovey, B. I.: An analysis of figure rotations, *J. Consult. Psychol.*, *25*:21–25, 1961.
89. Diller, L.: The Bender gestalt test in hemiplegia. Unpublished data.
90. Birch, H. G., and Diller, L.: Rorschach signs in organicity: a physiological basis for perceptual disturbance, *J. Project. Techn.*, *23*:91–108, 1959.
91. Frostig, M., Lefever, D. A., and Whittlesey, J. R. B.: A developmental test of visual perception for evaluating normal and neurologically handicapped children, *Percept. Motor Skills*, *12*:383–394, 1961.

DISCUSSION

As a result of findings that certain types of situations produce better performance by brain-damaged children than by normal individuals, considerable interest was expressed in the possibility of developing positive rather than negative tests indicative of the presence of brain damage. It was pointed out that a number of existing testing devices for other kinds of functional aberration, such as diabetes and epilepsy, involve the existence of positive indicators of the dysfunction. Another example is the Ishihara test for color blindness, in which individuals who lack color discrimination are able to make certain perceptions on the test cards that cannot be made by individuals who are normal in color discrimination. It was felt that increased emphasis should be placed upon what sick children can do that other children cannot do. If we could discover what brain-injured individuals can do better than normal persons, we would then undoubtedly be on the track of certain of the distinguishing mechanisms that underlie their functioning. Once again the analogy to color blindness was raised. It was pointed out that color-blind individuals are able to pierce camouflage that is entirely effective when viewed by individuals with normal color perception. Thus, in certain circumstances, a defect may be an asset.

As a direct extension of the problem involved in the development of positive tests for brain damage, the discussion moved to the more general topic of the functional meaning of psychological testing of brain-damaged children. It was pointed out that in a true sense, the psychological evaluation of a child is not so much to determine whether he is brain damaged. It was agreed that at our present stage of knowledge such an inference has insufficient validity. The object of psychological evaluation should be, rather, the identification of the particular patterns of cognitive and conative functioning of the individual so that regions of strength and weakness, as well as the circumstances for the development of optimal behaviors, might be identified. The degree to which the emphasis can be shifted from an identification of deficiencies to an identification of positive attributes in functioning will influence the degree to which psychological evaluation can provide a sound basis for educational planning and for the habilitation or rehabilitation of the child.

The group members who were not psychologists expressed considerable dissatisfaction with the patient classifications used in most psychological investigations. It was suggested that neurologists, psychiatrists, or neurophysiologists derive little benefit from such classificatory terms as exogenous, endogenous, cerebral palsied, brain damaged, etc. These terms lack explicitness in definition and have insufficient etiologic and prognostic meaning. As one consequence, in separate studies on children presumably suffering from an entity identified by the same name, quite different clinical, physiological, and behavioral findings exist.

It was believed that, to a considerable extent, the apparent disagreements in findings among investigators stemmed from the fact that these investigators were studying populations of children who differed significantly one from the other in the nature of their neurologic damage and in the time of life at which such damage had been sustained. Thus, the samples studied were basically incomparable. To illustrate the point, it was suggested that the primary basis for the differences in findings between Teuber and Reitan stemmed not so much from the amount of damage or from its site in the brain as from fundamental difference between the two populations studied. Teuber, for example, was not studying patients. He was studying ex-soldiers who had been injured during the war in the prime of their youth and who were called back for examination approximately ten years later, long after the acute stage of illness had passed. Most of these individuals were functioning well in the community, were working at gainful occupations, and had not spontaneously sought out clinical attention. Reitan, in contrast, studied persons who had come to the neurosurgery clinic because of significant current dysfunction, inability to continue gainful activity in the community, marked distress, and clearly evident signs of neurologic disorganization. In brief, one group consisted of individuals with static, noninterfering damage to the brain, whereas the other consisted of clinical cases who presented themselves to a hospital service with serious functional complaints.

It was suggested that a reconciliation of viewpoints and a clearer understanding of the psychologic functions which may in fact be disturbed by damage to the brain may require that considerably more attention be devoted to the definition of study populations and to the careful delineation of neurologic, functional, and historical characteristics.

The sociologists and psychologists participating in the discussion recognized the validity and cogency of these criticisms with respect to the inadequacy of definition of the clinical groupings but noted that such criticism stops short of a full analysis of the inadequacy of reporting. They felt that neurologic case reports on brain damage in children give too little attention to the social and familial background characteristics of the children studied and that not enough sophisticated behavioral analysis accompanies the detailed neurologic findings. This criticism, it was pointed out, was not raised defensively but in the interest of fuller multidisciplinary consideration of the problems involved in the formulation of research.

Considerable concern was expressed over the repetitiveness and duplication that seem to characterize the psychological investigation of brain-damaged children. In a sense, investigators appear to be exploring with refinements the same paths as have their predecessors instead of doing basically new or different work. It was suggested that too much of the research by psychologists is dominated by techniques, tests, or gadgets and that what appears to be lacking is the development of meaningful hypotheses which could lead to more intensive investigation of mechanisms underlying behavioral disturbance. The consensus was that this path of hypothesis-oriented investigation holds the greatest promise for fruitful future inquiry.

Two Strategies for Studying Perception in "Brain-damaged" Children

HERBERT G. BIRCH, M.D., PH.D. ARTHUR LEFFORD, PH.D.
Albert Einstein College of Medicine

MANY INVESTIGATIONS [1,2] as well as clinical evaluations have clearly indicated that disturbed perceptual or perceptual-motor functioning frequently accompanies central nervous system damage. Given such aberrant functioning as a fact, we have, as yet, little understanding of the nature of the underlying mechanisms or processes that result in the disturbed performances. Thus, failure to perform adequately on a block-design test, though frequently interpreted as the consequence of impaired perception, may in fact occur in patients who can recognize and discriminate the correct visual pattern but cannot organize the scattered blocks to reproduce correctly what they can see. Thus, as Birch and Bortner [3] have demonstrated, some brain-damaged patients who make erroneous block-design reproductions can nevertheless choose a correct reproduction over their own product when asked to identify the one which most closely resembles the model. These findings suggest that perception cannot be viewed as a single process and that a greater understanding of mechanisms underlying perceptual changes accompanying central nervous system damage requires a more detailed analysis of the perceptual phenomena themselves. The present paper reports on some of the strategies we have used in analyzing perception and on some of the findings. We hope that these findings will help to clarify and define some of the consequences.

Several models can be used for defining strategic approaches to the analysis of perception. Our first strategy derives from Sherrington's overview of the evolution of nervous system organization. In tracing the evolution of the role of the central nervous system in mediating the relation of the organism to the environment, Sherrington [4] has stated:

> The naive would have expected evolution in its course to have supplied us with more various sense organs for ampler perception of the world. . . . The policy has rather been for the nervous system to bring the so-called

"five" into closer touch with one another. A central clearinghouse of sense has grown up. . . . Not new senses, but better liaison between old senses is what the developing nervous system has in this respect stood for. (Pp. 287–289.)

The generalization flowing from the findings of comparative neurophysiology receives considerable support from comparative psychology. In large part the understanding of the mechanisms underlying phylogenetic differences in the plasticity and modifiability of behavior has been based upon the recognition [5] that as one ascends in the vertebrate series from fish to man the unimodal sensory control of behavior comes to be superseded by multimodal and intersensory control mechanisms. The unevenness of the development of such an intersensory liaison is illustrated nicely by the behavior of the frog. As long ago as 1882, the naturalist-physician Abbott demonstrated [6] that the frog is incapable of modifying a visually determined response on the basis of information obtained through pain sensation. Thus, a frog that was permitted to strike at a live fly impaled upon a central post that was surrounded by a sharp palisade of stakes continued to strike at the moving fly despite the fact that every outthrust of its tongue resulted in its tongue being impaled upon the sharp points of the palisade. In Abbott's description, the visually determined striking response to the fly was continued even though the frog's tongue was ripped to shreds. Thus, no modulation of a visually determined response occurred as a consequence of a tactual pain stimulus.

In contrast, however, in the same organism, the visually determined striking response was capable of being modified by information received through gustatory avenues of stimulation. Thus, as Schaeffer [7] has pointed out, a frog in a very few trials will learn to inhibit its visually determined striking response to a bitter hairy caterpillar. Again, in experiments in our own laboratories, the visually determined response of a frog to a moving target was seen to be rapidly inhibited when the target was coated with a bitter substance, such as quinine. Therefore, in the frog, gustatory stimulation is capable of modulating and modifying visually determined response, whereas tactual stimulation apparently is not. In contrast to the amphibian, the normal adult mammal may, under appropriate conditions, adequately integrate information deriving from all sense avenues, and this liaison constitutes one of the major functions of the cerebral cortex.

In man considerable evidence has been amassed [8] to suggest strongly that even for relatively simple sensory functions the effects produced by the application of a stimulus to a given sense organ are continuously modified by ongoing activity in the other sense modalities. Such findings have added substance to the early speculations of such pioneers in the study of behavioral development as Baldwin,[9] who, more than a half-century ago, sought to analyze the development of perceptual-motor control in terms of the age-specific emergence of visual-kinesthetic interrelations. Although Baldwin restricted his consideration to the problem of motor control, it is clear, as we have suggested elsewhere,[10] that similar considerations may underlie the development of perception and cognition. Despite the potential importance of the establishment of interrelations among the separate sense modalities for behavioral maturation, little evidence is available on the development of the functioning of sensory interactions and interrelationships.

Frequently items of evidence as well as impressions derived from general observations of children serve to support the presumption that changing relations among the sense modalities are characteristic features of child development. In infants and young children, sensations deriving from the viscera and from stimuli applied to the skin surface appear to be predominant in directing behavior, whereas at these ages information presented visually or auditorily is relatively ineffective. As the child matures, the teloreceptive modalities assume an even more prominent position in the sensory hierarchy until, by school age, vision and audition appear to become the most important sensory modalities for directing behavior. Such hierarchical shifts are orderly and seem to be accompanied by increased intersensory liaison in normal children. Such changes may be considered as one basis for the development of human behavioral complexity, in that, with them, the child comes simultaneously to be dominated less by his internal state and more by the external environment and less by any single stimulus than by the interrelations among stimuli reaching him through his different avenues of sense.

INTERSENSORY STUDY

These considerations led to the study of normal intersensory development in children and to the investigation of such functions in neurologically damaged individuals. The sensory systems studied were vision, kinesthesis, and haptic touch. (By a haptic stimulus we mean one that is mediated through touch and active exploratory movement of the hand.) The subjects were asked to judge whether simultaneously presented stimuli in pairs were the same or different in shape. The same blocks were used as the visual and haptic stimuli. As a visual stimulus, the block was placed on the table directly in front of the subjects where it could be seen. For haptic stimulation, the subject's hand, behind an opaque screen, was placed on the Seguin Block by the experimenter. The subject then actively explored the form with his hand outside his field of vision. Kinesthetic information was provided by placing the subject's arm behind a screen and, with the arm out of the subject's sight, passively moving it through a path describing the geometric form. This was accomplished by placing a stylus in normal writing position in the subject's hand. The examiner gripped the stylus above the point at which it was held by the subject and then moved the stylus and hand through the path of a track inscribed in a linoleum block which described the geometric form. The tracks were made in 4″ by 6″ linoleum blocks, inscribed

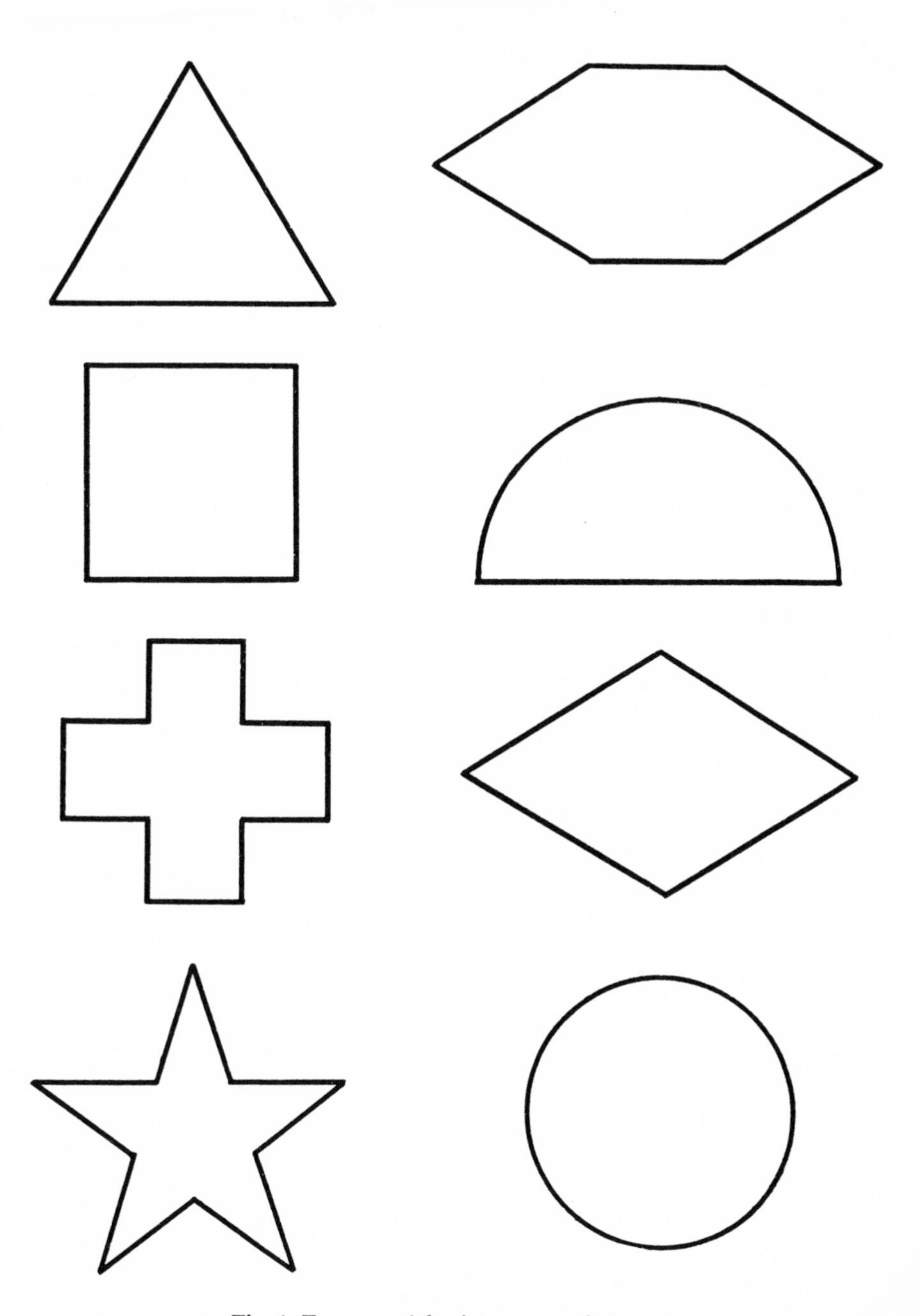

Fig. 1. Forms used for intersensory judgment.

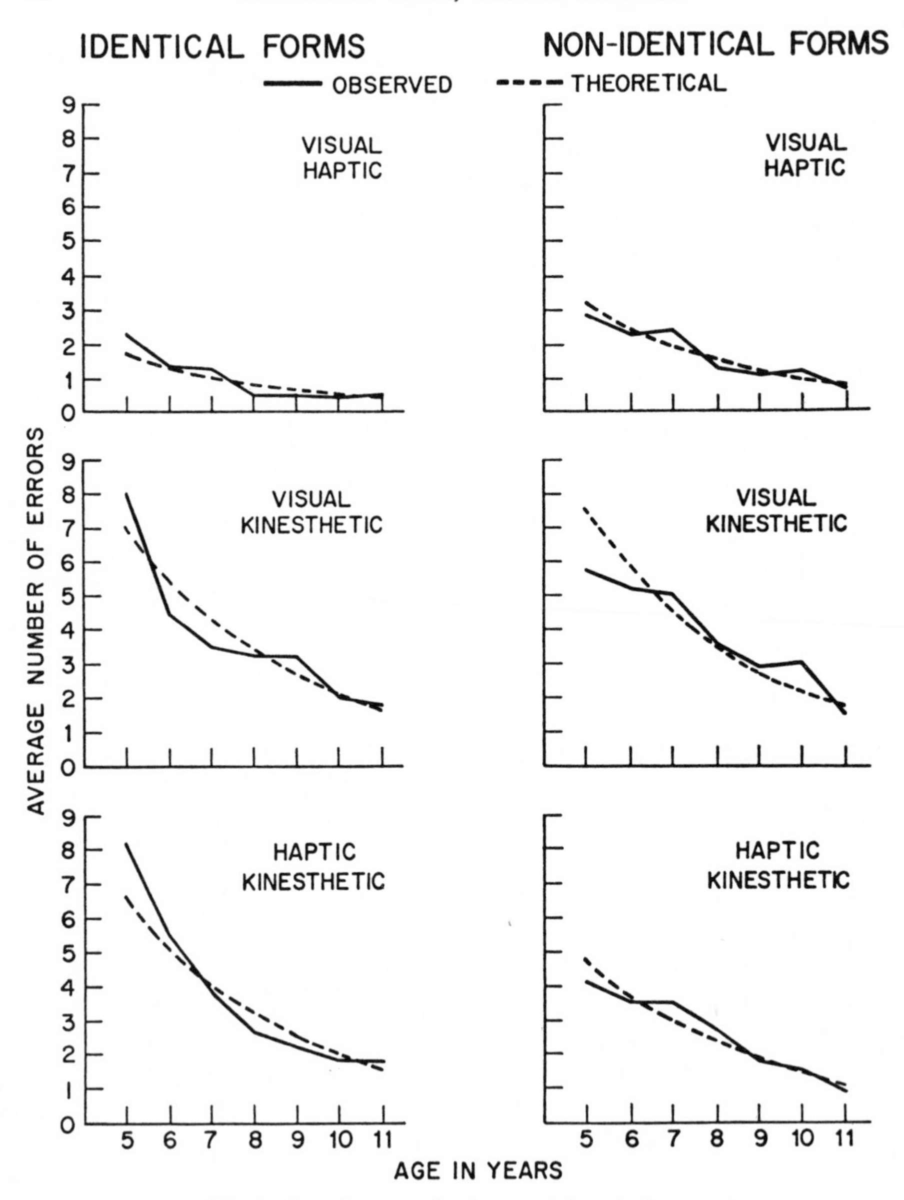

Fig. 2. Growth curves for intermodal equivalence.

to a depth of one eighth of an inch. The outlined dimensions of the tracks were of the same sizes and shapes as the various blocks used for visual and haptic stimulation. The forms used are shown in Figure 1.

Having described briefly the technique, we would like to present some preliminary findings. We can see from Figure 2 that for normal children errors decrease with age for all conditions of sensory interaction and resemble the curves of exponential decay functions. The empirical findings and theoretical curves plotted from the Thompson growth equation do not differ at the 1-percent level of confidence.

The column headed "Identical Forms" contains the results obtained from judging the *same* geometric form in both sense modalities. The column headed

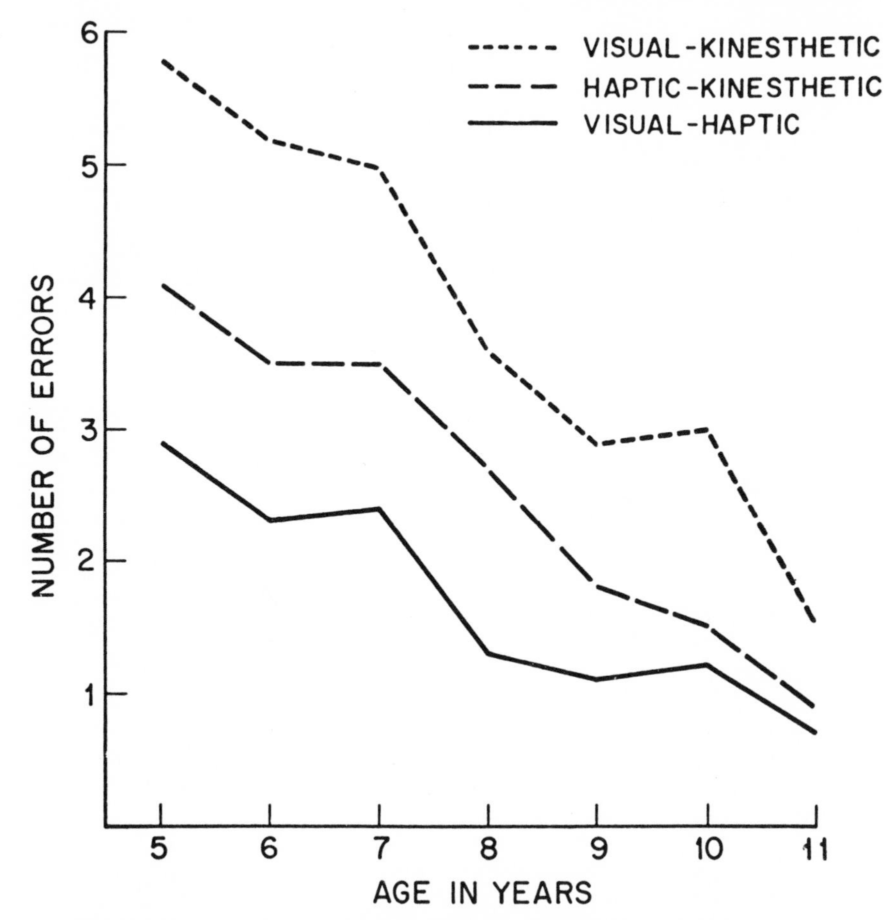

Fig. 3. The average errors made in judging non-identical or different forms.

"Non-identical Forms" indicates the results obtained from judging *different* geometrical forms in both sense modalities. It will be noted that by age five visual-haptic interaction appears to be relatively well established as compared to visual-kinesthetic and haptic-kinesthetic interaction.

The relations between different sensory systems develop at different rates, and in Figure 3 we can observe the effect of the specific sensory combination

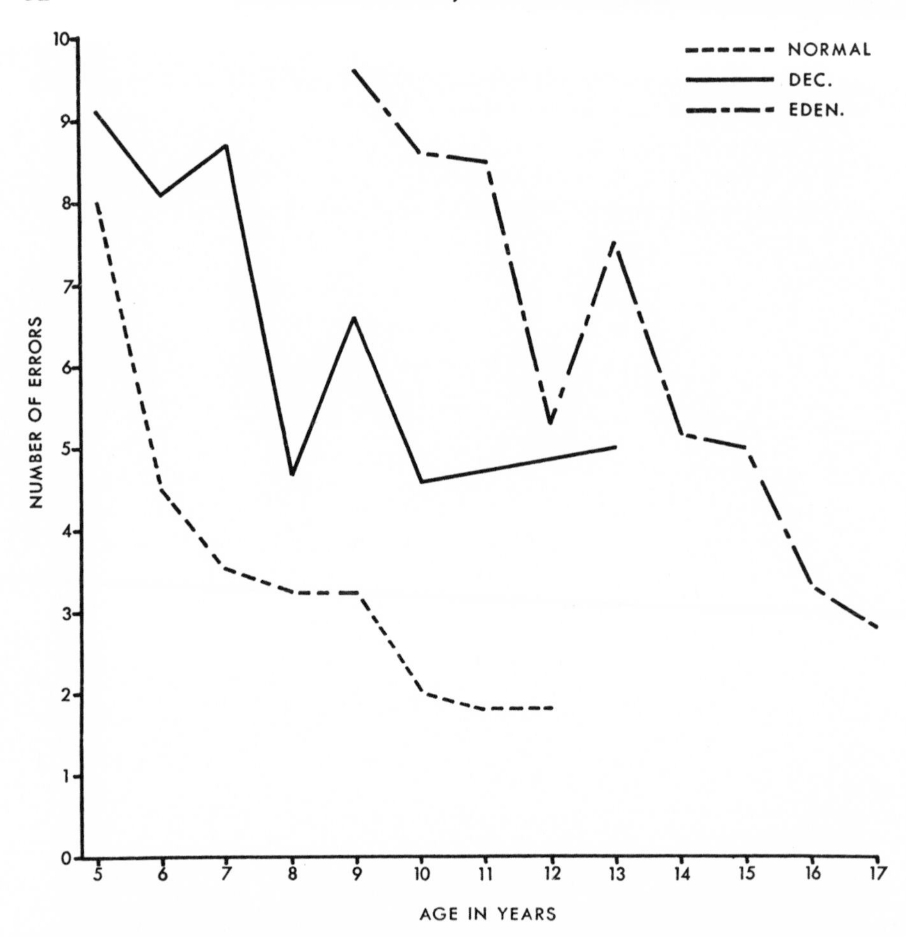

Fig. 4. The functioning of normal and retarded groups on the visual-haptic judgment of identical forms. The DEC (Developmental Evaluation Clinic) group was comprised of children who had in common the presenting symptoms of retarded speech development. The Edenwald group was comprised of older mentally retarded children in an institutional setting.

on intersensory functioning. It can be noted that visual-haptic judgments are less difficult than haptic-kinesthetic judgments, which in turn are less difficult for the child than visual-kinesthetic judgments.

When normal children are compared with groups of neurologically impaired children in this type of functioning, clear difference in intersensory functioning can be noted. Several groups of neurologically impaired children were studied: a group of children with retarded speech development, several groups of mentally retarded children, a group of epileptic children, and a group of cerebral-palsied children.

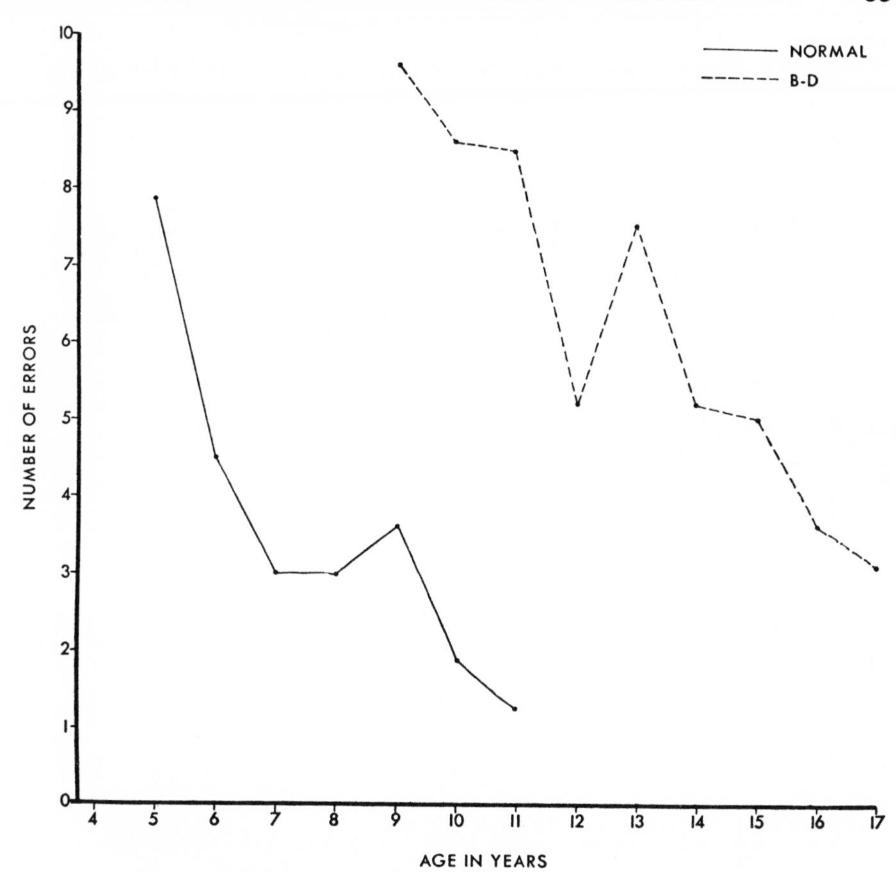

Fig. 5. Visual-kinesthetic judgments in normal and abnormal children.

In Figure 4 the functioning of the normal group is contrasted with the retarded groups on the visual-haptic judgment of identical forms. We note that the performance of the abnormal groups on visual-haptic judgment of identical forms tends to be poorer than that of the normal group.

In Figure 5 the normal group is contrasted with the retarded groups on the visual-kinesthetic judgment of identical forms. It is interesting to note here that with a change to the visual-kinesthetic function the differences between the groups became markedy accentuated.

In Figure 6 the normal group is contrasted with the older retarded group on the haptic-kinesthetic judgments. Here one can note the enormous variability in performance in the abnormal group, a characteristic that raises problems in the consideration of the data. Because of this variability, we have often found it useful to consider abnormal cases on an individual case basis rather than on a group basis.

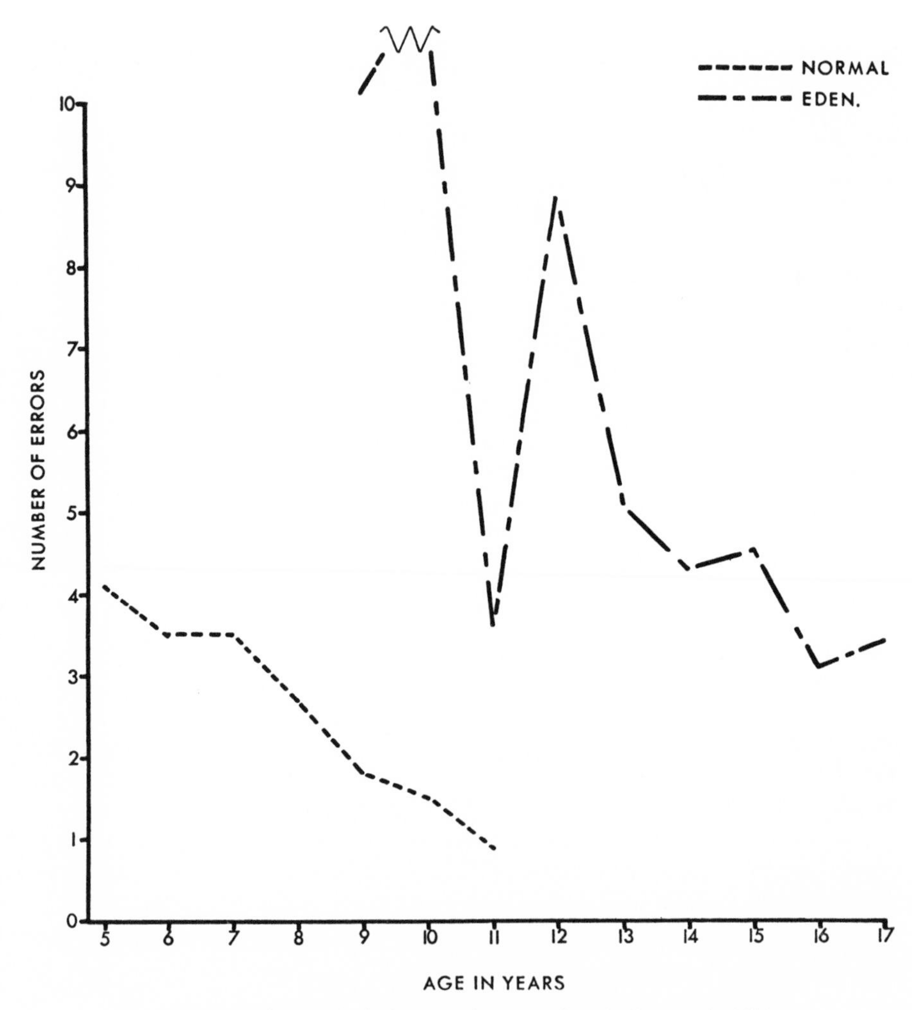

Fig. 6. Haptic-kinesthetic judgments in normal and abnormal children.

PERCEPTUAL-MOTOR STUDY

The second strategy with which we have been concerned views complex perceptual activity as involving a number of processes. We have considered perceptual functioning in terms of such features as perceptual discrimination, analysis, and synthesis. Further, we have attempted to relate these aspects of the complex act of perceiving to the organization of motor functioning.

Recognition was studied by testing the subject's ability to discriminate perceptually among a set of 12 geometric forms which included those forms studied in detail on the motor task (Fig. 7). Perceptual analysis was studied by asking the subjects to find in a whole figure isolated parts of the figure,

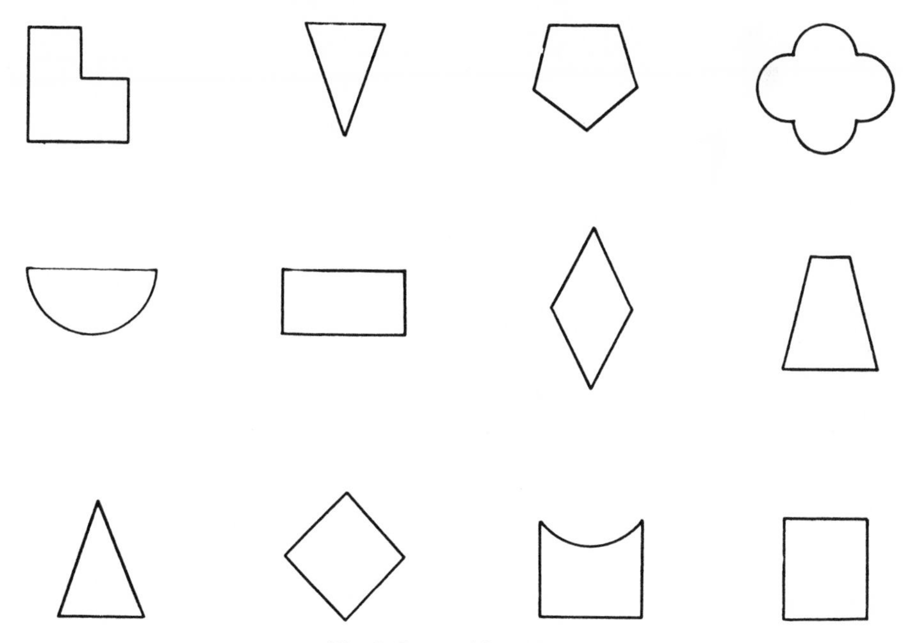

Fig. 7. Recognition forms.

such as angles or sides of triangles and diamonds (Fig. 8). Perceptual synthesis was studied by asking the subjects to select one of four sets of lines which could be used to construct a whole figure (Fig. 9).

In Table I the number of correct responses made by normal and cerebral-palsied children on the perceptual discrimination task are presented. Although the functioning of the cerebral-palsied children is somewhat poorer and the difference between them and the normal children statistically significant, the difference in functional significance is slight.

Table I

Differences in the Discrimination of Form Between Normal and Cerebral-Palsied Children

Age in Years	Norm	C-P
5	11.2	10.2
6	11.4	9.8
7	11.5	9.9
8	11.5	11.3
9	11.9	9.4
10	11.6	12.0
11	11.6	11.5

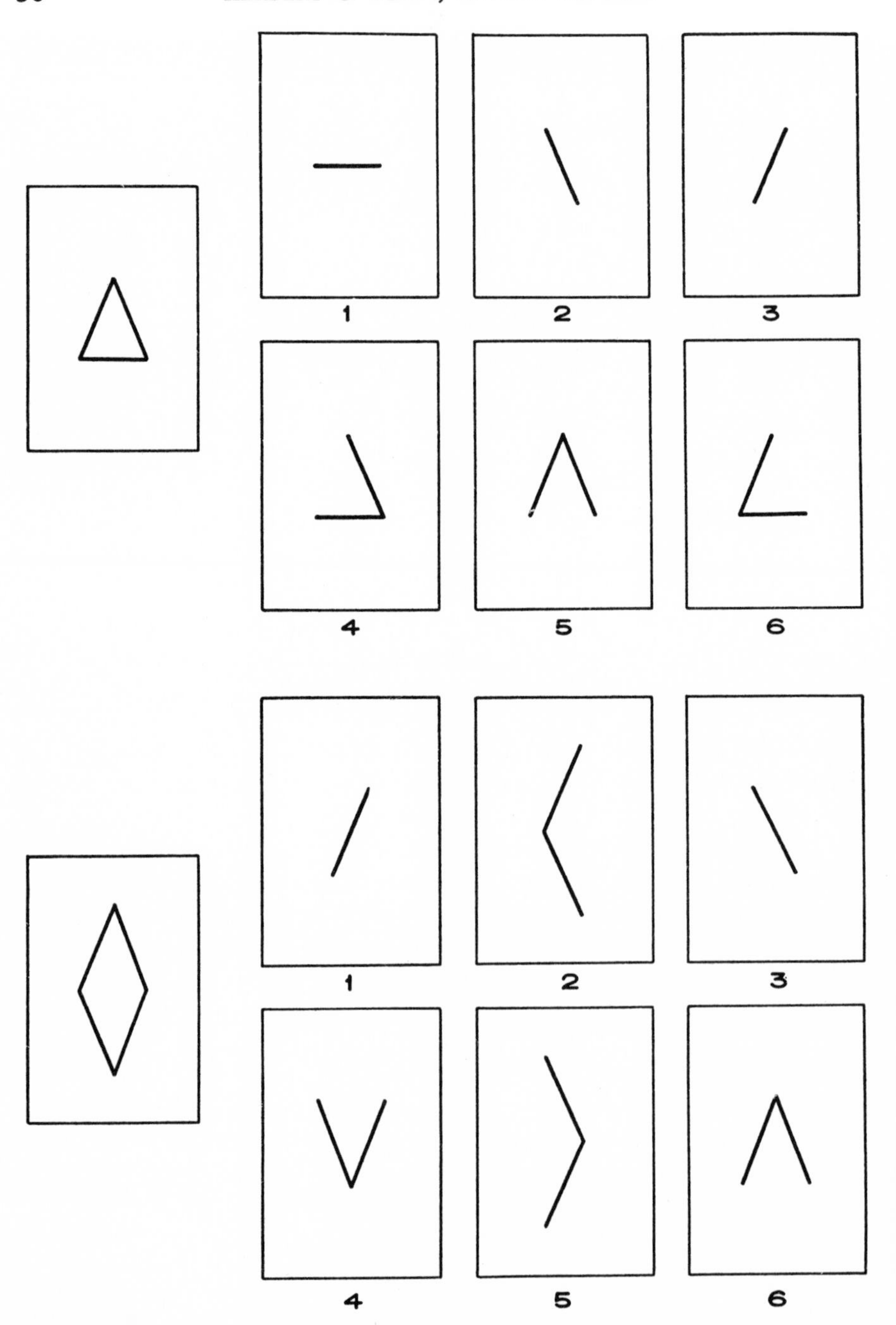

Fig. 8. Analysis of forms.

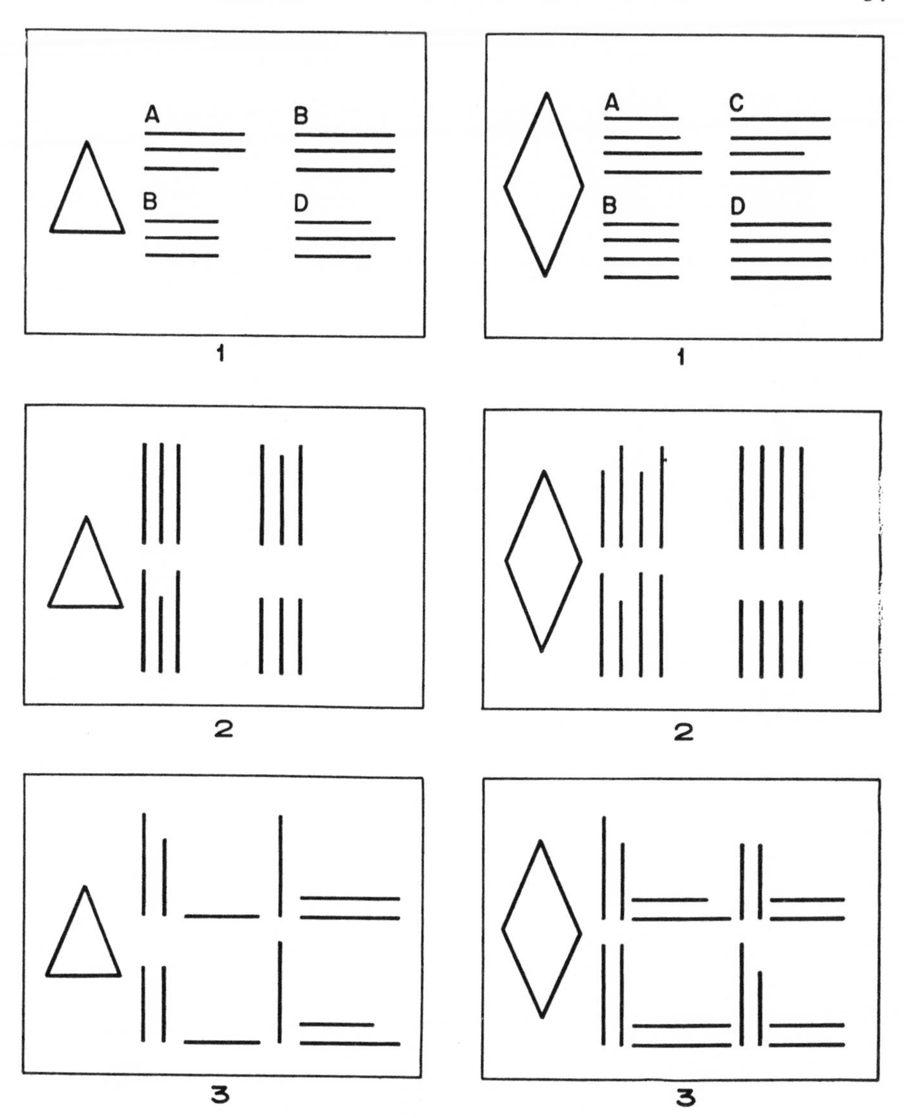

Fig. 9. Synthesis of forms.

The findings are quite different with respect to the ability to perform perceptual analysis of a whole figure (Table II). It will be noted that the cerebral-palsied group does considerably worse than the normal group. Both groups show development with age, but the normal group shows a considerably accelerated performance. By age 12, the normal group makes a maximum score of six whereas the cerebral-palsied children only start to approach the maximum by age 18. Therefore on the perceptual analysis test, in spite

Table II

Differences Between Normal and Cerebral-Palsied Children in the Ability to Analyze Visual Percepts

Age in Years	Norm	C-P
5	3.8	1.2
6	4.4	2.4
7	4.5	2.6
8	5.4	3.3
9	5.2	2.4
10	5.4	3.8
11	5.7	2.4
12	6.0	4.3
13		3.6
14	Max.=6	4.3
15		4.2
16		5.0
17		4.7
18		5.5

of relatively normal discrimination recognition functioning, the development in the neurologically damaged group seems to be markedly atypical.

Perceptual synthetic functioning is even more disturbed in the cerebral-palsied group of children. As may be seen in Table III, perceptual synthetic ability develops with age in the normal group but shows no significant developmental trend in the neurologically impaired children.

Table III

Differences Between Normal and Cerebral-Palsied Children in the Ability to Synthesize a Visua Percept from its Elements

Age in Years	Norm	C-P
5	1.3	1.0
6	2.5	0.8
7	1.9	0.9
8	2.5	0.3
9	2.1	0.8
10	2.9	0.8
11	2.7	0.5
12	2.7	0.7
13		0.6
14	Max.=3	1.0
15		0.7
16		0.8
17		0.9
18		0.6

DISCUSSION

The findings reported can most appropriately be viewed as illustrations of methods whereby one can begin to define some of the primary defects in basic developmental mechanisms that underlie deficient performance in "brain-damaged" children. Because the groups of neurologically abnormal children were insufficiently specified with respect to the nature, locus, and extent of their nervous system damage, all comparisons between the normal and abnormal groups must be considered as suggestive rather than definitive. However, even when viewed with caution, certain of the results are sufficiently striking to warrant comment.

The evidence for normal children strongly confirms the view that the elaboration of intersensory relations represents a set of developmental functions showing age-specific characteristics and markedly regular curves of growth. At the very least, the emergence of such relationships appears to be delayed in the "brain-damaged" children, a factor which may seriously limit possibilities for the normal utilization and integration of environmental information. Given such a primary defect, the opportunity to develop bizarre integrations may be enhanced and aberrant paths of development reinforced. The dangers would probably be greatest where the developmental environment and educational situation made demands for intersensory integration between modalities that were least adequately integrated. Since the development of interrelations among all sensory modalities are not equally affected by damage to the nervous system, the possibility exists that the opportunities for relatively normal development may be enhanced if educational stress is placed upon experiences which emphasize the utilization of the most adequately integrated systems.

The findings obtained in the study of levels of perceptual functioning are also indicative of certain fundamental differences between normal children and certain types of "brain-damaged" children. Although the cerebral-palsied children studied were a heterogeneous group, there is little doubt as to the fact that all were brain injured. It is of interest that these children differed from the normal only little in their ability to make simple perceptual discriminations and recognize different geometric forms. However, despite relatively normal levels of perceptual recognition, the cerebral-palsied children were significantly defective in both their perceptual analytic and synthetic abilities. Most marked was the gross deficiency in perceptual synthesis, where no curve of improvement in function was exhibited by the brain-injured children over an age span from 5 to 18 years.

Although it is too early in the course of this research program to draw firm conclusions from the findings, there is little doubt that the strategies evolved have significant potential for the study of neurologically damaged children.

REFERENCES

1. Bender, L.: *A Visual Motor Gestalt Test and Its Clinical Use,* American Orthopsychiatric Association, New York, 1938.
2. Strauss, A. A., and Lehtinen, L.: *Psychopathology and Education of the Brain Injured Child.* Grune & Stratton, 1947.
3. Bortner, M., and Birch, H. G.: Perception and perceptual-motor dissociation in cerebral palsied children, *J. Nerv. Ment. Dis., 130*:49–53, 1960.
4. Sherrington, C.: *Man on His Nature.* Cambridge University Press, 1951.
5. Birch, H. G.: "Comparative Psychology," in *Areas of Psychology,* ed. F. A. Marcase. Harper & Bros., 1954.
6. Abbott, C.: The intelligence of batrachians, *Science, 3*:66–67, 1882.
7. Maier, N. R. F., and Schneirla, T. C.: *Principles of Animal Psychology.* McGraw-Hill, 1935.
8. London, I. D.: Research on sensory interaction in the Soviet Union, *Psychol. Bull., 51*:531–588, 1954.
9. Baldwin, J. M.: *Mental Development in the Child and the Race.* The Macmillan Co., 1897.
10. Birch, H. G., and Lefford, A.: Intersensory development in children, *Monogr. Soc. Res. Child Develop., 28*:5, Serial No. 89, 1963.

Behavioral Manifestations of Cerebral Damage in Childhood

LEON EISENBERG, M.D.
Johns Hopkins University Medical School

WHAT CLINICAL LOGIC, if any, lies behind the diagnosis of "brain damage"? The physician has *inferred* the existence of an underlying structural defect from the history he has obtained, the behavior he has observed, and the examinations he has undertaken. In the strict sense, this diagnosis is warranted only when direct visualization, tissue biopsy, or specific laboratory findings confirm brain pathology. However, since certain neurologic signs correlate so highly with brain damage, we can proceed confidently with diagnosis when these signs can be elicited. Moreover, a clear history of trauma, infection, metabolic disorder, or the like may be sufficient for a valid diagnosis. Let us note that such data merely permit the assertion that the brain is damaged; it is quite another matter to conclude that the disordered behavior is a necessary consequence of the demonstrated damage.[1]

The difficulty posed by most cases seen in the psychiatric clinic is that the neurologic findings and the laboratory results are at best equivocal, and the history is nonspecific. The psychiatric diagnosis has been based on the behavior syndrome. Here, the clinical syllogism runs about like this: children with known brain damage exhibit, or may exhibit, such and such behavior; the patient under study displays similar behavior; ergo, he is brain damaged. Unfortunately for the syllogism, children with evident brain damage may show remarkably little impairment in intellectual and emotional behavior, and the behavior syndromes they do display are bewilderingly varied.

The neurologist of traditional persuasion will be tempted to smile knowingly and to suggest that psychiatrists not jump in where neurologists fear to tread. Certainly, the frequency of the diagnosis of brain damage would decline spectacularly if we limited it to cases with unequivocal sensory or motor defect or both. By so doing, we would undoubtedly cut down on false positive diagnoses—but at the cost of far too many false negatives.

At that, the problem of false positives would remain with us. The existence of a hemiparesis, for all the assurance it affords us of a lesion in the motor pathways, hardly constitutes a final demonstration that deviant behavior in the same patient has similar antecedents; we have all seen patients with motor lesions who are nonetheless unimpaired in intellectual function. It is merely that the demonstration of the motor lesion increases the likelihood that other lesions sufficient to account for the disordered behavior may also be present. We judge this to be true because of the frequent association of intellectual deficit with cerebral palsy and because of the multiple lesions found in those patients who come to autopsy. It should not need emphasis here that there is far from a one-to-one correlation between necropsy findings and behavioral deficits and that very similar patterns of behavior appear in children with little to suggest injury and much to support psychogenesis. In the individual case, we had best proceed with circumspection even in the presence of neurologic signs.

As to the false negatives that would result from a restrictive definition, there is extensive epidemiologic evidence that children with behavior disorders but without other neurologic manifestations have a disproportionate loading of fetal and neonatal complications known to be associated with central nervous system pathology.[2] I submit, then, that we cannot accept the alluring proposition that we restrict the diagnosis of brain damage to cases with the classic neurologic findings. Let me at once add that, in making this diagnosis, we should specify the criteria upon which we base our diagnosis, the level of confidence we assign to it, and the type of syndrome the patient exhibits; the greatest fallacy of all is the common assumption that there is *a* brain-damage syndrome.

The difference in usage of the term—*i.e.,* diagnosis from behavior disorder vs. diagnosis from reflex changes—often leads to bitter disputes between clinicians who mistake a difference in interpretation for a difference in findings. I have been challenged more than once by neurologists who behave almost as if I had violated jurisdictional lines in making an "organic" diagnosis. The terminology is overlaid by other gratuitous meanings. To many physicians, "organic" brain injury conveys irreversibility and hopelessness, whereas psychogenesis suggests remediability.[3] Surely, I need not expand upon the absurdity of this dichotomy, but it is necessary to recognize its ubiquity if we are to be prepared to understand the otherwise inexplicable emotion with which physicians and teachers, no less than parents, resist this diagnosis.

The surplus of meanings does not end at this. In clinical practice, one finds that mention of "brain" in a diagnostic context suggests to parents tumor, trauma, and operation, all with grim overtones. Whether or not these concerns are verbalized, they must be dealt with openly by the physician, for they are almost universal. In this age of parental anxiety, the physician must be alert to self-blame by parents who are all too prone to guilt for not having sought medical attention sooner, or for having left the child momentarily unattended when the supposed brain trauma occurred, or for having passed on defective heredity, or the like.

Thus, in "brain damaged" and "brain injured" we deal with terms that arouse disproportionate alarm, that convey to many an unwarranted pessimism, that are often difficult to substantiate with precision, and that are applied to children of remarkably disparate clinical types: some grossly defective, some intellectually acute, and others bright in some functions and dull in others; some hyperkinetic, some apathetic, and others unpredictable. Yet I would argue that it would be profitless to attempt to outlaw these terms and search for euphemisms to replace them. What we must recognize is that when we have assigned the patient to this general category the diagnostic task has just begun; we must go on to specify (*a*) the type of disorder, (*b*) the areas of function secondary to damage, (*c*) the loci, and (*d*) the causative disease. That this will be difficult in no way relieves us of the obligation to attempt it.

With this in mind, let us consider some of the clinical manifestations of brain damage and attempt to relate them to neurophysiological and developmental principles. Rather than review a complete list of the characteristics found in the brain-damaged child,[4,5] I shall select three major ones for a somewhat detailed examination. These characteristics are: (*a*) deviations in tempo, amount, and pattern of motor activity, (*b*) abnormalities in attention, and (*c*) intellectual deficits.

HYPERKINESIS

Hyperkinesis is the behavior syndrome most often described in the brain damaged. The child is constantly on the move, into things, difficult to restrain, and upsetting to the most patient adult. Note well that this description applies to the normal child at least at some moments. The behavior might be considered appropriate in given social settings; one need only observe children on the school ground during recess as they give a remarkable imitation of Brownian movement. Thus, it is not that the brain-damaged child is doing something the normal one cannot but that he does it when he should not and, probably, that he does it more often. This last statement has yet to be documented by careful quantitative study [6] but is the common report of parents and other caretakers.

In view of its nuisance value, it is not surprising that this syndrome should be the one most often described by clinicians. Indeed, one is tempted to conclude that "brain damaged" is the expletive uttered by the clinician vainly trying to restrain for examination a writhing whirling miniature dervish. But other brain-injured children may be torpid and inert. Perhaps the most consistent relation between brain defect and behavior is to be observed in the mongoloid child, whose placid and tranquil behavior is no less noteworthy for being pleasant to deal with.

Both types, the overactive and the inert, point to pathology in the control of behavior. Observation of the normal child suggests that he possesses the requisite energy for hyperkinetic behavior. One need not hypothesize excess drive to explain hyperkinesis; it seems more parsimonious to suppose that it results from lack of inhibition and that torpidity results from an excess of inhibition.

In a series of psychopharmacologic studies,[7–11] we have demonstrated that stimulants such as dextroamphetamine and methylphenidate are useful in controlling hyperkinetic (and aggressive) behavior disorders in children and adolescents; that phenothiazines such as prochlorperazine and perphenazine may be no better than placebo; and that phenobarbital can be considerably worse. This paradoxical effect—a reduction in activity by a drug classed as a stimulant for its effects in adults—has yet to be explained adequately, though it has long been noted. There are no studies of stimulants in normal children to compare with those in normal adults. Our subjects were selected for treatment because of hyperkinesis; some were grossly brain damaged; others were not obviously so. Thus, whether this effect is a function of age or of age plus pathology cannot be stated. If stimulants act to enhance neural responsiveness, one might suppose that their therapeutic potency results from a relatively greater enhancement of the activity of inhibitory than excitatory systems in these young patients. It is our hope that we may obtain clues to the nature of the physiologic defects in hyperkinetic children by isolating the specific changes in function produced by stimulant drugs.*

ABNORMALITIES IN ATTENTION

Although the motor disorders are more readily noticeable, the abnormalities in attention have the greater impact on adjustment because they interfere with cognitive development. A child learns most efficiently when he attends. The brain-damaged child has difficulty in focusing his attention selectively and in sustaining it. In the extreme, he is at the mercy of every extraneous sight and sound in his environment. He fails to apprehend what is of moment because he is distracted by the trivial and the transient. In this, he behaves like the normal infant and very young child.

Though this pattern is the more frequent one, some of these youngsters dis-

* Laufer and his coworkers[12,13] have demonstrated that children with the hyperkinetic behavior syndrome, when contrasted with children with other psychiatric disorders in their in-patient population, demonstrate a low threshold for photo-Metrazol activation of the EEG by the technique of Gastaut.[14] They have further shown that dextroamphetamine results in a significant raising of this threshold value toward that characteristic of their comparison group. It is their view that the basic neurophysiologic deficit in hyperkinetic children resides in diencephalic dysfunction which allows the cortex to be flooded with visceral and sensory impulses normally filtered out in the diencephalon. On the basis of Bradley's experimental data,[15] they suggest that dextroamphetamine raises synaptic resistance in the diencephalon and thus enhances its capacity as a filter. The differential effect of this drug in the child patient and the normal adult remains to be explained.

play its contrary: a perseverative preoccupation with detail and a consequent failure to respond appropriately to changing stimuli. Still others show partial and varying attention defects that are not the same from day to day or even from hour to hour. This leads all too often to invidious comments from the teacher that "he could if he would" because sometimes he does.

Focusing attention is, on the one hand, a process of enhancing responsiveness to a limited field, on the other, a matter of inhibiting response to the numerous competing stimuli ever present in the environment. In part, this is built into the very structure of the central nervous system. Excitation of a cutaneous receptor results in a topographically localized response, with a spot of maximal activity, a wider zone of moderate response, and a wide surround of inhibition.[16] The inhibitory surround, by cutting down on response to competing stimuli, enhances the impact of the central event. Cells subserving this inhibitory function are found in cord, cuneate nucleus, thalamus, and cortex. Inhibitory influences on cortical activity can also be initiated from the reticular system.[17] Pathways from cortex to reticular system provide a mechanism for cortico-reticulo-cortical inhibition. In this way, signals arriving at a primary receptive zone can initiate a depression of response in other cortical zones. Interference with these precisely interdigitated inhibitory systems might very well be the basis for the attention defects observed in so-called diffuse minimal brain damage, in which no gross lesion with motor or sensory consequences can be identified.

The attention deficits will, of course, have important consequences for learning and intelligence. The child so afflicted will be impaired not only in the fund of knowledge he acquires but also in the acquisition of the so-called "abstract attitude," the prerequisite for complex problem-solving behavior. In abstracting the class characteristic of a stimulus pattern (its squareness or roundness, for example) from its particularities (size, color, brightness, etc.), the initial task is to reduce it to a canonical form—that is, to minimize the impact of its particular size by reducing it toward a standard size, and so on.[18,19] The inhibitory systems associated with the sensory apparatus subserve just such a function; in addition to their role, already described, in cutting down on background, they diminish the primary response itself toward a modal value; in this, they function like the automatic volume control in a radio, reducing gain when the signal is too loud. Error in this control system for self-regulation of sensory intake, resulting from brain damage, would inevitably complicate the task of the higher-order mechanisms which, in some way as yet unknown, then abstract the essence of the form from the partially "de-particularized" stimulus pattern.

INTELLECTUAL DEFECTS

The intellectual defects found following brain damage vary widely—from highly circumscribed deficit in some children to generalized depression of intelligence in others. It is customary to rely upon intratest and intertest scatter as indices of brain damage as opposed to so-called nonspecific mental deficiency,[5] but a note of caution is necessary in this regard: scatter is found among normals, among anxious children, and among subcultural retardates to an extent greater than that recognized by those who rely upon it as a specific sign. Group differences in respect to variability exist, but there is great overlap.

The extent of functional impairment after brain injury will depend upon at least five biological factors: size of lesion, location of lesion, whether the lesion is static or active, whether it is focal or diffuse, and developmental age at time of occurrence. (To simplify discussion, consideration of social and psychological factors that interact with the biological will be deferred until the last section of this paper.) Unfortunately, so little is known of these factors in childhood that attempts to suggest general principles can be only speculative; in the hope of sharpening discussion, I shall formulate just such "principles" with clear warning that they should not be mistaken for established fact.

FACTORS IN FUNCTIONAL IMPAIRMENT

Given the locus, we anticipate greater consequences from larger lesions, though in no straight-line relationship. Below a critical mass, a lesion may have no detectable effect upon behavior; very much beyond it, one may observe no further loss in the same functions but rather the appearance of new functional deficits.

Given the size, we anticipate differential effects related to locus of lesion; this is certainly so for involvement of somesthetic, motor, and visual cortex. Beyond these areas, relatively little is known of cerebral localization in children. Studies with adults [20] indicate some specificity of defects resulting from lesions in major cortical zones, but the story is far from clear; clinical experience with children leads to the impression that specificity is, if anything, even less precise than in the adult.

Given the locus and the size, we anticipate greater consequences from an "active" than a "static" lesion. (In this context, active is taken to mean electrically active rather than progressive; obviously, the expanding tumor or the degenerative disease will produce increasingly serious malfunction.) The static lesion is "subtractive" in its effect; the behavior deficits associated with it represent the less efficient adaptive function of the brain reorganized after the loss. The electrically active lesion produces, in addition to these effects, those resulting from its unregulated and abnormal electrical storms.[21] These discharge bursts impair the function of normal areas by making them refractory to afferent input and by usurping their efferent channels. In some patients, anticonvulsant or surgical therapy that succeeds in eliminating focal discharge from such lesions leads to impressive functional gains. The great variability in day-to-day performance frequently noted in the brain damaged suggests that such electrical bursts may be a prominent factor in their clinical difficulties.

The remaining factors—diffuseness of lesion and age of child at time of acquisition—are even more difficult to assess. Usually, we have no reliable signposts of either. If we may judge from the differences between post-traumatic and postencephalitic syndromes, we would conclude that the diffuse lesion is apt to have more marked *intellectual* consequences than the focal one. Obviously, this depends upon extent and locus, as well. However, I am impressed by the severity of the intellectual deficit I have observed among children who have had no localizable lesion—that is, no major motor or sensory defect and no localizing laboratory findings but grossly defective behavior following prenatal and perinatal pathology.

Other behavior aberrations in the diffusely brain damaged vary markedly as the children grow older. The hyperkinetic syndromes are likely to diminish by late childhood and to disappear almost entirely by adolescence. Presumably this reflects the increased capacity for inhibition normally associated with maturation. On the other hand, I have seen a number of brain-damaged adolescents who display disordered thinking and bizarre behavior clinically reminiscent of schizophrenia. Is this a relatively direct consequence of the brain lesions or, as seems more likely, an outcome of personality development in the presence of increased vulnerability to stress (limited adaptive capacity) and of traumatic social experience? How often does it occur, and in what types of children? Only comprehensive longitudinal, as opposed to biased cross-sectional, studies will enable us to provide a "natural history" of this disorder that may supply answers to these questions.

What can be said of time of onset as a variable? All of us have seen the school-aged child who emerges from coma following head injury with a marked aphasia but then goes on to a surprisingly total recovery, a phenomenon less frequently observed among adults. To explain this, we invoke such concepts as relative undifferentiation and consequent greater functional potentiality in the immature cortex.

The data from animal experiments on differential age effects are mostly limited to motor behavior. Ablation of motor cortex or sectioning of pyramidal tracts in the young cat, monkey, or chimpanzee results in much less motor deficit than the same lesion in the adult animal; [22–26] it has been suggested that this stems from the fact that direct cortical connections to spinal motoneurons are only gradually established during the first year of life.[27] But it should also be noted that effects of neonatal motor lesions are more severe in chimpanzee than in monkey and in monkey than in cat. Man is the most vulnerable to lesions in the corticospinal system at each age, although an appreciable age effect may remain.

The clinical example cited a moment ago—of the school-aged child with aphasia—described the impact of a lesion on an intellectual function (speech) that had already emerged. Brain injury during prenatal or neonatal life may have a far more destructive and permanent impact. That is to say, one sees children damaged during this period who never acquire speech. In the absence of pathologic studies, it is not possible to say whether these cases merely represent gross and overwhelming lesions (and that we just do not recognize the lesser ones, for which the organism has compensated) or whether injury before speech acquisition is even more devastating than similar injury in the adult. If the latter proposition is true, then a plot of effect of lesion against age of acquisition would be curvilinear, major effects occurring early and late, with the dip in the curve occurring in relation to the normal age of attainment of the ability.

These major early effects may result from secondary consequences of the primary lesion—that is, the loss of a given area might lead to a failure of the development of interrelated areas dependent upon it for stimulation to maturation; thus, a limited zone of tissue destruction in the embryo could have widespread consequences.* Admittedly, this is no more than speculative; it is at least equally likely that the communication problems associated with prenatal damage stem from a widespread distribution of lesions acquired during this period, with consequent distortion of the entire cerebral development.

ENVIRONMENTAL CONTRIBUTIONS

Important as is the role of the organic lesion in determining certain of the behavioral characteristics of the brain-damaged child, it is no more the sole determinant than is his genetic structure. The behavior that emerges is equally dependent upon the nature of the environment in which he develops. This separation of the two aspects is useful simply for convenience of discussion but does violence to the actual process of development, the essence of which is interaction. The psychological deficits we observe in the patient who has suffered early cerebral injury cannot be taken to imply that the tissue destroyed is in itself the sole cause of the entire pattern. The injury might have impaired an elementary psychological function, the lack of which could then distort subsequent development. Thus, complex functions, the anatomical equipment

* A wide variety of experimental studies in animals, corroborated by clinicopathological correlations in man, have demonstrated anatomically remote, though specific, consequences of primary lesions in major neuronal systems. (1) Loss of the major afferent input to a nucleus leads to cell deterioration and loss. Enucleation of the eye results in *transneuronal degeneration* in the lateral geniculate.[28,29] Similarly, destruction of the cochlea results in *transneuronal degeneration* in first-order nuclei (ventral cochlear) as well as second-order nuclei (lateral superior olive and lemniscal and contralateral medial trapezoid).[30] (2) Cortical ablations lead to *retrograde degeneration* in dependent thalamic nuclei,[31-33] presumably as a result of concomitant destruction of thalamic axons projecting to cortex. (3) *Retrograde transneuronal degeneration* (in mammillary nuclei after removal of cingulate cortex) has been shown to be a function of the age of the organism when the lesion is made, the more severe effects occurring in the neonate.[34,35] The severity of these transynaptic effects (1 and 2) has been shown to vary with the species, the age of the animal, and the system studied.[28,30,34,36] The available evidence, though incomplete, is thus compatible with the hypothesis that injury in prenatal or early neonatal life may have more wide-ranging anatomical results. A related but separate problem is the differential vulnerability of the brain at different stages of development to specific insults such as anoxia, toxins, viral agents, etc.

for which might otherwise be intact, could have failed to evolve. Whenever the injury is such as to impair the development of the capacity to symbolize (language), all subordinate functions which are ordered by language will develop less than optimally and all patterns of social interaction will be grossly impaired.

One might at first blush be inclined to expect the impact of environment on the brain-damaged child to be less than that on the normal. After all, has not his fate largely been determined by his lesion? But this is true only to the extent that the lesion may set limits upon ultimate attainment in the best of possible environments. One can in fact demonstrate that the brain-damaged child is more at the mercy of his environment than the normal child.

For the adequately endowed child, a wide variety of environments suffice to permit adequate if not optimal development. For the handicapped child, limited in his adaptive capacity, there is a considerable restriction in the number of environments within which effective development is possible. School programs are designed with the average child in mind. They provide an opportunity for overlearning the required tasks and so take into account the variability in average performance. The brain-damaged child needs more than this usually sufficient quantitative surplus and often a qualitatively different kind of learning experience. Only if these both more numerous and special experiences are provided will he be able to progress. The deficits in performance we observe may represent not at all the inherent handicap of his disease but rather the most he has been able to accomplish in the absence of what he needed. We cannot conclude from the fact that he *has* not learned to read by the methods adequate for the ordinary child that he *could* not, if attempts were made to bypass his deficiencies by making use of other sensorimotor channels.

Can the factors impairing abstract ability be remedied? Piaget has demonstrated an age sequence in the development of thinking. Recent studies suggest that this process is responsive to the provision of specific learning experiences, the principles of which can be transferred to a general class of problems.[37] We know, further, that the formation of "learning sets" is a central aspect of problem-solving.[38] The brain-damaged child who fails to respond to conventional tutelage may be capable of moving ahead if we begin by simplifying the challenge we present and then tax him with progressively more complex tasks. Even if the supposition that inhibitory functions are impaired in these children is correct, it is clear that this is not a total failure but a relative one. Reinforcement of the channels he does have could well enhance their efficiency and impact. We cannot at this point state whether the defects in "abstract ability" in the brain injured can be corrected, but a negative conclusion is not warranted in the absence of systematic efforts to bypass his learning barriers.

The dependence of the brain damaged upon his environment is nowhere more clear than in his family relations. His defect, if it is obvious at birth, may alter parental attitudes toward him. What is the impact on the development of maternal feelings of having a child who does not respond as he should, who is a source of frustration rather than pride? Parental behavior may be so skewed as to induce in the child the very patterns of disturbance we would have recognized as psychogenic had the presence of brain damage not preempted our attention. We can sympathize with the difficulties of a parent confronted by a youngster who behaves well one day and poorly the next for no apparent reason, who provides embarrassment rather than pride when he brings home his report card, and so on. Yet must we not first consider what it means to the child if he finds himself rejected for something he cannot control and does not understand?

How the child thinks about himself has a major influence on his behavior. The child's image of himself has two main sources: the way he sees others viewing him and what he sees himself as able to do—and hence to be. Others' views are first his parents' views. If they cannot provide the warm acceptance that underlies the sense of personal worth for the normal child, the inner core of his self-concept will be one of worthlessness. His extrafamilial experiences with peers and teachers often further self-depreciation as others display impatience with his limitations and shun his company. Even with the good fortune of having sympathetic parents and companions, he must daily face the painful realization of his incompetence at play and at work. No "reassurance" will satisfy him that he is capable as a person when he sees that he is not.

Inability to control the outbursts of wild and aggressive behavior to which he is vulnerable leads to a sense of powerlessness, to guilt for the consequences of his misbehavior, and to fear of the harm he may do in moments of loss of control. Such children plead for external controls upon their behavior; "permissive" child-rearing practices multiply the problem and increase the burden of guilt.

Many of these youngsters come to think of themselves as bad, stupid, and doomed to lifelong failure. With such a self-concept, they may simply abandon any effort to restrain the behavior that gets them into difficulty. Viewing themselves as incompetent, they behave as incompetents, even in circumstances within their coping capacity. Some, despondent of gaining acceptance through constructive actions, seek a place in the sun via traits which at least compel a response from others; even though the response is negative, it is an acknowledgment of their importance. One sees such children acting as clowns. Having been ridiculed when laughter was the very opposite of what they sought, they maintain the fiction that they are play-acting and seek the notoriety they fear they cannot escape.

Thus, much of the difficult behavior that is seen in association with the brain-damage syndromes stems not from the anatomical deficits but from their social consequences for personality development; that is, a significant component of the behavior disorder is a psychogenic phenomenon, for which organic elements are a necessary but not a sufficient condition. Implicit in this view is a conviction that an environment able to respond to special needs constructively could result in a much higher level of ultimate function.

Specifically, this entails family guidance and planned educational opportunities. Unfortunately, many child guidance clinics will not accept such patients for care because they are viewed as "organic" problems not appropriate for psychotherapy. They are accepted at neurology clinics, but all too often with insufficient attention given to the psychological aspects of management. Yet these patients and their parents are in great need of psychological assistance. These families have all the problems any family might have had plus the special difficulties associated with these disorders, which highlight and exaggerate family weaknesses that might otherwise have remained within tolerable limits.

Some communities now have classes for the brain damaged. Without overlooking the advance this represents, we must also recognize the inadequacies in the concept behind many of these programs. All too frequently, they agglomerate children with highly disparate needs simply because they bear a common label. Trained and interested teachers are hard to find; hence the teacher given this chore may be a misfit the principal hopes to get out of his way by an assignment to the equivalent of an educational Siberia. Even the interested and able teacher is handicapped because there is so little systematic research into the special problems and methods of remedial education for this group of children.

There are, however, clear indications for preventive intervention. As we noted earlier, disorders of brain function are associated with complications of pregnancy and parturition.[39,40] These, in turn, are associated with class and ethnic-group membership.[41,42] What we see in these children is the result of double handicap: organic lesion and cultural deprivation. Thus, provision of better health care for pregnant mothers at high risk, improvement of life circumstances through adequate welfare levels and foster care where needed, enriched preschool and school programs, and the like can be expected to lessen the burden of neuropsychiatric complications that assails these children. Even as we undertake further studies of the basic issues, we must accept a social responsibility to apply what *is* known to prevent further casualty and to ensure the best care available for those already victimized.[43]

REFERENCES

1. Eisenberg, L.: Conceptual problems in relating brain and behavior, *Amer. J. Orthopsychiat., 30*:37–48, 1960.
2. Rogers, M. E., *et al.:* Prenatal and paranatal factors in the development of childhood behavior disorders, *Acta Psychiat. Neurol. Scand.,* Suppl. 102, 1955.
3. Eisenberg, L.: Emotional determinants of mental deficiency, *Arch. Neurol. Psychiat., 80*:114–124, 1958.
4. Eisenberg, L.: Psychiatric implications of brain damage in children, *Psychiat. Quart., 31*:72–92, 1957.
5. Clements, S. D., and Peters, J. E.: Minimal brain dysfunctions in the

school aged child, *Arch. Gen. Psychiat.*, *6*:185–197, 1962.
6. Schulman, J. L., and Reisman, John: An objective measure of hyperactivity, *Amer. J. Ment. Defic.*, *64*:3; 455, 1959.
7. Eisenberg, L., *et al.:* A psychopharmacologic experiment in a training school for delinquents, *Amer. J. Orthopsychiat.*, 1963. In press.
8. Molling, P. A., *et al.:* Committed delinquent boys; the impact of perphenazine and of placebo, *Arch. Gen. Psychiat.*, *7*:70–76, 1962.
9. Eisenberg, L., *et al.:* Effectiveness of psychotherapy alone and in conjunction with perphenazine and placebo, *Amer. J. Psychiat.*, *117*:1088–1093, 1961.
10. Cytryn, L., *et al.:* The effectiveness of tranquilizing drugs plus supportive psychotherapy in treating behavior disorders of children, *Amer. J. Orthopsychiat.*, *30*:113–128, 1960.
11. Whitehouse, D., *et al.:* A comparison of methylphenidate, phenobarbital and placebo in hyperkinetic behavior disorders. Unpublished manuscript.
12. Laufer, M. W., *et al.:* Hyperkinetic impulse disorder in children's behavior problems, *Psychosom. Med.*, *19*: 38–49, 1957.
13. Laufer, M. W., and Denhoff, E.: Hyperkinetic behavior syndrome in children, *J. Pediat.*, *50*:463–474, 1957.
14. Gastaut, H.: Combined photic and metrazol activation of the brain, *Electroenceph. Clin. Neurophysiol.*, *2*:249–261, 1950.
15. Bradley, P. B.: The effect of some drugs on the electrical activity of the brain of the conscious cat, *Ibid.*, *5*: 471, 1953 (Suppl. III).
16. Mountcastle, V. B., and Powell, T. P. S.: Neural mechanisms subserving cutaneous sensibility, *Bull. Johns Hopkins Hosp.*, *105*:201–222, 1959.
17. French, J. D., *et al.:* Projections from cortex to cephalic brain stem (reticular formation) in monkeys, *J. Neurophysiol.*, *18*:74–95, 1955. See also Segundo, J. P., *et al.:* Effects of cortical stimulation on electrocortical activity in monkeys, *Ibid.*, *18*:236–245, 1955.
18. Pitts, W., and McCulloch, W. S.: How we know universals. The perception of auditory and visual forms, *Bull. Math. Biophys.*, *9*:127–147, 1947.
19. McCulloch, W. S., and Eisenberg, L.: "Integrative Aspects of the Nervous System." Basic Science Lectures, Walter Reed Army Research and Graduate School, Washington, 1949.
20. Teuber, H. L.: "Some Alterations in Behavior After Cerebral Lesions in Man," in *The Evolution of Nervous Control from Primitive Organisms to Man.* A.A.A.S., Washington, 1959, pp. 157–194.
21. Morrell, F.: Interseizure disturbances in focal epilepsy, *Neurology*, *6*:327–344, 1956.

21a. Morrell, F.: Effect of focal epileptogenic lesions and their ablation upon conditioned electrical responses of the brain in the monkey, *Electroenceph. Clin. Neurophysiol.*, *8*:217–236, 1956.

22. Kennard, M.: Reorganization of motor function in the cerebral cortex of monkeys deprived of motor and premotor areas in infancy, *J. Neurophysiol.*, 1:477–496, 1938.
23. Kennard, M.: Cortical reorganization of motor function, *Arch. Neurol. Psychiat.*, *48*:227–240, 1942.
24. Tower, S. S.: The dissociation of cortical excitation from cortical inhibition by pyramid section and the syndrome of that lesion in the cat, *Brain*, *58*: 238–255, 1935.
25. Tower, S. S.: Pyramidal lesion in the monkey, *Brain*, *63*:36–40, 1940.
26. Walker, A. E., and Fulton, J. F.: Hemidecortication in chimpanzee, baboon, macaque, potto, cat and coati, *J. Nerv. Ment. Dis.*, *87*:677–700, 1938.
27. Kuypers, H. G. J. M.: Corticospinal connections: postnatal development in the Rhesus monkey, *Science*, *138*:678–680, 1962.
28. Matthews, M. R., *et al.:* Transneuronal cell degeneration in the lateral geniculate nucleus of macaque monkey, *J. Anat.* (London), *94*:145–169, 1960.

29. Goldby, F.: A note on transneuronal atrophy in the human lateral geniculate body, *J. Neurol. Neurosurg. Psychiat.*, *20*:202–207, 1957.
30. Powell, T. P. S., and Erulkar, S. D.: Transneuronal degeneration in the auditory relay nuclei of the cat, *J. Anat.* (London), *96*:249–268, 1962.
31. Rose, J. E., and Woolsey, C. N.: A study of thalamo-cortical relations in the rabbit, *Bull. Johns Hopkins Hosp.*, *73*:65–128, 1943.
32. Rose, J. E.: Organization of the mammalian thalamus and its relation to the cerebral cortex, *Electroenceph. Clin. Neurophysiol.*, *1*:391–403, 1949.
33. Powell, T. P. S.: Residual neurons in the human thalamus following hemidecortication, *Brain*, *75*:571–584, 1952.
34. Cowan, W. M., and Powell, T. P. S.: An experimental study of the relation between the medial mammillary nucleus and the cingulate cortex, *Proc. Roy. Soc.* (Ser. B), *143*:114–125, 1955.
35. Gudden, B.: Experimentaluntersuchungen über das peripherische und centrale nervensystem, *Arch. Psychiat. Nervenkr.*, *2*:693–723, 1870.
36. Torvik, A.: Transneuronal changes in the inferior olive and pontine nuclei in kittens, *J. Neuropath. Exp. Neurol.*, *15*:119–145, 1956.
37. Kessen, W., and Kuhlman, C.: "Thought in the Young Child." *Monogr. Soc. Res. Child Develop.*, *27*:2, Serial No. 83, 1962.
38. Harlow, H. F.: The formation of learning sets, *Psychol. Rev.*, *56*:51–65, 1949.
39. Knobloch, H., *et al.*: The neuropsychiatric sequelae of prematurity, *J.A.M.A.*, *161*:581–585, 1956.
40. Lilienfeld, A. M., and Pasamanick, B.: The association of maternal and fetal factors with the development of cerebral palsy and epilepsy, *Amer. J. Obstet. Gynec.*, *70*:93–101, 1955.
41. Pasamanick, B., *et al.*: Socioeconomic status: some precursors of neuropsychiatric disorders, *Amer. J. Orthopsychiat.*, *26*:594–601, 1956.
42. Rider, R. V., *et al.*: Associations between premature birth and socioeconomic status, *Amer. J. Public Health*, *45*:1022–1028, 1955.
43. Eisenberg, L.: Possibilities for a preventive psychiatry, *Pediatrics*, *30*:815–828, 1962.

DISCUSSION

Because this paper emphasizes the detailed patterns of behavioral disturbance found in children with brain damage, one of the major themes of the discussion was a consideration of the validity of the stereotypes often used to describe the behavior of brain-damaged children. Particular attention was devoted to two issues: (1) the character of hyperkinetic behavior disturbances, and (2) the unevenness in function that is so often described in children with brain damage.

It was pointed out that, although for some years hyperkinesis has been reported as a major behavioral manifestation of brain damage in children, there are few if any objective studies on the amount of movement that such children do in fact exhibit. Only one preliminary study of the behavioral characteristics of brain-damaged children—that of Shulman * in Chicago—has attempted

* Shulman, J.: Paper presented at the American Academy of Pediatrics, 1962.

to compare the amount of kinesis in neurologically impaired children and in normal children of the same age. In this study, both groups of children were examined by time samplings of movement. The amount of movement engaged in was measured by a self-winding chronometer with the spring removed. The amount of elapsed time recorded on the watch worn by the child provided a direct index of the amount of activity over the sampling period. It is of interest that no significant differences in amount of movement activity per se were recorded between the neurologically impaired children described as hyperkinetic and their age-mate normal controls. In the light of such findings, the question naturally arose as to whether the hyperkinesis that had been reported referred to the amount of activity or to the lack of focus that characterized the activities of these children.

As the discussion proceeded, it became increasingly clear that our information about the hyperkinetic phenomenon is descriptively inadequate. When careful clinical histories are taken from the parent, one frequently finds that the child whom the mother has described as continuously and disturbingly active also, by her report, in certain circumstances spends a considerable portion of his day sitting without any gross movement in front of a television set watching cartoons or other simple visual presentations. Further, if the clinician observes behavior longitudinally, he notes that the greatest amount of undirected and disorganized motor behavior tends to occur in new situations or at the times of initial contact with new people or tasks. As familiarity increases, with either the person or the room, the behavior of the child tends to change and in later sessions appears to be less characteristically "hyperkinetic" than it was on initial examination.

Finally, the question was raised as to the possibility that certain aspects of the hyperkinetic pattern might have a familial basis. This view receives some support from the frequency with which parents of hyperkinetic children report that they themselves were described during their own early years as being fidgety, always moving about, and easily distracted.

It was generally agreed that our present knowledge cannot provide a definitive set of answers for the questions that have been raised in connection with hyperkinetic behavior. It was suggested that one potentially very productive area of research involves the detailed behavioral observation of children with brain damage, the determination of the conditions for and the periodicity of their hyperkinetic behaviors, and the analysis of the types of environment which tend to result in nonhyperkinetic functioning. Such investigation would provide us with a basis for deciding whether the problem we must deal with is that of overactivity per se, deriving spontaneously as a behavioral projection from patterns of neural dysfunction in the child, or whether we are dealing with another manifestation of undirectedness and inappropriateness of focus in behavior which, because of its incongruity to the demands of the social situation, is interpreted as hyperkinesis. In addition, such information may provide clues as to the kinds of environmental modifications that could reduce hyperkinetic behavioral disturbances and thus help to maximize the child's persistent contact with relevant aspects of his environment.

By direct extension, the discussion of the periodicity and unevenness of hyperkinetic behavioral manifestations led to a more general consideration of the fluctuation and instability observed in the more general psychological functioning of brain-damaged children. The little we know of the tempo and patterns of such fluctuations suggests that they are episodic. The father of one brain-damaged child was quoted as having said, "Some days it's like he's plugged in and you're with him. Other days it's as though the mechanism is disconnected and you can't make any contact at all." It was felt that these episodic fluctuations might underlie the typical patterns of variability that occur in intelligence test scores when such tests are administered to the same child over a period of years. High levels of function might occur on "good days" and lower levels of function on "bad days."

Consideration of the episodic and intermittent character—or, more correctly, the tempo—of the behavioral disturbances led to some attempts at an analogy between the behavior of brain-damaged children and certain of the phenomena observed in both clinical and experimental epilepsy. It was suggested that the episodic disturbances produced in contralateral hemispheres in animals when limited unilateral cortical foci are established might provide some theoretical basis for understanding the episodic course of the general behavioral abnormalities reported in children. However, existing information on electroencephalographic activities in brain-damaged children at the times of their greatest and least distractibility, though incomplete, does not seem to indicate that any consistent patterns of abnormal electrical activity accompany the different behavioral states. Such evidence can scarcely be considered conclusive; it may merely reflect the degree to which our standard methods of electroencephalographic evaluation are insufficiently sensitive to study the problem of a neural basis for behavioral dysfunction.

Some concern was expressed that the paper, in its consideration of the psychiatric problems of brain-damaged children, had placed primary emphasis on the behavioral manifestation of disturbance and had dealt insufficiently with strictly psychologic disturbances, or aspects of mental life. More specifically, the need was expressed for fuller consideration of the consequences of impulsive behavior, hyperkinesis, disturbance in perception, peculiarities in responsiveness, and low limits of threshold for the development of normal symbolizing abilities. It was emphasized that such symbolizing function and language-oriented behaviors might perhaps be the most specifically human characteristics of functioning, and that any psychiatric consideration of the behavior of brain-damaged children should in significant degree concern itself with this area.

It was pointed out that our information on the manner in which damage to the brain in childhood interferes with the development of symbolizing activity is most fragmentary. However, on the basis of the available evidence, the degree to which symbolic function is interfered with appears to be related to the time of life at which the damage is sustained. It was suggested that damage could result in early discontinuity of experience and early selectivity of bizarre aspects of the environment; if these serve to organize focused behaviors, the development of disturbed patterns of symbolization would almost inevitably result. The degree to which the reported deficiencies in abstract ability, capacities to generalize, and tendencies toward concretization in thinking are related to such abnormal developmental patterns cannot be specified at present.

A quite different approach to the possible mechanism underlying disturbed symbolization is reflected in the suggestion that the problem for these children may be not an inability to develop concepts but, rather, that the concepts they do possess are available for use only in special circumstances. Such a view seems to be supported by the findings of Birch and Bortner * that children who are unable to utilize abstract categories in their sorting behavior when the stimulus object and the objects to which it is to be matched have sensory similarities are able to utilize abstract concepts when sensory competition is removed. Thus, in a test where a green pen was used as an index object and the child was asked to match it with a bottle containing ink, a thimble, and a piece of green paper, the tendency was to match the green pen with the green paper. However, when white paper was substituted for green, the same patient said, "The pen goes with the ink bottle, because you need ink to write." These findings suggest that there is a hierarchical order of selection from among alternative levels of response, and that the brain-damaged individual is more sensitive to the sensory aspect of the situation than to the conceptual aspect.

The final question discussed was the interaction between the brain-damaged child and his family and home in the production of behavioral symptoms. In a number of studies, parents of brain-damaged children who showed behavioral disturbances appeared themselves to have serious personality disorders. These reported findings readily permit two quite different types of interpretation. On the one hand, they suggest that the disturbances of behavior found in the children were, at least in part, the result of faulty and inconsistent patterns of management to which they had been exposed in the home situation. On the other hand, it is equally possible that the patterns of personality and emotional disturbances noted in the parents were themselves a product of the effort to maintain an intact family despite the presence of a child with grossly abnormal behavior. The consensus of the group was that both of these interpretations probably have some validity and that our present body of information is insufficient to permit us to choose between them—to decide in specific cases which mechanism is operative, whether both are operative, and the degree to which each has made a functional contribution. Most certainly the problems raised by the findings suggest a fruitful region for further inquiry.

* Birch, H. G., and Bortner, M.: Stimulus Competition and Concept Usage. In preparation.

The Effect of a Brain-damaged Child on the Family

HOWARD R. KELMAN, PH.D.
New York Medical College

THIS DISCUSSION is an attempt to appraise present knowledge concerning the effects of brain-damaged children on the family. Rather than providing a detailed summary of the literature, this report will attempt, through a survey of relevant materials, to assess the evidence upon which current knowledge rests, and to review some approaches that have been employed to characterize family behavior. This analysis, it is hoped, will help to identify some salient issues and questions requiring further clinical and research exploration and attention.

In this discussion "brain damage" has been interpreted broadly to include children with a variety of impairments—motor, mental, behavioral, and sensory—stemming from defects in cerebral functioning, whatever the origin—disease, development, or trauma. (To have narrowed the definition to one particular neurologic or behavioral condition—"the brain-injured child"—might have simplified the task, but this restricted definition seemed untenable in the light of present knowledge of cerebral defect and its behavioral consequences.) Practical considerations precluded giving systematic attention to the large body of materials dealing with orthopedic impairments and psychiatric illness and emotional disorders, even though cerebral damage can occur in persons with these conditions and may be the primary etiologic agent in some disorders traditionally ascribed to psychogenic causes.

THE EVOLUTION OF CURRENT SOCIAL CONCERN

Brain damage per se is a relatively new terminological addition to the many ways in which children exhibiting certain symptoms have been classified. Historically, children with cerebral damage have been grouped into broad clinical categories reflecting for the most part the major areas of deficit: mental deficiency, cerebral palsy, epilepsy, and the like. This has been true at least where the impairment and its manifestations have been clearly visible. Where the impairment was less visible or the nature of the "organic" component more difficult to establish clinically, the behavioral symptoms were believed to be no different in origin from the more traditional psychogenic disturbances (where disordered behavior was involved) or mental retardation (where learning or communication disorders were of major concern). The overlap and confusion between these categories have become more apparent with increased knowledge and understanding of cerebral function.

It is important to note, too, that these categories had and continue to have a certain social character and significance. The mere labeling of a child as mentally retarded, cerebral palsied, or autistic continues to have implications regarding the range and type of medical treatment, educational, institutional, and other services that will be made available (or denied) to him and his family.[1–5,*] Also, social significance has been attached to the ascribed parental or familial etiologic involvement—stigma where the link was presumably genetic,[6–14] guilt and anxiety where the link was attributed to psychogenic processes.[15,16]

In general, children with milder, less visible forms of brain damage were not recognized as such and therefore received little special attention. On the other hand, the chronic, frequently multiple, and presumably irreversible deficits of children with gross damage engendered a climate of hopelessness and defeatism in which little more than diagnostic services or custodial care was made available to their families.[17] In this atmosphere, scientific interest in the families of such children was largely limited to investigations of parental or familial roles as etiologic agents or correlates. Cerebral defect and its behavioral expressions in children were attributed to familial inadequacy of either a genetic or a behavioral character.[18,19]

In contrast to this earlier period, marked by relative professional and programmatic sterility, the recent history of these overlapping fields of interest in childhood brain damage is characterized by rapid expansion and development of services and active scientific and programmatic debate and activity. This change has come about as a result of a number of interrelated forces. Technological, economic, and scientific changes in a period of accelerating industrial and urban expansion have reduced the social threat of the acute and infectious diseases.[20–22] As a consequence, the prevention and control of disability—the social consequences of chronic disease—has emerged as a major public health concern. This process has been accelerated by the growing realization that reliance on custodial institutional solutions has failed to reduce significantly the magnitude of the economic and social problems of chronic disability or to lessen their impact on the affected individual, his family, and the community. The emergence of rehabilitation as a field of practice and as

* See, also, pp. 100–114 of this volume.

a system of beliefs and values has reflected and in turn contributed to this shift of emphasis and social concern.[23–25]

In all of these efforts, particularly those focused upon children, the importance of soliciting the participation and cooperation of the family unit has gained increasing clinical and social recognition.[26,27] This is so not only because the family is legally, morally, and socially defined as the child's custodian but also because of the influence the familial environment can exert upon the medical and social well-being of the chronically disabled child.[28–30]

It is against the background of these and other historical developments that present social and scientific interest in families as therapeutic objects rather than as etiologic agents[31] has emerged. Knowledge of the familial consequences of such children is necessary, then, in order to define and to make clinical and social decisions concerning the range of social environments required by defective children. The definition of these environments will depend also, of course, upon the resources for care and management available in different family groups, the facilities and services made available by society, and the social, moral, and legally defined responsibility of the family to the damaged child.

Objective information concerning families is a prerequisite to a more rational definition and allocation of professional, familial, and societal resources. In the past such decisions were determined largely by moralistic and judgmental views. In the discussion that follows, the adequacy and utility of present knowledge will be weighed against the social and technical requirements for such information.

CURRENT VIEWS OF FAMILY IMPACT

Although interest in the familial consequences of brain-damaged children is relatively recent, even a cursory review of materials published during the past decade reveals considerable consensus. In essence, professional opinion asserts that these children constitute an actual or potential threat to the family unit; specifically, their demands for care and management are said to disrupt family routines, sharpen existing or create new strains in family relationships and roles, restrict extrafamilial social contacts, and threaten family morale. The severity and quality of the impact is seen to vary with: (*a*) the attributes of the disorder (type, severity, and multiplicity of deficits), (*b*) the attributes of the child (age, sex, ordinal position), and (*c*) the attributes of the family (quality of interpersonal bonds, economic and social status and resources, values and beliefs, and structural and demographic character). Although it has been noted that families are not affected uniformly and that some may not be adversely affected, the consensus is that the impact on family living is noxious. Opinions differ only on the strength or range of its toxicity.

Despite this high degree of consensus, however, scrutiny of the evidence upon which it rests suggests that this evidence is not altogether reliable and is of limited applicability. This is due largely to: (1) limitations in the range and quality of observations of families and family behavior; (2) limitations in the conceptual approaches used to interpret family behavior; and (3) assumptions of behavioral homogeneity within the diagnostic categories to which family behavior is related.

CHARACTER OF CLINICAL AND RESEARCH MATERIALS; THE EVIDENCE

Published materials bearing on the subject (excluding those geared toward parents or the lay public) may be grouped into several gross categories. The classification below is somewhat arbitrary but appears to be useful for purposes of this analysis.

1. The largest single category consists of *reports of practitioners* engaged in providing clinical services to children and their families. These materials tend to be "problem-oriented." They contain descriptions of problems reported to them by parents and family members; their interpretations of problems of families observed in the course of care and treatment; and their, or reported, impressions of the effects of treatment services. The bulk of these reports originates from workers in newly established specialized diagnostic, treatment, and educational programs.[11,32–44]

2. *Formally structured clinically based studies* are fewer in number. They consist of descriptions of populations using services, evaluations of services, and follow-up studies. For the most part, these efforts have been based on small populations also known to specially organized and newly established programs.[9,45–58]

3. *Systematic studies* of adequate scope are few and are confined to surveys of mentally retarded children or their families. These studies have investigated present and past correlates (including family) of institutional or community status of the child[59] or have focused on family organizational changes related to the presence of retarded children.[60–65]

The largely impressionistic quality of the clinical evidence, and the limited scope and generally retrospective character of the few systematic studies, raise methodological questions concerning its reliability. Important as these questions may be, however, they are not our major concern. Recognition of their biases does not necessarily imply that such studies have no use. What may be significant and revealing for future efforts is to consider the nature and meaning of the biases contained in these materials.

Selective Population Bias

In general, clinical and research materials are biased by the fact that they are based primarily upon populations who are mostly either "users" of newly established services or members of parent-sponsored organizations. The use by families, voluntarily or as a result of referral, of specialized facilities may be confined to one or another segment of the universe of families with defective children. Such families, thus, may be those whose lives have been particularly or uniquely affected by the fact of having a brain-damaged child.

The social and educational skills and experience that are necessary to identify and utilize potentially helpful services are apparently selectively distributed in our population. There is a body of knowledge which suggests that the movement of particular population subgroups to facilities (in the absence of legal compulsion applicable to all potential "users") is correlated with socio-economic, ethnic, and educational characteristics.[66–70] Similar patterns of "selective population recruitment" by facilities and of "self-selection" by families of defective children have also been noted.[63] This evidence, together with available descriptions of clinical and research populations,[9,60,64] suggests that "users" of newly established specialized services are largely white middle-class individuals or persons oriented toward middle-class values. Therefore, attributes which may be characteristic of the "users" of services cannot reliably be ascribed to the universe of families with such children.

Thus, it would appear that present materials would have their greatest applicability to population groups that seek services or help from special sources. Conversely, they would have more limited or questionable applicability and relevance to other social groups and to "non-users."

Observer Bias

Clinically based observations are likely to be circumscribed by a limited time perspective as well as by artifacts of the organization of clinical services. Clinical contacts are office-bound, sporadic, and short term and can yield, usually, only "cross-sectional" views of the family and its behavior.

Few clinical services are organized to permit long-term prospective views of patient-family interaction, and parent-child information obtained in retrospect may be distorted, in terms of the specific dimensions the clinician may be interested in evaluating and which may have prompted these families to seek out and to present themselves for such services. Although some clinically based research studies have sampled large populations of families, these studies too are dependent upon retrospectively derived data for comparison and analysis of family changes related to the presence of the damaged child. Virtually absent from the existing literature are longitudinal prospective family studies or observations or studies utilizing comparison populations of families of nondefective children or of children with other types of disorders. Certainty, then, regarding the antecedent and resultant family adaptational states in relation to the presence of the child (or even their uniqueness) is lacking because of these considerations.

Many clinical observers tend to generalize from their individual experiences to the larger universe despite the fact that their view of family function is narrowed by the office-bound, sporadic, and short-term character of clinical practice, by an almost exclusive focus on parent-child attitudes and relationships, and by the selective characteristics of populations who find their way to particular practice sites or whom they may "select" themselves because of their own biases.[71]

The need for longitudinal studies on populations of families unselected from the point of view of possible pathologic bias is obvious. Cross-sectional studies utilizing comparison populations can also be expected to yield useful data. The paucity of such studies may be due more to complexities and costs involved in obtaining data than to lack of recognition of their importance.

DEFINITIONS OF FAMILY IMPACT AND BEHAVIOR

Thus far we have reviewed some of the methodological problems and biases. Let us now consider questions arising out of the conceptual approaches. Whether explicitly stated or not, underlying these approaches are assumptions concerning the nature of family organization and the determinants of family behavior. Of particular concern are such questions as (1) How has "family impact" been defined and interpreted? and (2) How are differences or variability in family behavior in relation to the child explained?

Clinico-diagnostic Models

In general, most clinically based reports "explain" family behavior according to attributes of the child's disorder. Familial impact is defined largely in terms of parental attitudinal categories (accepting or rejecting, guilty or nonguilty parents) and/or psychological qualities of the family relationships (closely knit, warm, etc.). This conceptual approach has generated several related typologies of families and family behavior. [11,32,33,40,41,56]

The parents or families may be categorized in terms of the kind of problems they experience with the child—either reported problems or categories of problems established a priori by clinicians. Variations in family behavior are accounted for by variations in the severity, the multiplicity, or the range of the problems the child presents. The various typologies of family problems are differentiated into needs for different kinds of treatment services, such as short or long term, intensive or brief, and supportive or insightful.[42,72,73,]

Another view examines family or parental behavior in terms of the category or type of defect of the child—cerebral palsy, mental retardation, brain injury, schizophrenia, or epilepsy, for example. Variability in family behavior is accounted for by reference to various subtypes within the larger categories of defective children. Thus, there are parents of familial and nonfamilial retarded children, mildly or severely retarded children, hyperkinetic or withdrawn, etc.

The logic of these typologies of family behavior rests upon the following questionable or even untenable assumptions:

1. Within the categories and classifications employed, the behavior of the defective children is uniform and essentially static.
2. Family behavior is uniquely ordered according to the nature of the child's impairment.

From this it would follow that:

1. Knowledge of the child's impairment is sufficient to account for family behavior, and
2. Variability in family behavior is due to differences in the impairments of children.

The utility of these family behavioral typologies and others whose conceptual roots are embedded solely in the nature and evolution of the child's impairment is quite limited. This is so not only because present categories of childhood brain damage do not describe or delineate homogeneous, unchanging behavioral disorders but also because family behavior depends upon a variety of interacting forces, some inherent in the family unit and some originating outside of it. Finally, it should be noted that these typologies recognize only individual differences among families. Social and cultural uniformities and variations in the form and content of family life in relation to demands of damaged children are not dealt with, if they are recognized at all.

Despite the hazardous nature of their underlying assumptions, many clinically based reports do provide useful and necessary information concerning families. Those reports which yield descriptive information on the nature, range, and quality of the problems or the adaptive behavior of families succeed in implicating critical variables or hypotheses for more systematic investigation. The interpretation of family behavior or problems needs to be separated from the content of the observations or descriptions.

Moreover, these accounts may reflect the fact that present categories of brain damage are more social than clinical and reflect the different social significance in our society of these different disability groups. Thus, mental retardation is a category of defect covering many types of children who share, more or less, a common behavioral symptom—intellectual inadequacy—and who are viewed and dealt with as a group because of the social significance of this behavior symptom in our culture. Being labeled "mentally retarded" has implications concerning the range of health, educational, and social services which will be made available as distinguished from children not so classified.* Families of children within the same diagnostic category may, therefore, share a common core of experiences and problems (legal, social, psychological, etc.). However, whether the social significance of the fact of having a brain-damaged child in the family is sufficiently powerful to override prior differences in

* For an elaboration of this point, see pp. 100–114.

family organization and behavior or to cast subsequent family behavior into unique and persistent patterns is highly dubious.

The ready employment by many clinicians of these interpretations of family behavior has a certain plausibility not only for the reasons cited above but also because such views seem to fit well the demands and circumstances of clinical practice. The theory that family behavior is determined or explicable by the needs of the child is a corollary, so it would seem, of the view that the behavior of children (defective or nondefective) is explicable by or is attributable solely to parental behavior or attitudes. Such views have gained wide clinical acceptance in the fields of child development and child psychiatry.

The application, then, of "proven" theories of parent-child behavior to an area where the etiology of deviant behavior has been insufficiently understood has enabled these workers to offer reasonably plausible explanations of family behavior. Clinically, then, to attribute childhood behavioral deviance to parental behavior has a more reasonable chance of successful therapeutic applicability than no "theory" at all.

The Crisis Model

A more recent conceptual view appearing in the literature has defined or explained family behavior in relation to brain-damaged children as a crisis or chronic stress reaction.[9,12,62,74–79] In contrast to the static view of impact embedded in the attitudinal systems, the crisis situation is conceptualized as having a developing character. This longitudinal approach permits family units to be differentiated according to a variety of dimensions, such as (*a*) perceptions of initial impact; (*b*) family status or organization prior to onset; and (*c*) initial and subsequent coping techniques and outcomes.

This conceptual scheme does not regard particular sets of family behavior or attitudes as necessary or intrinsic to a particular disorder. Instead, family behavior is explained as a product of a field of action in which the event (the child's perceived deviant behavior), the familial definition of the event (the assessment of its social significance), and the past and present organization of the family all interact to produce family behavior typologies.

Despite the obvious advantages of a dynamic or developmental approach over more mechanical views of family impact, two serious limitations are apparent. First, the definition of an event as being a crisis depends upon its being so defined by the affected family, regardless of whether or not the event meets social or clinical criteria to "qualify" as a crisis. This implies that people who describe their life situations as being crisis-producing behave like people in a crisis situation. The event itself has no objective reality or meaning to the family until and unless it is so perceived or defined—and this one can know only in retrospect, after the fact.

This definition of family behavior, then, would yield data on only those families that have reacted to some objective phenomenon (any phenomenon) in terms that are defined by the ground rules of the model. Typologies of family behavior generated by this approach would not encompass, therefore, those families who may differently perceive the event or its consequences for them, or families whose behavioral reactions do not conform to some assumed norm of family crisis behavior. (Assumed also is a precise definition of childhood behavioral deviance as being "crisis-producing" at some arbitrary point in time.)

The failure of many families to present themselves at newly established treatment centers or to institutionalize their damaged children or even to join parent-sponsored organizations does not necessarily imply that a disorder has not been perceived or that family coping techniques have not been challenged. It does suggest that there may be modes of family reactions to the presence of a brain-damaged child which may be different from the patterns demonstrated by those families upon whom the bulk of existing clinical and research observations have been made.

An additional limitation of the crisis model, as it has been applied in this area, stems from the fact that it defines family impact and behavior essentially in terms of intrafamilial personal relationships and processes. (In this respect it resembles clinical definitions of family impact, though it is more highly sophisticated.)

Whether family behavior in relation to brain-damaged children is viewed as being determined by a particular parental attitudinal structure (intrinsic to the disorder of the child) or as arising out of a particular assessment of a threatening social situation, a similar theory of the determinants of family organization and behavior appears to be invoked. That is, families are viewed essentially in terms of the psychodynamics of interpersonal relationships or as a small system of interacting personalities. All or most of family behavior is seen as explicable in terms of this interaction or as the product of patterned organization or reorganization of diadic or triadic role relationships. In a sense, either or both viewpoints (presented here greatly oversimplified) regard family units as self-encased systems more or less impervious to outside influence. It is against this model of family organization and structure that the brain-damaged child is viewed as making demands and as being the primary, if not the sole, determinant of subsequent family behavior.

It may be that this family model fits well most of the families that find their way to the special sites from which they are observed clinically or who fall into accessible samples for more structured research study. (There they are fitted into clinical or research categories established a priori according to the underlying theoretical constructs or typologies created out of their responses to specially designed research instruments.) However, the applicability of this family organizational model—in this case derived from the middle-class nuclear family system—to "non-users" or to other population groups, particularly low-income and ethnic-minority families, requires further study. Knowledge of social class and ethnic differences in patterns of family organization, function, and stability [80–95] as well as behavioral differences in relation to health and disease states suggests that it may not be applicable.[67,96–100]

It is entirely possible, however, that present characterizations of familial effects and behavior accurately depict middle-class people in trouble. What is crucial here is not whether this model of family structure or behavior fits better or worse than another. This can be better determined by systematic investigation than by speculation. What is significant for purposes of this review is to see how the imposition of a particular theory or family model—in this case a "psychological" model—defines the nature of family consequences and the range of relevant variables to be observed.

The net effect of the assumptions and theoretical restrictions underlying present knowledge has been to narrow the range of definition of family effects so as to implicate essentially personality and psychological processes within the family unit. The critical variables then become the family members' psychological relationships and attitudes and the processes and transactions underlying their organization and changes in organization. This view not only restricts other possibly significant variables that have been implicated—socioeconomic and health, for example [63,65,101]—but also tends to relegate extrafamilial social forces (treatment services, environmental alterations) to lesser (if any) importance as determinants of family impact behavior.

In summary, then, present clinical and research knowledge about the effects of brain-damaged children on families is based essentially on selective populations of families. Efforts to relate present family behavior to prior family states is limited by the retrospective character of both clinical and research observations. Impact has been defined essentially in terms of its psychological significance for parents and family relationships. Family behavior has either been ascribed to the child's disorder or regarded as a product of a crisis situation affecting family role relationships. The characterization of impact, the restriction of family behavior to intrafamilial psychological variables, and the nature of the selection of available populations strongly suggest a middle-class bias. This bias may well fit the biases of clinic and research workers.

Controlled longitudinal investigations and systematic descriptive materials are not yet sufficiently available. Conceptual approaches have therefore been derived from work in related areas. The fit of these a priori frameworks requires more precise measurement on varied population groups and a more adequate descriptive base.

SOME REQUIREMENTS OF A MORE ADEQUATE BASIS FOR KNOWLEDGE

The achievement of a more valid and utilitarian body of information requires first an objective formulation of the clinical and social issues and questions. The identification of relevant data dictates the choice of methods and tools for collection and analysis. Theoretical interpretations of data should proceed from this base rather than circumscribe its character and scope.

It was suggested in the preceding discussion that present clinical and theoretical definitions of familial effects have emphasized psychological attributes at the expense of economic, health, and other variables which have been implicated clinically and explored in the few existing surveys.

The preoccupation of much of clinical effort with parental attitudes as primary determinants of child or family behavior or as predictors of response to treatment services seems highly questionable in view of the failure of these approaches to generate meaningful family behavioral typologies.[52,102,103] (This does not imply that moods, feelings, and emotional states are not clinically important. As behavioral phenomena these can be objectively described.) However, the real test of the "predisposing to behavior" qualities of attitudes—that is, their ability to predict behavior—lies in whether the predicted behavior actually occurs. Similarly, the usefulness of any theoretical system lies in its ability to depict and predict behavioral realities. Its internal consistency and reliability have nothing to do with whether the underlying assumptions are relevant in the first place.

Applicability requires a focus on *descriptions* of behavior as distinct from *interpretations* of behavior, which are concerned more with motive, attitude, and belief of the subject (or the observer). Much of present knowledge remains deductive and ascriptive with an inadequate emphasis on objective descriptions of the material conditions and the behavior of the family and of the behavior of the child. Descriptive analysis is not necessarily synonymous with unstructured anecdotal accounts nor do deductive and ascriptive interpretation imply illogical thought or constructs. What is being emphasized here is the creation of an empirical base of objective materials descriptive of the conditions and circumstances of the family and of the behavior of the child. From this base analytical or theoretical systems can be evolved, or borrowed models may be better measured. Without an adequate base of this kind, theories of impact on families, clinical assessments and interpretations, and the ratings of interviewers and observers of family function remain essentially subjective and judgmental.

This problem can perhaps be illustrated by reference to a study by this reviewer of the behavior of a group of families of mongoloid and a comparison group of families of nondefective children.[104] In this study both groups were compared for a variety of both intra- and extrafamilial behavior. One commonly employed indicator of social withdrawal, for example, is visiting behavior. In this study, families of mongoloid children were found to visit relatives, friends, and neighbors less frequently than did families of nondefective children. This would seem to be an indicator of social withdrawal were it not for the fact that the families of nondefective children *were visited* less frequently than families of mongoloid children independent of the class of visitor involved.

Another measure was extrafamilial organizational involvement. Here, too, significant differences were found. Although both groups' pattern of involvement were similar—that is, they belonged to similar kinds of organizations—the families of nondefective children belonged to more. Again this finding might be indicative of social withdrawal were it not for the fact that the families of mongoloid children were more active participants in the organizations to which they belonged.

A final example deals with measures of sharing or consensus in household roles. Patterns of decision-making were similar for both groups. "Consultative" were preferred to "nonconsultative" processes in assigning household tasks. Although families of nondefective children exhibited a greater use of consultative processes, the families of mongoloid children involved more family members in the sharing of household tasks.

Which measure of each of these three qualities of family behavior is the significant one? The decision will depend upon either the clinical bias or the underlying theoretical construct of the investigator. It is apparent, however, that any one choice would be equally subjective even though each has been objectively measured and can be replicated (assuming subjects are reliable informants). The net effect of making choices is to exclude from analysis or consideration the fact of differences which are revealed only when the same behavior is viewed differently. What may really be of importance is the *fact* of difference—differences in qualities of behavior which may be empirically related to the realities of the physical, social, and psychological demands made upon this group of families of mongoloid children.

We noted also in the earlier discussion that present knowledge is based largely on selected populations, usually those seeking or using services. But not all families seek or use specialized services, since there is no institutionalized compulsion, legal or moral, for them to do so. It may be that "non-users" in this context are "users" in other contexts. Also, many "non-users" may have a different range of problems whose very nature may dictate modifications of the content of present services directed to parents and families who are "users" (guidance, counseling, training, etc.).

Present knowledge seems largely to exclude low-income and ethnic-minority families essentially because of their failure to present themselves in large numbers for newly established specialized treatment services. Yet the urgency for study of these family groups is all the more compelling since there is evidence that some precursors of cerebral damage (prematurity, inadequate prenatal care and diet, etc.) are found more frequently in such population subgroups [105,106] and they have fewer resources to help recognize and deal with these problems.*

Present knowledge has also tended to view changes in family behavior as being determined primarily, if not solely, by the presence of the defective

* Two studies now in progress [107,108] may yield useful data on childhood cerebral defects in low-income and ethnic-minority populations.

child in the family or the familial assessment of its social and psychological significance. Although this interpretation may "fit" the families upon whom the bulk of present knowledge depends, the applicability of this conceptual approach to families seen in other contexts, or to other sociocultural types of family units, is indeed questionable.

For several years this reviewer has participated in a preventive-medicine clerkship teaching program for medical students. Families for this program are chosen from among those known to a Health Department child health station. Defective children, in this case *not* the index child, have been identified in this population of low-income and ethnic-minority family groups. The daily lives of these families seem ordered by the exigencies of earning a living and the maintenance of social well-being for all family members rather than by the sole demands of the damaged child. The "deviance" is recognized, but it is not assigned the same priority of familial concern and resources as more pressing health, economic, housing, and educational needs and problems.

So, too, an exploratory study of families of children known to a municipal hospital out-patient rehabilitation service for children failed to reveal essential differences in the quality of "impact" between families of children with polio and those with children who were retarded and cerebral palsied. In both groups of families the physical and social hardships were additive upon a base of daily struggle in a low-income population in which priorities were assigned to more urgent concomitant family health and social problems.

Assumptions of homogeneity of family behavior or impact implied in current models of the family are no more tenable than are assumptions of homogeneity of behavior implied in present classification schemes for brain-damaged children. How, then, may family behavior or alterations in family behavior be studied and explained? An approach to developing data necessary to answer these questions requires that such behavior be viewed as a product of the interaction of several related but separately derived factors.

On the one hand, there is *the fact of a child with brain damage,* which exists as a real phenomenon independent of its recognition and assessment as such by the family. The underlying cerebral condition, as well as the behavioral sequelae, has a structure and course of development which may produce over time a changing picture of symptoms and behavioral consequences. Such changes are a product not only of the natural history of the cerebral disorder but also of the changing age and social status of the child.

The family itself is *an evolving social and cultural unit* with a history, a life style, and a structure that preceded the entry of the damaged child into its midst. As the family moves through its life cycle, its future course is molded by the same variety of social forces that affect all families as well as by the demands of the damaged child. The addition of any child, damaged or not, to a family will alter prior family behavior and organization.

Family-child interactions are conditioned by the *particular societal* contexts within which they occur. This is so because such contexts: (1) define the norms for determination of childhood behavioral deviance; (2) determine the range of familial and societal responsibilities for such children; and (3) depending upon the socioeconomic status of the family, they proscribe the range of available familial resources, physical and social.

It is only through prospective long-term observation of these family-child interactions, beginning prior to the "biasing" of the family by the child's presence (or by utilizing populations whose selection biases are known), that the evolution of needs, the perceptions of problems, and the behavioral alterations of different family groups can be differentiated and understood. Whether it is appropriate to group families' needs and problems according to the present categories of the child's disorder can be determined only in the context of studies that involve comparison populations, similarly selected.

A final point concerns the nature of the issues to which knowledge of families is to be applied and to which clinical and research efforts are related. Not infrequently, embedded in these issues are questions of a moral or ethical character. Such questions require objective scrutiny and reformulation in order to avoid narrow proscription of effort and thinking. Thus, for example, the observation that infants subjected to maternal deprivation showed disturbance in later behavior [109] was translated into near-doctrinaire notions of the evils of maternal separation.[110] This in turn led to the belief that the child's own family, regardless of its character, was superior to any substitute environment.

Similarly, public and professional opinion is sharply divided on such social issues as whether institutional or home care is superior [111–115] or whether one form of organization of services is more economical or effective than another.[1,23,116,117] The real problem is not whether institutional care per se is better (or worse) than home rearing per se but rather whether care in a particular institution with a specific program or home care in a particular family environment (and for a specific time) will better meet the assessed specific needs of a given child.[118] There is no intrinsic virtue to either home or institutional care except as these values may be assigned to one or another of these child-rearing environments by particular social or cultural groups in achieving definite ends or goals for the child.

The evolution of issues such as these coincides with continuing expressions of concern regarding the status of the family as a social institution and how well it is doing its job. Families, too, have not been immune to the effects of broad underlying social, economic, and technological forces. Health, income, educational, occupational, and other changes have altered the form, content, and material conditions of family life.[119–121] There is today sharp controversy as to whether, and to what extent, such changes have enhanced the stability and well-being of different family groups and their members.[122,123] Special social problems affecting family life have been identified for particular family groups including those with low incomes,[124,125] ethnic minorities,[126,127] those with long-term ill or disabled children or adult members,[55,128–134] and those with multiple problems.[135] Much attention has been paid to the creation of social and other supports whereby families may be enabled to achieve more effective preventive and therapeutic roles in relation to the wide variety of social and health problems that have been linked to family malfunction.[76,136–142]

In essence, what is being called into question is whether society's traditional reliance upon the family for the care and well-being of the child—sick or well—is still valid or appropriate under conditions of twentieth-century living. The resolution of this and related questions involves a wide range of legal, moral, and social considerations and decisions, for in our society primary responsibility for the child is firmly fixed upon the family by moral and legal sanction. Only under clearly specified conditions of danger to the health or safety of others or of familial incompetency are other social institutions required to assume this responsibility.

In matters affecting normal children, however, society recognizes that the individual family cannot make technical decisions concerning education and health. Families are legally bound to present their children for schooling and for vaccination, for example. But where demonstrations of adult capabilities are lacking or where children may threaten to become social liabilities as adults, societal assumption of responsibility is more narrowly restricted. Such children are not systematically sought out by any social or health agency, and the family's circumstances are not assessed. In short, there is no formal, or even informal, compulsion placed upon the family to do anything about the matter if it does not choose to.

The absence, then, of clearly defined mandates to other social institutions to share (or assume) responsibility for the care and training of defective children along with (or even instead of) the family means, in effect, that such families will have to provide as best they can for the disabled child and to distribute their resources among the members of the family unit according to their own capacities and values. Where decisions concerning the welfare of the family are required, these will be made in the final analysis by the family alone, although it may consult with kin and with members of the professional community beforehand. If the family's individual "diagnosis" of the situation specifies removal of the defective child from the family midst, the only apparent means of resolving critical problems has been institutional placement.

Recent developments of more comprehensive community-based services for brain-damaged children and for their families [116,117] may be viewed, then, as attempts to provide a range of social alternatives. These developments, it was earlier noted, have called into question traditional medical, educational, and social-welfare practices. Changing forms of practice or demands for such change have given rise to new questions requiring new definitions of practice goals and problems. Knowledge of the effectiveness and applicability of these alternatives, and of the requirements for care and management of defective children for different family groups, is necessary if these resources are to be used more appropriately. The absence of valid information vitiates these attempts and wastes human efforts and resources. It is in relation to issues such as these that knowledge of the familial consequences of brain-damaged children becomes socially significant and meaningful.

SUMMARY

This discussion has focused on the adequacy of present knowledge of the family effects of children with cerebral defects. This has been attempted through a macroscopic review of the available materials rather than a detailed summation of their contents. Its purpose has been to identify for further discussion some salient issues and questions that condition the social utility of present knowledge and concepts.

It has been implied that clinical and theoretical generalizations which characterize present views of the impact of these children upon their families go beyond the methodological and conceptual limitations of the underlying evidence and assumptions. Present information appears largely to be based on impressionistic observations and/or interpretations involving selected populations. Impact has been defined in retrospect and viewed essentially as an affective dislocation of parental or familial interpersonal relationships. The nature of observer, population, and theoretical bias suggests a middle-class orientation and definition of family effects. Systematic studies of scope focused on family behavior per se are sparse. Prospective investigations of changes in family behavior involving comparison populations, especially on low-income and ethnic-minority families, seem called for.

Some suggestions have been offered for establishing a more adequate knowledge base in further clinical and research efforts.

REFERENCES

1. *Basic Considerations in Mental Retardation, A Preliminary Report,* Report No. 43, Committee on Mental Retardation, Group for the Advancement of Psychiatry, New York, 1959.
2. *Cerebral Palsy, A Social Problem,* Proceedings of a Symposium conducted by United Cerebral Palsy of of New York City and The Study Group of Social Workers in C.P., New York, 1953.
3. Falther, A.: "Family, Friends, and Frustrations," in *Total Rehabilitation of Epileptics—Gateway to Employment.* Office of Vocational Rehabilitation, U.S. Dept. of Health, Education, and Welfare, 1962.
4. Katz, A. H. (ed.): *Mental Retardation and Social Work Education,* Wayne State University Press, Detroit, 1961.
5. Klapper, M.: *Basic Concepts in Community Planning for the Cerebral Palsied,* United Cerebral Palsy Associations of N.Y. State, 1954.
6. Boles, G.: Personality factors in

mothers of cerebral palsied children, *Genet. Psychol. Monogr., 59*:159–218, 1959.
7. Freedman, A. M., *et al.:* "Family Adjustment to the Brain-Damaged Child," in *Modern Introduction to the Family*, eds. Bell and Vogel. Free Press, 1960, pp. 555–562.
8. Kanner, L.: Parent's feelings about retarded children, *Amer. J. Ment. Defic., 57*:375–383, 1953.
9. Kanof, A., *et al.:* The impact of infantile amaurotic familial idiocy (Tay-Sachs disease) on the family, *Pediatrics, 29*:37–45, 1962.
10. Kelman, H. R.: Some problems in casework with parents of mentally retarded children, *Amer. J. Ment. Defic., 61*:595–598, 1957.
11. Kozier, A.: Casework with parents of children born with severe brain defects, *Social Casework, 38*:183–188, 1957.
12. Mandelbaum, A., and Wheeler, M.: The meaning of a defective child to parents, *Social Casework, 41*:360–367, 1960.
13. "Mongolism—A Symposium," *Quart. Rev. Pediat.*, May, Aug., Nov. 1953.
14. Wortis, H. Z.: Some aspects of the parent-child relations in cerebral palsy, *Cereb. Palsy Rev., 15*:8–9, 1954.
15. Clausen, J. A., *et al.:* The impact of mental illness on the family, *J. Soc. Issues, 11*:4, 1955.
16. Jackson, J. K.: The adjustment of the family to alcoholism, *Marriage and Family Living, 18*:361–369, 1956.
17. *The Mentally Subnormal Child*, Technical Report No. 75, World Health Organization, Geneva, 1954, p. 46.
18. Goddard, H. H.: *The Kallikak Family*. The Macmillan Co., 1919.
19. Perry, S. E.: Some theoretic problems of mental deficiency and their action implications, *Psychiatry, 17*:45–73, 1954.
20. Lerner, M.: Mortality and morbidity in the United States as basic indices of health needs, *Ann. Amer. Acad. Polit. Soc. Sci., 337*:1–10, 1961.
21. Parsons, T.: Some trends of change in American society, *J.A.M.A., 167*:31–36, 1958.
22. Simpson, H. S. (ed.): *The Changing American Population,* A Report of the Arden House Conference, Institute of Life Insurance, New York, 1962.
23. *Mental Disorders: A Guide to Control Methods,* American Public Health Association, New York, 1962.
24. Tobis, J. S.: Rehabilitation of the handicapped child, *New York J. Med., 56*:2354–2360, 1956.
25. Wright, R. D.: Rehabilitation's wave of the future, *Arch. Phys. Med. Rehab., 43*:395–400, 1962.
26. Chen, M. A., and Cobb, S.: Family structure in relation to health and disease, *J. Chronic Dis., 12*:544–567, 1960.
27. Galdston, I. (ed.): *The Family—A Focal Point in Health Education.* International Universities Press, New York, 1961.
28. Cardwell, V. E.: *Cerebral Palsy: Advances in Understanding and Care,* Association for the Aid of Crippled Children, New York, 1956.
29. Denhoff, E.: The impact of parents on the growth of exceptional children, *Except. Child., 26*:271–274, 1960.
30. Denhoff, E., and Holden, R. H.: Family influences on successful school adjustment of cerebral palsied children, *Except. Child., 21*:5–7, 1954.
31. Tisza, V. B.: Management of the parents of the chronically ill child, *Amer. J. Orthopsychiat., 32*:53–59, 1962.
32. Bice, H. V., *et al.:* Group counseling with mothers of children with cerebral palsy, *Social Casework, 30*:104–109, 1949.
33. Grebler, A. M.: Parental attitudes toward mentally retarded children, *Amer. J. Ment. Defic., 56*:475–483, 1952.

34. Holt, K. S.: The home care of severely retarded children, *Pediatrics, 22*:744–755, 1958.
35. Weingold, J. T., and Hormuth, R. P.: Group guidance of parents of mentally retarded children, *J. Clin. Psychol.*, Monograph Supplement No. 9, 1953, pp. 20–26.
36. Jensen, R. A.: The clinical management of the mentally retarded child and his parents, *Amer. J. Psychiat., 106*:830–833, 1950.
37. Kelman, H. R.: Parent guidance in a clinic for mentally retarded children, *Social Casework, 34*:10, 1953.
38. Kugel, R. B.: "Changes in the Concept of Training and Care of the Mentally Retarded Child Within the Family Group," *Casework Papers, 1961,* Family Service Association of America, New York, pp. 143–149.
39. Mahoney, S. C.: Observations concerning counseling with parents of mentally retarded children, *Amer. J. Ment. Defic., 63*:81–86, 1958.
40. Mayer, E. R.: Some aspects of casework help to retarded young adults and to their families, *J. Soc. Work Proc., 7*:29–48, 1956.
41. Miller, E. A.: Cerebral-palsied children and their parents, *Except. Child., 24*:298–302, 1958.
42. Sheimo, S. L.: Problems in helping parents of mentally defective and handicapped children, *Amer. J. Ment. Defic., 56*:42–47, 1951.
43. Wortis, H., *et al.:* The home visit in a cerebral palsy treatment program, *Amer. J. Occup. Ther., 8*:260–262, 1954.
44. Wortis, H., and Margolies, J. A.: Parents of children with cerebral palsy, *Med. Social Work, 4*:110–120, 1955.
45. *A Five Year Study of Brain-Damaged Children,* The Mental Health Center, Springfield, Ill., 1962.
46. Barsch, R.: Explanations offered by parents and siblings of brain-damaged children, *Except. Child., 27*:286–291, 1961.
47. Baumann, M. C., *et al.: A Report on Brain-Damaged Children,* The Mental Health Center, Springfield, Ill., 1957.
48. Caldwell, B. M., and Guze, S. B.: A study of the adjustment of parents and siblings of institutionalized and non-institutionalized retarded children, *Amer. J. Ment. Defic., 64*:638–651, 1960.
49. Caldwell, B. M., *et al.:* Reactions of community agencies and parents to services provided in a clinic for retarded children, *Amer. J. Ment. Defic., 65*:582–589, 1961.
50. Caldwell, B. M., *et al.:* Factors associated with parental reaction to a clinic for retarded children, *Amer. J. Ment. Defic., 65*:590–594, 1961.
51. Graliker, B., *et al.:* Attitude study of parents of mentally retarded children: II. Initial reactions and concerns of parents to a diagnosis of mental retardation, *Pediatrics, 24*:819–821, 1959.
52. Klebanoff, L. B.: Parental attitudes of mothers of schizophrenic, brain-injured and retarded, and normal children, *Amer. J. Orthopsychiat., 29*:445–454, 1959.
53. Koch, R., *et al.:* Evaluation of parental satisfaction with the medical care of a retarded child, *Pediatrics, 23*:582–584, 1959.
54. Schipper, M. T.: The child with mongolism at home, *Pediatrics, 24*:132–144, 1959.
55. Schonell, F. J., and Watts, B. H.: A first study of the effects of a subnormal child on the family unit, *Amer. J. Ment. Defic., 61*:210–219, 1956.
56. Thurston, J.: Attitudes and emotional reactions of parents of institutionalized cerebral-palsied retarded patients, *Amer. J. Ment. Defic., 65*:227–235, 1960.
57. Wortis, H., and Cooper, W.: The life experience of persons with cerebral palsy, *Amer. J. Phys. Med., 36*:328–344, 1957.
58. Zuk, G. H.: The religious factor and

role of guilt in parental acceptance of the retarded child, *Amer. J. Ment. Defic., 63*:139–147, 1959.
59. Windle, C.: Prognosis of mental subnormals, *Amer. J. Ment. Defic.* (Monograph Supplement), *66*:118–128, 1962.
60. Farber, B.: Effects of a severely mentally retarded child on family integration, *Monogr. Soc. Res. Child Develop., 24*:4, Serial No. 71, 1959.
61. Farber, B.: Family organization and crisis; maintenance of integration in families with a severely mentally retarded child, *Monogr. Soc. Res. Child Develop., 25*:1, Serial No. 75, 1960.
62. Farber, B., *et al.:* "Family Crisis and the Decision to Institutionalize the Retarded Child," *Research Monograph,* NEA, Series A, No. 1, 1960.
63. Saenger, G.: *Factors Influencing the Institutionalization of Mentally Retarded Individuals in N.Y.C.,* New York Interdepartmental Health Resources Board, Albany, 1960.
64. Saenger, G.: *The Adjustment of Severely Retarded Adults in the Community,* New York Interdepartmental Health Resources Board, Albany, 1957.
65. Tizard, J., and Grad, J. C.: *The Mentally Handicapped and Their Families.* Oxford University Press, 1961.
66. Beck, D. F.: *Patterns in Use of Family Agency Service,* Family Service Association of America, New York, 1962.
67. Cornely, B., and Bigman, S. K.: Cultural considerations in changing health attitudes, *Med. Ann. D.C., 30*:191–199, 1961.
68. Elling, R., *et al.:* Patient participation in a pediatric program, *J. Health Hum. Behav., 1*:183–191, 1960.
69. Koos, E. L.: *The Health of Regionville.* Columbia University Press, 1954.
70. Wylie, C. M.: Delay in seeking rehabilitation after cerebrovascular accidents, *J. Chronic Dis., 14*:442–451, 1961.
71. Hollingshead, A., and Redlich, F.: *Social Class and Mental Illness.* John Wiley & Sons, 1958.
72. Carr, B.: Problems confronting parents of children with handicaps, *Except. Child., 25*:251–255, 1959.
73. Krupp, G. R., and Schwartzberg, B.: The brain-injured child: a challenge to social workers, *Social Casework, 41*:63–69, 1960.
74. Caplan, G.: Patterns of parental response to crisis of premature birth, *Psychiatry, 23*:365–374, 1960.
75. Farber, B.: Perceptions of crisis and related variables in the impact of a retarded child on the mother, *J. Health Hum. Behav., 1*:108–118, 1960.
76. Hill, R.: Generic features of families under stress, *Social Casework, 39*:139–150, 1958.
77. Klein, D. C.: "Preventive Intervention in Individual and Family Crisis Situations," in *Prevention of Mental Disorders in Children,* ed. G. Caplan. Basic Books, 1961, pp. 283–306.
78. Parad, H. J., and Caplan, G.: A framework for studying families in crisis, *Social Work, 5*:3–15, 1960.
79. Waldfogel, S., and Gardner, G. E.: "Intervention in Crisis as a Method of Primary Prevention," in *Prevention of Mental Disorders in Children,* ed. G. Caplan. Basic Books, 1961, pp. 307–322.
80. Davis, A.: American status systems and the socialization of the child, *Amer. Sociol. Rev., 6*:345–354, 1941.
81. Frazier, E. F.: "The Impact of Urban Civilization upon Negro Family Life," in *Modern Introduction to the Family,* eds. Bell and Vogel. Free Press, 1960, pp. 101–111.
82. Havighurst, R. J., and Davis, A. A.: Comparison of the Chicago and Harvard studies of social class differences in child rearing, *Amer. Sociol. Rev., 20*:438–442, 1955.
83. Klatskin, E. H.: Shifts in child care

practices in three social classes under an infant care program of flexible methodology, *Amer. J. Orthopsychiat., 22*:52–61, 1952.
84. Kohn, M.: Social class and parental values, *Amer. J. Sociol., 64*:337–351, 1959
85. Koos, E. L.: Class differences in family reactions to crisis, *Marriage and Family Living, 12*:77–78, 1950.
86. Lewis, H.: "Child-Rearing Practices Among Low-Income Families," *Casework Papers, 1961,* Family Service Association of America, New York, pp. 79–92.
87. Littman, R. A., *et al.:* Social class differences in child rearing: a third community for comparison with Chicago and Newton, *Amer. Sociol. Rev., 22*:694–704, 1957.
88. Maccoby, E. E., and Gibbs, P. K.: "Methods of Child Rearing in Two Social Classes," in *Readings in Child Development,* eds. W. E. Martin and C. B. Stendler. Harcourt, Brace & Co., 1954.
89. Miller, S. M., and Riessman, F.: The working class subculture: a new view, *Social Problems, 9*:86–97, 1961.
90. Pettit, L.: Some observations on Negro culture in the U.S., *Social Work, 5*:104–109, 1960.
91. Rainwater, L., *et al.: Workingman's Wife.* Oceana Publications, New York, 1959.
92. Sears, R. R., *et al.: Patterns of Child Rearing.* Row, Peterson, 1957.
93. Sussman, M. B.: The help pattern in the middle class family, *Amer. Sociol. Rev., 18*:27, 1953.
94. White, M. S.: Social class, child rearing practices, and child behavior. *Amer. Sociol. Rev., 22*:704–712, 1957.
95. Wilensky, H. L., and Lebeaux, C.: *Industrial Society and Social Welfare,* Russell Sage Foundation, New York, 1958.
96. Caudill, W.: *Effects of Social and Cultural Systems in Reactions to Stress,* Pamphlet 14, Social Science Research Council, New York, 1958.
97. Deutsch, M.: "Minority Group and Class Status as Related to Social and Personality Factors in Scholastic Achievement," Monograph No. 2, The Society for Applied Anthropology, N.Y. State School of Industrial and Labor Relations, Cornell University, 1960.
98. Simmons, O. G.: *Social Status and Public Health,* Pamphlet 13, Social Science Research Council, New York, 1958.
99. Yankauer, A.: The relationship of fetal and infant mortality to residential segregation, *Amer. Sociol. Rev., 15*:644–648, 1950.
100. Yankauer, A., *et al.:* Social stratification and health practices in child bearing and child rearing, *Amer. J. Public Health, 48*:732–741, 1958.
101. Holt, K. S.: The influence of a retarded child on family limitations, *J. Ment. Defic. Res., 2*:28–36, 1958.
102. Frankiel, R. V.: *A Review of Research on Parent Influences on Child Personality,* Family Service Association of America, New York, 1959.
103. *Parent Education and the Behavioral Sciences,* Children's Bureau, U.S. Dept. of Health, Education, and Welfare, 1960.
104. Kelman, H. R.: "Mothers' Perceptions of the Effects of Non-institutional Mongoloid Children upon their Families." Doctoral dissertation, New York University, 1958.
105. Pasamanick, B., and Knobloch, H.: "Epidemiologic Studies on the Complications of Pregnancy and the Birth Process," in *Prevention of Mental Disorders in Children,* ed. G. Caplan. Basic Books, 1961, pp. 74–84.
106. Pasamanick, B., and Lilienfeld, A.: Association of maternal and fetal factors with development of mental deficiency: I. Abnormalities in the prenatal and paranatal periods, *J.A.M.A., 159*:155–160, 1955.
107. Freedman, A. M.: Long range an-

terospective study of premature infants, *World Ment. Health, 14*:1–8, 1962.

108. Masland, R. L.: "Researches into the Prenatal Factors that Lead to Neuropsychiatric Sequelae in Childhood," in *Prevention of Mental Disorders in Children,* ed. G. Caplan. Basic Books, 1961, pp. 52–73.
109. Bowlby, J.: *Maternal Care and Mental Health,* World Health Organization, Geneva, 1951.
110. *Maternal Deprivation,* Child Welfare League of America, 1962.
111. Centerwall, S., and Centerwall, W.: A study of children with mongolism reared in the home community as compared with those reared away from home, *Pediatrics, 25*:678–685, 1959.
112. Farrell, M. J.: The adverse effects of early institutionalization of mentally subnormal children, *Amer. J. Dis. Child., 91*:278–281, 1956.
113. Garber, R. S., *et al.:* Do we need institutions for epileptics? *J. Med. Soc. New Jersey, 52*:27–29, 1955.
114. Slobody, L. B., and Scanlan, J. B.: Consequences of early institutionalization in mental retardation, *Amer. J. Ment. Defic., 63*:971–974, 1959.
115. Tizard, J.: Residential care of mentally handicapped children, *Brit. Med. J., 1*:1041, 1960.
116. *The Evaluation and Treatment of the Mentally Retarded Child in Clinics,* Proceedings of a training institute, New York Medical College and the National Association for Retarded Children, New York (no date given).
117. Wellin, E., *et al.:* Community aspects of mental subnormality; a local health department program for retarded children, *J.A.M.A., 50*:36–42, 1960.
118. Birch, H. G., and Belmont, L.: The problem of comparing home rearing versus foster-home rearing in defective children, *Pediatrics, 28*:956–961, 1961.
119. Ginzberg, E. (ed.): *The Nation's Children: Part 1. The Family and Social Change,* The White House Conference on Children and Youth. Columbia University Press, 1960.
120. Pollak, O.: Interrelationships between economic institutions and the family, *Soc. Sec. Bull., 23*:9–15, 1960.
121. Titmuss, R. M.: Industrialization and the family, *Soc. Serv. Rev., 31*:54–62, 1957.
122. Schorr, A. L.: Family policy in the U.S., *Int. Soc. Sci. J., 14*:452–467, 1962.
123. Schorr, A. L.: *Filial Responsibility in the Modern American Family,* Division of Program Research, U.S. Dept. of Health, Education, and Welfare, 1960.
124. Epstein, L. A.: Some effects of low income on children and their families, *Soc. Sec. Bull., 24*:12–17, 1961.
125. Harrington, M.: *The Other America: Poverty in the United States.* The Macmillan Co., 1962.
126. Handlin, O.: *The Newcomers.* Anchor Books, Doubleday & Co., 1962.
127. Padilla, E.: *Up From Puerto Rico.* Columbia University Press, 1958.
128. Gibbs, N.: "Psychological Aspects of Cerebral Palsy," in *Recent Advances in Cerebral Palsy,* ed. R. S. Illingsworth. Little, Brown & Co., 1958, pp. 108–131.
129. Glaser, H. H., *et al.:* Comprehensive medical care for handicapped children: I. Patterns of anxiety in mothers of children with rheumatic fever, *Amer. J. Dis. Child., 102*:344–354, 1961.
130. Katz, A. H.: *Parents of the Handicapped; Self-Organized Parents' and Relatives' Groups for Treatment of Ill and Handicapped Children.* Charles C. Thomas, 1961.
131. Levy, J. H.: *Parent Groups and Social Agencies.* University of Chicago Press, 1951.
132. Lewis, R. S., *et al.: The Other Child: The Brain-Injured Child.* Grune & Stratton, 1960.

133. Rose, J. A.: "The Prevention of Mothering Breakdown Associated with Physical Abnormalities," in *Prevention of Mental Disorders in Children,* ed. G. Caplan. Basic Books, 1961.
134. Schwentker, F.: "Social Management of Epilepsy," in *The Diagnosis and Treatment of Convulsive Disorders in Children,* ed. S. Livingston. Charles C. Thomas, 1954.
135. Willie, C. V., and Rothney, W. B.: Racial, ethnic, and income factors in the epidemiology of neonatal mortality, *Amer. Sociol. Rev., 27*:522–526, 1962.
136. Bordua, D. J.: *Sociological Theories and Their Implications for Juvenile Delinquency,* Children's Bureau, U.S. Dept. of Health, Education, and Welfare, 1960.
137. Cumming, J. H.: The family and mental disorder: an incomplete essay, *Milbank Memorial Fund Quart., 39*:185–228, 1961.
138. Green, A. W.: "The Middle-Class Male Child and Neurosis," in *Modern Introduction to the Family,* eds. Bell and Vogel. Free Press, 1960, pp. 563–572.
139. Myers, J., and Roberts, B. H.: *Family and Class Dynamics in Mental Illness.* John Wiley & Sons, 1959.
140. Naegele, K. D.: "Some Problems in the Study of Hostility and Aggression in Middle-Class American Families," in *Modern Introduction to the Family,* eds. Bell and Vogel. Free Press, 1960, pp. 417–428.
141. Parsons, T., and Fox, R.: Illness, therapy, and the modern urban American family, *J. Soc. Issues, 8*:31–44, 1952.
142. Sanua, V. D.: Sociological factors in families of schizophrenics, *Psychiatry, 24*:246–265, 1961.

DISCUSSION

The discussion of this paper concerned itself primarily with the specific considerations involved in the decision about institutionalizing the child. Consensus was expressed that this decision is never a simple one and that neither the family nor the child is well served by a simple, prescriptive approach—that a series of factors must be considered by the physician or the social agency to which the family comes for guidance. A clear understanding of the degree of disability present in the child and of the prognosis for his functional outcome is crucial, since the decision made by the family may hinge upon these factors.

The structure and value system of the family are also highly relevant. Certain types of families, because of religious, ethnic, or social conviction, have found that, in certain circumstances, the presence of a handicapped child has increased family cohesiveness and contributed to growth of the family as a social unit; other types of families find that the presence of a handicapped child within the family is extremely disruptive. For these reasons, the professional who is trying to help families make such decisions must bear in mind that there is no single family type in the United States. One discussant noted that, in particular, patterns of family organization within the Negro community have been shown, by Franklin Frazier and others, to differ within themselves and from the prevalent white middle-class model customarily used as the stereotype for family organization.

The decision to institutionalize or to retain a child within the family cannot be made without a detailed consideration of the availability within the community of services for children with special dysfunctions. Thus, the decision to keep a child at home is made much more easily when special educational and guidance facilities are readily available. In the absence of such resources, the family may not be able to contribute effectively to the development of the child.

The Social Environment and Individual Functioning

STEPHEN A. RICHARDSON, PH.D.
Association for the Aid of Crippled Children

BRAIN INJURY is a widely used term with many meanings. Beyond its specific denotation of a lesion in the brain, it provides a general umbrella under which cluster a wide variety of symptoms and diagnostic categories: mental retardation with organic involvement, cerebral palsy, epilepsy, the hyperkinetic impulse disorder, syndromes of cerebral dysfunction, "the brain-damaged child." Whichever term is used, the symptoms may be broadly characterized as having two patterns: first, a predominating and obvious defect which may or may not be accompanied by other functional deficits—*e.g.*, cerebral palsy with severe motor involvement, or severe general mental retardation; second, no single outstanding deficit but rather a miscellany of functional deficits that are not immediately apparent and often are difficult to recognize—*e.g.*, perceptual, behavioral, learning, and emotional malfunctions.

The purpose of this paper is to consider these two general patterns of symptoms in terms of how they come to attention, what kinds of action are taken, and the consequences for the child's over-all socialization and development.

We shall begin with the simplest possible assumptions, adding complexity only as required by the demands of the inquiry. Let us consider first the varieties of experience necessary for the adequate socialization of the child.

The child's functioning is intimately related to the social and economic environment in which he lives; this environment both influences and is influenced by his functioning. From the almost infinite number of possible environmental factors, we shall select those that may be critical for his adequate socialization and development.

EXPERIENCES NECESSARY FOR ADEQUATE SOCIALIZATION

Obviously no definitive classification of experiences necessary for the child's adequate socialization can be drawn up at the present stage of knowledge, but the following may be regarded as illustrative of the types on which there would be some measure of consensus.

Maintenance (food, clothing, shelter, cleanliness, protection against illness and injury)
Exercise
Exploration of the physical and social environment
Development of communication skills
Social relationships
Affiliation with social collectives such as a family, school, peer group, or club
Successes
Support and love
Internalization of certain norms and values
Play and fun
The opportunity to express feelings
Increase in responsibility with increasing age
Adequate social stimulation
A variety of role models
Some consistency in the behavior of others toward the child

These experiences interact with a set of functional characteristics that may be affected as a consequence of brain injury. Again, the following listing is illustrative rather than exhaustive and is intended to provide a basis for raising questions.

Human Functions Affected by Brain Injury

Motor functioning
Level of physical activity
Degree, manner, and intensity of response to the physical and social environment
Growth (the degree to which the child's development approaches the norms for various development sequences)
Appropriateness of affective reactions
Reception of, reaction to, and initiation of communication
Level of cognitive functioning
Social relationships
Consistency of behavior

Fig. 1. Functioning in children and the varieties of experience necessary for adequate socialization.

FUNCTIONS → / NECESSARY VARIETY OF EXPERIENCES ↓	Motor	Activity level	Response to physical and social environment	Growth	Affective reactions	Sensory and perceptual	Cognitive	Social relation-ships	Consistency of behavior
Maintenance									
Exercise									
Exploration of environment									
Communication skills									
Social relationships									
Affiliations with collectives									
Successes									
Support and love									
Internalization of norms and values									
Play and fun									
Expression of feelings									
Increases in responsibility									
Intellectual stimulation									
A variety of role models									
Some consistency in the behavior of others									

Figure 1 shows the interrelationship between the necessary experiences and human functions. We shall focus initially on human functioning and examine how a single functional impairment or a syndrome of impairments jeopardizes the child's opportunity to gain experiences necessary for his adequate socialization. Later we shall consider ways in which the social environment of the child and the experiences he derives from it influence and modify his functioning. For example, a child's level of cognitive functioning may appear low because of an unrecognized perceptual impairment. His inability to meet the demands and expectations in a school setting, coupled with the resultant partial withdrawal of love and support by his parents, who are ambitious for him to do well at school, places the child under a stress to which he may respond, for example, by fantasy and withdrawal from reality. This leads to increasingly inappropriate affective reactions on the part of the child until what began as a perceptual impairment develops into a severe emotional disturbance because of his lack of the successes, love, and support he needs for adequate socialization.

This general schema is broader in focus than the traditional medical diagnostic viewpoint. First it does not focus on pathology alone and, instead of using such diagnostic labels as cerebral palsy, brain injury, or epilepsy, views malfunctioning in a broad context of human functioning. Medical treatment, by contrast, although related to the child's functioning, generally focuses sharply on a specific malfunction and rarely takes into account the consequences and implications of the child's functioning for his ability to obtain necessary experiences or the extent to which treatment will influence this ability. This concentration on restoration of a specific function is satisfactory if full restoration is achieved. But where treatment can only partially improve functioning, this limited focus is inadequate because it fails to take into account the full consequences for the child.

For example, a normally intelligent child with mild to moderate cerebral palsy has a major presenting symptom—motor impairment of the legs—which directly reduces his opportunity to obtain exercise and explore the physical environment. A program of bracing and physical therapy can reduce the direct effects of motor impairment and increase his opportunities for exercise and exploration. But both before and after treatment there are much more indirect effects of this motor impairment on the kinds of experience the child will obtain. It has been shown that he is less likely than the child without motor impairment to be given increased responsibility with increasing age;[1] he will be less liked by his peers than the child without motor impairment;[2] and he will have a more restricted social environment.[3] In other words, there is a discrepancy between the limitations on the child's experiences that stem necessarily or directly from a specific functional impairment and the limitations that in fact occur.

THE CHRONOLOGICAL SEQUENCE IN WHICH MALFUNCTIONING COMES TO NOTICE

The consequences of various malfunctions may be better understood if they are ordered in the chronologic sequence in which they come to notice. This sequence is largely dependent on the ages at which there are sufficiently well-established norms to permit a diagnosis of "abnormal." The following is an approximate chronological ordering.

Motor functioning
Activity level
Responsiveness
Developmental landmarks
Appropriateness of affective reactions
Communication skills
Cognitive functioning
Play and social relations
Inconsistency in behavior

Early parental concern centers on the biological functioning and the physical appearance of the child because they are readily noticeable and because the child's earliest demands are predominantly biological. The parents are sensitive to these cues and are likely to bring their concerns to a physician, nurse, druggist, chiropractor—whoever they feel has competence in dealing with biological questions. Thus, biological malfunctioning, especially in its more severe forms, can be identified and brought to medical attention early. In making a diagnosis, the practitioner is likely to consider a number of long-established diagnostic categories which implicate brain injury: cerebral palsy, mongolism, hydrocephalus, epilepsy. To gain further evidence for establishing such diagnoses, the physician is likely to consider etiological data such as symptoms of pregnancy complication, difficult or prolonged labor and delivery, a high bilirubin level in the neonate, or febrile episodes in infancy. Because of the short time span since birth, the existence of such evidence can often be explored and reviewed. When biological malfunction appears in other children, the insult is often traumatic and apparent—for example, the child falls or receives a violent blow on his head; such damage is apt to come to medical attention promptly and to have clear etiologic evidence suggestive of brain injury.

Affective responses, communication skills, and social and cognitive functions, on the other hand, develop later in children, and there is far less systematic knowledge of what constitutes normal variation rather than abnormal deviance and about the point in time at which concern becomes justified that abnormality is present. These nonbiological functions are so broad in range that there is no one professional diagnostic and treatment specialty to which the parents may turn for guidance and even for the available knowledge. Instead, there is an incomplete division of labor among the educator, pediatrician, psychiatrist, psychologist, and social worker. Even where there is some consensus about the presence of abnormality in some of the later-appearing functions, the range of etiologic factors that may be implicated is far wider than in infancy and it becomes infinitely more difficult to discriminate between biological and environmental factors. Even if brain injury was a causative factor, many intervening variables may have influenced the child's present functioning. Even from this brief discussion, the importance and the varied consequences of the chronological sequence in which functions emerge become apparent.

RECOGNITION OF AND REACTION TO MALFUNCTIONING

An obvious striking malfunction due to brain injury will be identified quickly. There is real danger, however, that the obvious malfunction will so arrest the attention of the examiner that less apparent forms of malfunctioning may be neglected. For more than a decade, for example, predominate attention was given to motor malfunctioning in cerebral palsy, and emphasis was placed on surgical correction, bracing, and physical therapy. Only recently has there been recognition that a child with cerebral palsy may also have perceptual impairment which may seriously interfere with his ability to learn in school.

In the second characteristic syndrome of brain injury there is no single, outstanding malfunction but the child's over-all patterning of functioning becomes a source of concern and there is a miscellany of symptoms which may include any of the areas of functioning we have listed. These are still ill-understood patterns of malfunctioning. And although the label "brain injury" has been used, it is difficult to establish that injury to the brain has actually occurred. Thus the prognosis and the planning of effective treatment is severely hampered by lack of knowledge. Given this set of conditions, it becomes important to determine how children with any given syndrome of this type come to notice and how reactions to them may vary.

Research in social psychology has demonstrated that the perception of one person by another is an enormously complex process. From the almost infinite number of cues that a person provides through his range of functioning, people will variously select certain ones for attention. The behavioral cues that are meaningful, relevant, and salient for one perceiver may be very different from those selected by someone else. Among the factors that influence this selective process of the perceiver are his background of experience and the nature of the relationship between the perceiver and the perceived.

This variation in the perception of a child can easily be demonstrated by asking a variety of people who know a specific child to "tell me about him." The child's father, sister, schoolteacher, doctor, and minister would not give the same descriptions. Very few of the differences would be errors. Rather they would be a function of the different relationships the perceivers have with the child, the different contexts in which they see him, their differences in training and background experiences. The variation and complexity of these descriptions will increase with the age of the child as his range of functioning increases and he becomes involved in an increasingly complex array of activities and interpersonal relations. With this introduction, let us now examine some of the factors that influence perception of the kind of malfunctioning that is not generally apparent or striking.

The arousal of suspicion and the identification of particular forms of malfunctioning frequently occur through the child's difficulty or inability to live up to expectations and demands. The nature of these demands and expectations vary from those that apply with great uniformity to all children in a society (*e.g.*, the acquisition of bladder and bowel control; attending school between certain ages and meeting a series of academic demands, which increase in number and complexity with chronological age; the expectation that a child will give affection in reaction to receiving affection, that he will acquire certain forms of control over expression of his feelings, etc.), through those in which there is variation, to those which may be almost idiosyncratic to particular parents.

All persons do not place the same expectations and demands on a child. What we pick out for special attention derives in part from the role we play in society vis à vis a particular child. These roles carry various expectations that are placed on us by the society and that in turn require us to expect certain things of children, to prepare children to meet the expectations, and to impose certain demands. During the early years of life the parents play the main role but, as the child grows older, additional persons take on certain of the demand and expectation tasks—siblings, relatives, neighbors, teachers.

The role of parenthood derives from a lifetime of experience and implicit and explicit training. Because of the diversity in people's temperaments, backgrounds, and abilities, the parental role is highly variegated. Thus there will be marked differences from one family to another in the expectations and demands placed on a child. For example, parents of limited intelligence living in a low-income, crowded slum with a low level of social and economic aspiration may have a low expectation for the level of cognitive functioning of their children and place little inhibition on the child's aggression. In fact, they may be concerned if the child does not express aggression. On the other hand, a child with such a level of cognitive and affective functioning but with parents of high intelligence, living in a high-income suburb and having high social and economic aspirations, will have very different demands and expectations placed on him, and his behavior will very early be defined as malfunctioning. In short, although the parents generally hold widespread responsibility for their child's upbringing, the demands they make of their child and how they perceive his functioning depend on the family's social environment and on the personality and temperament of the parents.

From school age on, an increasing number of people come into contact with a child, having responsibilities for special phases of his growth and development; *e.g.*, the teacher places cognitive demands on the pupil and helps him to develop in the classroom setting, where there is an unusual opportunity to make comparisons between children in their ability to learn. It is no wonder, then, that cognitive malfunctioning often first comes to the notice of a teacher. In the same way, because of more specific roles vis à vis the child, the physical education instructor is in an unusually good position to notice inadequacies of motor functioning, and a recreation leader working with groups of children may be sensitive to inappropriate affective reactions.

With specialized training, a person's perception of certain areas of functioning becomes sensitized, but often at the cost of inattention to other areas of functioning. For example, in the health services a child psychiatrist, an orthopedist, an internist, and a urologist would have very different views of a child. There is little systematic knowledge on the manner and extent that selective perception of other people is influenced by occupational roles. One of the reasons why physicians may have difficulty in identifying certain areas of malfunctioning is that they may not make any demands during their examinations which would require a child to reveal such malfunction.

The perception of malfunctioning in a child may well be influenced by the frame of reference in which the child's problem is presented—either by the parents or by some other person—to the person asked to help in evaluation and treatment. For example, when a parent, concerned about his child's intellectual ability, brings the child to a psychologist, does the psychologist test for mental ability only—or does he also make a more general evaluation, either in his initial assessment or by referring the child to clinicians with other areas of competence? To the extent that the perceptual frame of reference used in presenting a case to a practitioner by the parents and patient influences the practitioner's evaluation, diagnoses, and treatment, to this extent does it become an issue worthy of study.

THE WITHDRAWAL OR IMPOVERISHMENT OF NECESSARY SOCIAL EXPERIENCES

The extent to which any child, with or without brain injury, obtains necessary social experiences depends heavily upon his parents and their social environment. If some of these experiences are abnormal, impoverished, or withheld, there may be serious consequences for his socialization and the full development of his functioning.

This consequence is illustrated in a number of studies and reports. Children reared in institutions who have received adequate maintenance but very little of the other necessary experiences are likely to exhibit retardation in cognitive functioning, disturbed affective reactions, and apathetic responses to the social environment.[4,5] Social impoverishment of the kind experienced by children living in slum areas may well lead to inadequacies in school performance and present an appearance of cognitive malfunctioning.[6–8] Populations in areas of high social disintegration show a higher prevalence of psychiatric symptoms than those in areas in which social disintegration is not present.[9,10] Preliminary results from a study done in Aberdeen (personal communication from R. Illsley, Ph.D.) indicate that children of low socioeconomic status have a higher prevalence of reading handicaps than children of high socioeconomic status. These data suggest that a child may exhibit forms of malfunctioning often associated with brain injury even though the etiological factors derive almost wholly from his lack of some of the experiences necessary for adequate socialization.

There is a less direct way in which impoverishment of experience is associated with malfunctioning from one generation to the next. Women who have been reared under conditions in which the necessary experiences were either lacking or impoverished have been shown to have more difficulty in reproduction and to produce more malfunctioning children than women whose developmental and current living experiences were more satisfactory. This has been most clearly demonstrated in the studies of Baird and his colleagues.[11,12] Using such criteria as complications of pregnancy, stillbirth, prematurity, and congenital anomalies apparent at birth, they have shown that lower-class women have lower reproductive efficiency than upper-class women.

REACTIONS TO SYNDROMES OF MALFUNCTIONING

The problem confronting the person responsible for diagnosis and treatment of a malfunctioning child is to assess the relative contributions of the biologic insult and the social environment. To examine this problem we need to look at some of the ways in which people's reactions to malfunctioning can affect children's experiences in ways that increase and complicate malfunctioning or, on the other hand, reduce malfunctioning and strengthen other functions.

How do individual reactions to various syndromes of malfunctioning in children influence a child's experiences? In the absence of systematic knowledge, we can only bring together studies that touch on the issue and consider the problem. A number of studies show that a person with a visible physical handicap experiences difficulty in encounters with other persons and in the development of social relationships, has fewer affiliations, less opportunity for fun and play, less adequate social stimulation and less increase in responsibility with increased age.[13–16] That this is not the direct result of the restrictions imposed by malfunctioning is shown by the extent to which these difficulties are encountered by persons with facial disfigurements who have no physical impairment.[17] We must infer that some of the difficulties encountered stem from the reaction of others to the handicap or malfunctioning. Direct evidence for this comes from a study that obtained a preference order of different visible handicaps by showing six drawings of a child. The pictures were identical except that one child had no handicap and each of the remaining five had a specific handicap different from that of the other four. The nonhandicapped child was most liked, and the average ranking of the various handicaps occurred with such consistency among different sets of subjects that a widespread cultural uniformity was suggested in preferences toward different handicaps.[18,19] As for children who exhibit aggressive and destructive behavior, clinical studies suggest that reactions from others include the arousal of anxiety and counterhostility or, alternatively, withdrawal.

This fragmentary evidence suggests that certain malfunctions in children may so disturb the persons responsible for his socialization as to further jeopardize a child's chance of obtaining the varieties of experiences he needs for adequate socialization. Additional work is needed to examine the extent to which different syndromes of malfunctioning have disturbing effects on other people and whether the degree and type of disturbance varies with different cultural and subcultural contexts.

If a child has no single outstanding deficit but rather a miscellany of functional deficits, the recognition and diagnosis of the syndrome of behavior may take a long time and be marked by considerable confusion and contradiction. During this interval, those who care for the child will exhibit the almost universal need to seek the meaning of and explanation for the child's disturbance. In the absence of knowledge, the child's guardians may seize on all kinds of rationales. The diversity of explanations evidences the extent to which there is still extant in our culture beliefs about malfunctioning that range from superstitions which can be found in chapters of the Old Testament to scientific and pseudoscientific theories. Because these beliefs may influence behavior, they must be given serious consideration. An extreme example is the rationale that the child is possessed of devils. This may produce reactions that would lead to punishment, constriction, and isolation of the child. A less extreme rationale, but one having a similar consequence, is that the child is stubborn, obstinate, naughty, or a troublemaker. A humanitarian philosophy such as "there is that of God in every man" may lead to kindly, loving reactions and a seeking for and development of the child's behavioral assets.

Certain rationales and patterns reactive to deviant functioning may especially influence parents if the parents feel guilt stemming from an implicit or explicit belief that the sins of the father are visited upon the children. This may bring into play protective possessive behavior exempting the child from demands and responsibilities. It may also lead to withdrawal to the extent of complete rejection of the child and to mutual recriminations between husband and wife. We should also consider carefully the diagnosis of brain injury in terms of the effects of so labeling a child. Although it may be of value in providing an explanation that reduces the parents' sense of guilt and feelings of inadequacy, it may also have unfavorable and unintended consequences such as reducing the practitioner's feeling of responsibility for carrying through a comprehensive evaluation and developing a plan of treatment.

Another individual difference in reaction to deviant functioning is the relative emphasis the parent places on himself and on the deviant person. For some, a malfunction may heighten self-centeredness: "What have I done?" "Why should this happen to me?" "What are my friends going to think of me?" For others, the focus and concern may be for the child alone or for the family as a whole.

The person with clinical responsibility is confronted with unusually difficult decisions in dealing with children with brain injury. He often cannot fulfill his customary and expected role in our society of providing diagnosis and treatment with the expectation of cure. Instead he must deal largely with unknowns and situations in which no clear-cut course of action is available. There are a number of reasons why in these circumstances it is difficult for the practitioner to share his uncertainty and perplexity with the child's guardians: it does not meet their strong need for an answer—preferably a simple answer—to their problems; we are an action-oriented society in which action in and of itself has virtue; the practitioner may fear that his inability to meet their expectations may result in a loss of confidence and in their going to quacks and charlatans, who may respond to demands for action by prescribing treatment that may be harmful. Finally, it is difficult for any person to tell others he does not have the knowledge expected of him. Despite these difficulties, some practitioners are able to share with the child's guardians what is and is not known about the child's problem and what can and cannot be done for him. Retaining the guardians' confidence, he can then work out with them the wisest possible decisions for the child's over-all development in the light of what information does exist. To do this requires consideration not only of the child but the whole family situation and over-all circumstances as well. This is a difficult and time-consuming task.

The practitioner has open to him other courses of action. He may refer the child to some other source for treatment; he may fit the child into a diagnostic category which suggests treatment that might be helpful; he may try to dispel the parents' concerns by suggesting a wait-and-see or he'll-grow-out-of-it attitude. The less knowledge and skill the therapist possesses, the more likely he is to routinize his treatment into standard operating procedures that he uses with little regard for their appropriateness and without a systematic attempt to evaluate the effectiveness of the treatment.

It is very natural to select from the full range of the child's deviance those impaired functions which the practitioner feels he has some competence to remedy and to ignore—intentionally or unintentionally—other impaired functions about which he has no special knowledge or competence. Although the child's malfunctioning may have serious effects on the parents, and these effects may in turn have important consequences for the child, the practitioner may choose to regard these problems as outside his purview.

When parents come to define their child as someone who needs special attention and help, a wide variety of search patterns for help are possible. We know most about the search patterns used by those parents who seek out medical or educational help, but very little about those of parents who adopt less conventional approaches. Koos found that low-income members of the community feared and hesitated about using physicians, and that they frequently consulted the druggist, the neighbors, and the chiropractor for diagnosis and treatment.[20] Rainwater, in studies of working-class women, suggests that people differ widely in the extent to which they feel they have control over their environment and their lives.[21,22] These feelings range from an extremely active approach, in which an aggressive hunt is initiated and sustained in seeking solutions of problems, to a high degree of passivity and fatalism, in which very little seems feasible to alter the course of events. The latter extreme, Rainwater believes, is more characteristic of unskilled working-class families. This passive view, of course, has considerable validity from the standpoint of ability to pay for health and related services. However, even where free services are available, there may be ignorance of or reluctance to use these services. As long as studies of patterns of search for care are focused on hospital- and clinic-patient populations, considerable bias in the direction of emphasizing more conventional search patterns will occur.

THE INSTITUTIONALIZATION OF SERVICES FOR DEALING WITH MALFUNCTIONING

Any society develops an elaborate set of arrangements to ensure that children receive certain experiences deemed necessary for adequate socialization. For normal children, a progressive life course is mapped by the society, with some variation left to the discretion of the parents and local authorities. It is required, for example, that after a given age the child should attend school, but this may be public or private; for many, a course of religious instruction and experiences is set. Some formal affiliation with other children for purposes of recreation is common, and, from birth on, residence in a family unit is expected and enforced by social and legal action. Certain expectations and demands are made on social, emotional, and cognitive behavior in these various settings and are enforced within limits that depend on the child's age and sex.

A child with functional deviance may find it difficult or impossible to adhere to or even closely approximate these expected courses of behavior. If the abnormality is recognized early and falls into an established medical or educational category, society may have developed alternative courses to which the child may be diverted and which temporarily or permanently exempt him from certain demands. One such course may consist of remedial therapy with a view to returning the child to the normal life course—for example, the provision of prostheses, remedial educational instruction, psychotherapy, medication, surgery, etc. These remedial actions take place when the functional abnormality has a hopeful prognosis, provided early therapeutic treatment is given. If the prognosis is less hopeful, or if there is no known effective therapy, special provisions for alternative courses of growth and development are evolved, such as special schools or classes, or placement of the child in an institutional setting.

The establishment of special provisions is influenced by the numbers of children with a given abnormality, the extent to which the functional abnormality has been recognized and named, its severity, and the extent to which it has received public interest.

Recently some school authorities have set up pilot programs for "the brain damaged" child, but, in the absence of well-established and generally accepted diagnostic procedures, they are confronted with the dilemma of whom to accept and not to accept. It is unfortunate that the planning of special educational arrangements is based on medical diagnostic classifications, particularly when special education recommendations derive principally from physicians who have little or no competence as educators. As a result, children are organized in classes on the basis of groupings such as mental retardation, emotional disturbance, cerebral palsy, and epilepsy rather than on rational educational criteria. Thus every class so constituted has such a heterogeneous array of educational problems that little teaching is possible except on an individual basis.

Increased responsibility on the part of educational authorities for educational diagnosis will lead to an increased impetus on research on the learning process, the obstacles to learning that are presented by various forms of malfunctioning, the forms of teaching therapy, and the criteria for grouping children so as to facilitate educational and personal growth.

Although the heaviest responsibility of the school is the development of cognitive skills, it has enormously important secondary responsibilities for providing children with almost all other experiences necessary for socialization. These secondary effects are even more important for a child with limited cognitive skills and should be planned in terms of a careful over-all assessment of the full range of his functions and the extent to which he is receiving the experiences he needs. Such an evaluation requires the placing of the medical evaluation within the framework of over-all educational planning.

The central on-going responsibility for children rests with their parents. The institution of the family is supported by the society through its laws, its educational, health, and welfare institutions. The parents who have a child with an atypical or ill-understood syndrome of malfunctioning may be in great need of the society's help but may find organized services for children unwilling or unable to provide support or service. This unwillingness will be in direct relation to the bureaucratization and departmentalization of services and the extent to which the child fails to fit the classification schemes used. For example, parents will have much greater difficulty in finding services and help for their child if he has a visible physical handicap and is emotionally disturbed than if he had one or the other malfunction, because services generally operate in mutually exclusive diagnostic classifications.

We very much need more understanding of the enormously varied capacities of families to maintain in the home a child with atypical malfunctioning and the varied ways in which community institutions—educational, health, recreation, and welfare—deal with "atypical cases." In the absence of parents, or where the home setting is not deemed appropriate, alternative institutional arrangements have to be made for a child with or without malfunctions.

Although institutions play an important role in the care of children with functional impairments, surprisingly few systematic studies exist of such institutions, and, indeed, there is no adequate classification scheme generally available by which the characteristics of different institutions may be compared. Studies of institutions that serve adults have suggested that there are certain inherent conflicts between the needs of an institution and its staff on the one hand and the needs of the people served on the other.[23–26] Dentler and Mackler,[27] for example, have demonstrated in a study of the assimilation of children into a residential institution for retarded children that the administrative practices used to keep order have the effect of breaking up informal social groupings and inhibiting the development of skill in social relations. There are very few institutions for children in which the goals and objectives for the children are sufficiently explicit so that the institutional practices can be evaluated in the light of these goals. It is more common to find that the functioning of the institution can better be understood on the basis of institutional needs, which remain covert and include such factors as survival, autonomy, and the convenience and comfort of the staff. In the absence of explicit goals and treatment criteria, institutions may rapidly become only custodial in character.[28]

The schema presented in this paper was in part derived from Tizard.[29] He planned a residential institution with a view to its providing the variety of experiences necessary for adequate socialization. In this institutional setting, retarded children were found to show marked improvement in functioning in contrast to their responses in a more traditional form of total institution.

For a child with functional impairment, the question is often raised as to whether institutional treatment is wise. The schema we have used provides a basis for assessing the present status of the child both functionally and experientially. It is then possible to assess a number of alternative forms of institution, which may include total institutionalization and many combinations of home and institutional care: foster parents; an arrangement by which several foster children live together with a man and wife in an ordinary residential area; a colony of cottages in each of which live a number of children with cottage "parents"; or the more traditional "barrack" type of institution. A number of combinations of care practices are evolving in which the resources of the child's own parents are supplemented by day-care centers and various forms of help in the child's home.

At present the consideration of these alternative patterns of care is largely marked by contention and dogma. Although the schema we have suggested for consideration of alternatives is only rudimentary, it does provide a rational basis for considering for a particular child whether, and in what way, a particular form of institutional care may be helpful. By manipulating an institutional environment or finding some combination of home and institutional environment, it also may be possible to broaden the variety of experiences a child needs and thus influence favorably his functioning where direct focus on a functional impairment and its restoration may not only fail but have unfortunate, unintended consequences for other functions and for the child's experiences.

REFERENCES

1. Shere, M. O.: The socio-emotional development of the twin who has cerebral palsy, *Cereb. Palsy Rev.*, *17*:16–18, 1957.
2. Richardson, S. A., Goodman, N., Hastorf, H. A., and Dornbusch, S. M.: Cultural uniformity in reaction to physical disabilities, *Amer. Sociol. Rev.*, *26*:241–247, 1961.
3. Barker, R. G., and Wright, H. F.: *Midwest and its Children: The Psychological Ecology of an American Town.* Row, Peterson, 1955.
4. *Maternal Deprivation,* Child Welfare League of America, 1962.
5. Bowlby, J.: *Separation Anxiety; A Critical Review of the Literature,* Child Welfare League of America, 1962, pp. 251–269.
6. Deutsch, M., and Brown, B.: Some data on social influences in Negro-white intelligence differences. In press: *J. Soc. Issues.*
7. Cherry, E.: "Communication in the Elementary School Classroom." Paper presented at the Society for Research in Child Development, April 1963.
8. Conant, J. B.: *Slums and Suburbs.* McGraw-Hill, 1961.
9. Leighton, D. C., Harding, J. S., Macklin, D. B., McMillan, A. L., and Leighton, A. H.: *The Character of Danger; Sterling County Study of Psychiatric Disorders and Socio-Cultural Environment.* Basic Books, 1963.
10. Leighton, A. H., Lambo, T. A., Leighton, D. C., Hughes, C. C., Murphy, J. M., and Macklin, D. B.: *Psychiatric Disorder Among the Yoruba.* Cornell University Press, 1963.
11. Baird, D.: Environment and childbearing, *Proc. Roy. Soc. Med.*, *46*:53–59, 1953.
12. Illsley, R.: Social class selection and class differences in relation to stillbirths and infant deaths, *Brit. Med. J.*, *2*:1520–1531, 1955.
13. Gowman, A. G.: Blindness and the role of companion, *Social Problems,* *4*:68–75, 1956.
14. Barker, R. G., and Wright, H. F.: *op. cit.*
15. Davis, F.: Deviance disavowal; the management of strained interaction by the visibly handicapped, *Social Problems,* *9*:120–132, 1961.
16. Macgregor, F. C., Abel, T. M., Bryt, A., Lauer, E., and Weissmann, S.: *Facial Deformities and Plastic Sur-*

gery; A Psychosocial Study, American Lecture Series, No. 174. Charles C. Thomas, 1953.
17. *Ibid.*
18. Richardson, S. A., *et al.*: *loc. cit.*
19. Goodman, N., Richardson, S. A., Dornbusch, S. M., and Hastorf, A. H.: Variant reactions to physical disabilities, *Amer. Sociol. Rev.*, *28*:429–435, 1963.
20. Koos, E. L.: *The Health of Regionville.* Columbia University Press, 1954.
21. Rainwater, L., and Weinstein, C. K.: *And the Poor Get Children.* Quadrangle Books, Chicago, 1960.
22. Rainwater, L., Coleman, R. P., and Handel, G.: *Workingman's Wife.* Oceana Publications, New York, 1959.
23. Goffman, E.: *Asylums.* Anchor Books, Doubleday & Co., 1961.
24. Burling, T., Lentz, E. M., and Wilson, R. N.: *The Give and Take of Hospitals.* G. P. Putnam's, 1956.
25. Rapoport, R. N.: *Community as Doctor.* Tavistock Publications, London, 1960.
26. Stanton, A. H., and Schwartz, M. S.: *The Mental Hospital: A Study of Institutional Participation in Psychiatric Illness and Treatment.* Basic Books, 1954.
27. Dentler, R. A., and Mackler, B.: The socialization of retarded children in an institution, *J. Health Hum. Behav.*, *2*:243–252, 1961.
28. Barton, R.: *Institutional Neurosis.* J. Wright, Bristol, England, 1959.
29. Tizard, J.: Residential care of mentally handicapped children, *Brit. Med. J.*, *1*:1041–1046, 1960.

DISCUSSION

The discussion centered around the types of life situations and the opportunities for interpersonal relationships that could best contribute to the development of positive social functioning in the child with brain damage. There was a tendency—as there frequently is in the consideration of this issue—to counterpose the rearing of children in institutional settings with their growth and development within their own families. It was pointed out that the opposites thus posed are unrealistic and in a sense represent stereotypes wherein the institution is viewed as cold, impersonal, and segregating and the home is viewed as having all the virtues of warmth, friendliness, kindness, and love. In actual practice, neither homes nor institutions are homogeneous, and both must be considered concretely and specifically if any sensible conclusion is to be reached.

It was pointed out that institutions could be considered both with respect to their formal character as organized social structures and with respect to the objectives that they purport to serve. The first formal characteristic generally noted about any institution is its size. There was some opinion that the size of the institution per se need not determine its character or affect its atmosphere—that even in large institutions the child can develop well socially and personally provided that the personnel is carefully selected and that thoughtful, detailed consideration is given to his developing needs.

Current opinion seems to favor the organization of large institutions around a cottage framework within which it becomes possible for close and intimate relationships to be established between small groups of children and significant adults. Such a view represents a set of feelings rather than a belief based upon substantial evidence; in fact, we have very little evidence as to the relation of specific forms of institutional structure to the development of the child. There was general agreement that this area of knowledge requires a considerable amount of detailed inquiry.

One view about institutional size stressed the fact that as size increases there is a proportionate increase in the size of the catchment areas from which the patients are drawn and, consequently, in the distance of the institution from the child's home and community. Concern was expressed that the mere fact of such physical distance could result in lengthening periods of institutionalization and diminishing contact between the child and his community. Such a process might contribute significantly to the permanent institutionalization of the child and make more likely his total exclusion from his home community.

Considerable dissatisfaction was expressed with the failure of some institutions clearly to specify their functions. Perhaps the most undesirable feature of institutions is their use as "disposition areas" into which a child is sent when he has been totally excluded from his family and community. A much more valid institutional function, it was felt, is for observation and diagnosis to assess the child's patterns of functioning and to determine the circumstance most conducive to his optimal level of functioning. Such a function could be combined with treatment organized according to a plan whereby, after periods of intensive therapeutic activity within the sheltered and highly structured environment of the institution, the child could periodically be returned to the community and permitted to function on the basis of the gains that had been made in the institution. When the child reached a new developmental stage, or when specific problems in his functioning within the community arose, he could be returned to the institution for specific therapeutic or educational intervention.

Such a pattern of management requires a close and continuing relation between the institution, on the one hand, and the family and the community, on the other. The child would be sent to the institution not merely because he could no longer be contained within his home environment but because of the specific contributions that the institution could better make to his personal and social growth. Although a few experiments with such intermittent patterns of community and institutional living exist, we lack as yet a sufficient body of experience by which to evaluate their usefulness.

The final phase of discussion noted a tendency on the part of both planners and investigators to use psychiatric institutions as their models for institutional study. It was felt that this type of institution may well have very special characteristics and that the degree to which experiences within them can be generalized to settings which have a stronger educational and habilitation focus is not yet clearly established. It was emphasized, therefore, that a considerable amount of research is required on institutions, particularly those concerned with the care, habilitation, and education of neurologically impaired children.

Some Epidemiological Aspects of Congenital Brain Damage

ERNEST M. GRUENBERG, M.D., D.P.H.
College of Physicians and Surgeons, Columbia University

I WOULD LIKE TO ATTEMPT a general description of what we have been talking about. What do we mean by the terms "cerebral palsy," "brain damage," and so forth? It seems to me that what we have been talking about—and what many of us have been worrying about in our professional work—is the fact that there is a group of behavioral disorders of function seen in children who are known to have had some kind of damage to their central nervous systems.

Dr. Kennedy (see pp. 13–22) has outlined beautifully the type of reasoning that is used to conclude that a particular child's central nervous system has been damaged at some time in the past. We notice that some youngsters known to have had brain damage manifest behavioral abnormalities such as hyperkinesis, difficulties in learning what their teachers think they should learn, difficulties in concentration, difficulty in analyzing and synthesizing figures that they are capable of recognizing, etc.

These manifestations that occur in brain-damaged individuals we can call a "brain-damage syndrome." Figure 1 is a sort of logic-diagram that specifies what I believe to be the general consensus on the subject. The oval at the left represents a group of children known to have damaged brains. The cross-hatched area of this oval represents those children who have behavioral elements in their clinical picture. The oval at the right includes these children but extends to include also another group of children: those with similar behavioral manifestations but for whom there is no clear-cut evidence, of the type described by Dr. Kennedy, that brain damage has occurred. Because the behavioral manifestations are similar, we suspect that they, too, have experienced damage, and so we label them "brain damage?" This is perfectly reasonable, since brain damage obviously can lead to many different manifestations, and there is no good reason for assuming that every damaged brain will be mani-

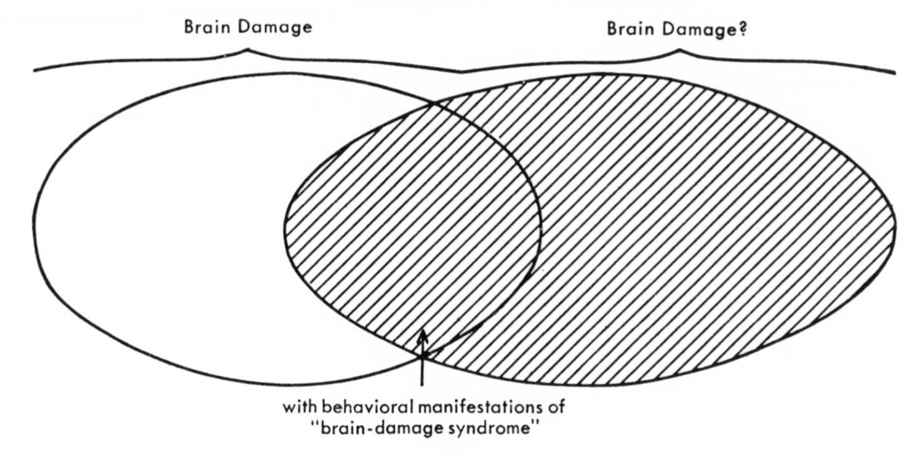

Fig. 1.

fested by both the more focal manifestations and the more general behavioral manifestations. This justifies the suspicion that some cases of behavior disorders are due to brain damage even when it can't be proved.

If the group of cases with the "brain-damage syndrome" in the absence of clear evidence of brain damage are to be thought about clearly, we should, perhaps, give it a name. We might, facetiously but not inappropriately, call it the "damaged-oid syndrome" or, more euphoniously, the "organoid syndrome." (Fig. 2.)

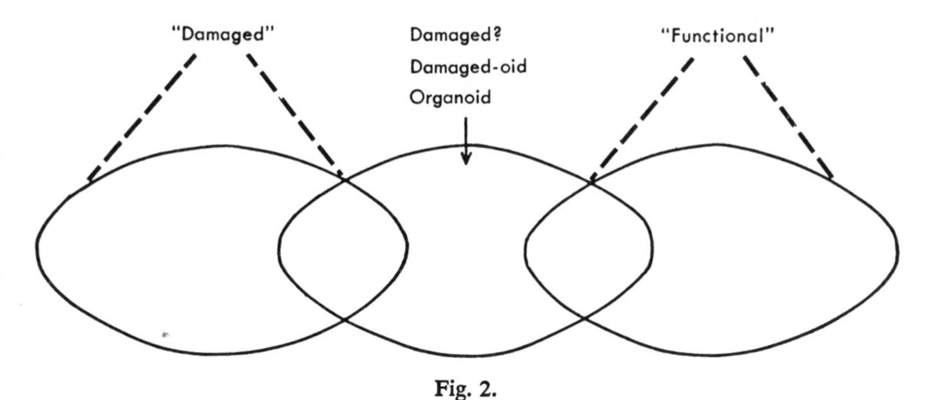

Fig. 2.

We know definitely that there are cases with "organoid" syndromes such as reading disability or impulsive behavior which from their history and course and total picture can clearly be judged to have experienced a "functional" disorder of psychogenic origin. Many cases could be cited to prove this point, but since I do not believe it is in dispute, there is no point in adducing evidence to prove it.

Secondly, I would like to raise the following questions regarding this organoid syndrome or, rather, the organic syndrome plus the organoid syndrome. Who manifests these syndromes? Where? When? How many people manifest them? From what segments of the population do these cases come? What kinds of causes are producing them? What might be done about it? The Greek word for asking these questions is "epidemiology."

Epidemiology is often thought of as a narrow, dry, pedestrian study of the numbers of cases of illness existent in a population. In fact, it is much more. It not only studies the distribution of prevalence rates in different populations but also seeks to understand the forces that make prevalence rates higher in one population than in another. As the father of American epidemiology, Wade Hampton Frost, put it: "Epidemiology at any given time is more than the total of its established facts. It includes their orderly arrangement into chains of inference which extend beyond the bounds of direct observation. Such of these chains as are well and truly laid, guide investigation to the facts of the future; those that are ill made fetter progress." [1]

This is what we have all been doing: we have been going beyond the established facts and trying to anticipate what are likely to be the facts of the future. We have been trying to avoid types of reasoning likely to obstruct future investigation.

The general phenomenon of the organoid syndrome has been studied very rarely. Hardly anyone will descend to the level of looking for all the cases in the population that fit these criteria. Yet there is an extensive literature that tries to account for the observations of Goddard,[2] Lombroso,[3] and others that families seem to have a wide variety of handicaps. Certain families seem to be at high risk of producing the intellectually handicapped and dysocial cases. Others have noted that these families tended to be poor. In fact, some have pointed out that, with or without positive family histories, the poor have a higher prevalence of brain-damaged persons.

Explanations of these general trends fall into a few groups:

1. The Eugenical.—Like beget like, and if the unfit stopped begetting, the numbers of unfit would decline.
2. The Social Darwinist.—The poor are poor because they are poor biological stuff. To the fittest go the rewards.
3. The Euthenical.—The poor are handicapped because their living conditions are undesirable; if they had a better environment, the number of cases would drop.

Although more sophisticated formulations occasionally occur, most of the older theories can be classified as representing one or more of these schools of thought.

The theories are not mutually exclusive. But stated baldly like this, they tend to embarrass us. It is a little humbling—not to say humiliating—to realize that they have simply gone out of fashion without being really defeated or replaced by better explanations. Perhaps general thinking has yielded to highly specific thinking, and we are simply embarrassed when asked to state our opinion regarding these theories.

Generally instead of relating ourselves to these broad theories, we ask much more specific questions, such as "Can maternal rubella produce mental retardation without microcephaly or only with microcephaly?" Such specific questioning leads to investigations which advance knowledge.

So much for a quick look at some of the generalizations regarding the epidemiology of chronic brain syndromes of congenital origin.

Three recently published reviews [4,5,6] of available knowledge of the origins and determinants of the distribution of congenital brain syndromes present evidence regarding the specific causes of specific syndromes. The first and most important of these reviews, that by MacMahon,[4] is based on epidemiological evidence regarding physical damage to the fetal brain. From the third [6] we can get some perspective on known causes of permanent brain damage. There is a long list of poisons—most of them introduced into the environment by advancing technology. More than fifteen specific infections—some rare, others common—are known to be capable of producing permanent brain damage. Although measles is about to come under control, we do not know how large a role it plays in producing permanent brain damage. Perhaps it is very important. Meningitis is much more important in some parts of the world than it is here. Is the common condition rubella causing more or less brain damage than syphilis, which is dying out? No one seems to know, but I would put my bet on syphilis at this time in the United States. There are fewer than ten specific genes recognized as leading to congenital brain syndromes. These each occur in something like one in 25,000 to 50,000 births, and I suppose that this small acknowledgment would not satisfy most eugenicists.

What do we know regarding the distributions of the organoid syndromes? There are two well-established facts regarding these distributions not accounted for by the eugenicists, the Social Darwinists, or the advocates of euthenics. Figure 3 and Table I show the age-specific prevalence of mental deficiency or oligophrenia according to the criteria of different investigators. A large proportion of the clearly brain-damaged and almost all of those with the organoid syndrome would be included in these data. They have in common a remarkable drop in prevalence after the age of 13—to less than half of what it was around the age of 13—although the drop does not appear so dramatic on the logarithmic scale.

How can this drop be explained? The most obvious explanation is that the school acts as a case-finding agent and that it is not in contact with the children after the age of 14; the rest of the community is not so observant of the intellectual defects. Another mechanism is the high mortality rate associated with some forms of brain damage. However, the drop in prevalence is so great

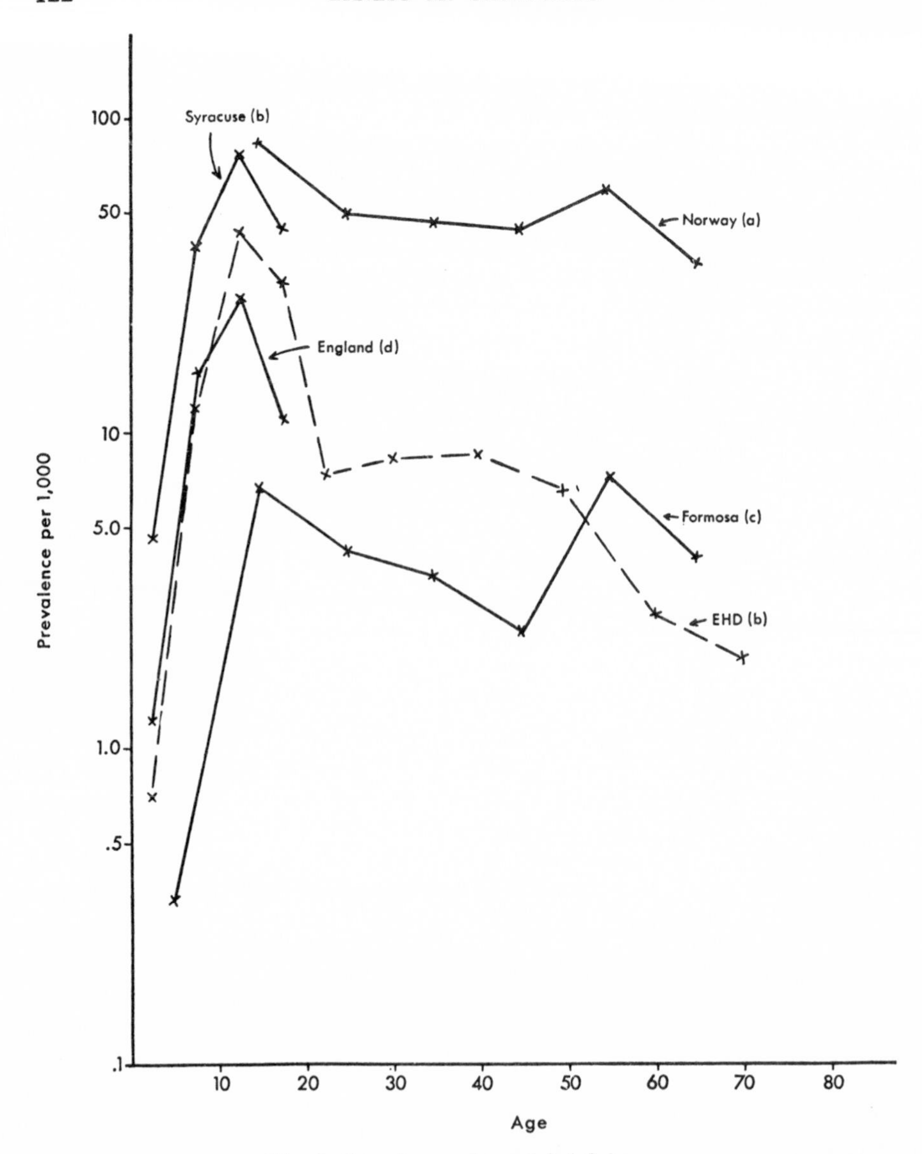

Fig. 3. Prevalence of mental deficiency.

that to account for it in terms of mortality would require that more than 100 percent of the deaths at age 13 were among the cases and that no deaths occurred among the rest of the population. Thus, although differential mortality rates may be invoked to explain part of the drop in prevalence, they can't explain all of it.

A third explanation, which I think has much merit but remains purely conjectural at this time, can be called the "schologenic hypothesis." This hypothesis is based on the notion that what is being reported is a functional disequilibrium between the individual and his environment; we take it for granted that society assigns roles in a reasonable way and that those who fail to fulfill roles have something wrong with them. I think we have grounds for questioning this assumption.

This idea can perhaps best be illustrated by reference to the history of the automobile. At first, only a small proportion of mankind was thought capable of mastering this new gadget—perhaps 5 percent of the males. This is similar to our present ideas regarding who should attempt to fly jet planes. But today

Table I

Prevalence of Mental Subnormality per Thousand

AGE	SYRACUSE	FORMOSA	NORWAY	ENGLAND	So. SWEDEN	EHD
0–4	4.6			0.12	9.0	0.7
0–9		0.3				
5–9	39.3			15.5	16.0	11.8
10–14				25.6	21.0	43.6
10–19	44.5	6.7	82.1			
15–19				10.8	19.0	3.2
20–24						7.2
20–29		4.1	48.8	8.4	10.0	
25–34						8.1
30–39		3.5	45.5	5.7	16.0	
35–44						8.3
40–49		2.3	43.2	5.4	3.0	
45–54						6.4
50–59		7.2	57.6	4.9	8.0	
55–64						2.6
60–69		3.9	33.6	2.9		
65–74						1.9

we expect some 95 percent of both males and females to master the operation of the automobile. And they do. What has changed in the past fifty years is not the nature of men and women but the automobile.

If we think of school grades in the same way, we can ask what part of the range of fifth graders the school's work is adapted to as compared to first graders. Logically, one would expect the school curriculum to be adapted to the children in each age group. This assumption gains plausibility in a child-centered culture and even more so in school systems operated by educators who avow a child-centered ideology. However, a careful appraisal of the forces determining curriculum for each grade in our schools will lead, I believe, to the conclusion that curriculum is affected by many other factors and that empirical data regarding the abilities of children in each age group are, in the first place, remarkably scarce and, in the second place, of relatively small importance. The social forces represented by society as a whole, historical traditions of education, and the internal structure of school systems themselves all play a large role.

Hence it is not impossible that some grade levels may be less adapted to the characteristics of the children for whom they are organized than other grade levels. It is in this sense that I think that Dr. George Stevenson's suggestion of "schologenic deficiency" is worth attention; not that schools produce deficiency, but that school organization can lead to a higher incidence of functional disequilibrium between the school environment and the children at some ages than at other ages.

The other remarkably well-established generalization about the distribution of the organoid syndrome is that many more boys than girls exhibit this syndrome. One explanation is similar to the "schologenic hypothesis" regarding age-specific prevalence. It states that schools are better adapted to the female child than to the male child. Unfortunately for this hypothesis, the data show that male cases outnumber female cases in the pre-school years and also in the clearly organic cases at all ages. Hence, we cannot accept this as more than a partial explanation. A second explanation points to the larger head sizes of boys than of girls at birth and their consequent greater liability to head injury. This may well play a role in some cases but makes no sense in conditions such as mongolism. A third possible mechanism refers to the fact that the genetic, particularly the chromosomal, composition of boys is different from that of girls. One can conjecture sex-linked susceptibilities to damaging agents, and there is no evidence to refute this suggestion. This genetic concept can be seen in an inverted form as well, but it is rather disturbing to some well-established preconceptions regarding male-female differences to suggest that males might tolerate brain damage during fetal life better than females, in the sense that the case-fatality rate is lower in male fetuses. Since the evidence is so good that male mortality exceeds female mortality in general, at every age level and also during fetal life as well, it may seem contradictory to suggest that case-fatality rates might be higher in females who have central nervous system damage than in males. Of course, this possibility is only seemingly in contradiction to the general phenomenon of higher male mortality rates and on close examination cannot be ruled out because it is paradoxical or because it requires an assumption regarding sex ratios at conception. The available evidence does not permit us to rule it out. Actually, weak as they are with respect to diagnosis, Record and Smith's Birmingham data on mongolism[7] suggest that paranatal mortality rates are higher in female mongols than in male, and their evidence as well as other evidence suggests that, at a few years of age, male mongol death rates are higher than female. This could be true of several other disorders and would account for the higher prevalence of male cases.

The sex ratio in the prevalence of the organoid syndrome remains an important unexplained fact and a potential clue regarding causes. As far as the sex ratios of the prevalence of intellectual handicaps is concerned, I believe that our available data *underestimate* the male excess because our devices used to estimate the frequency of intellectual defects, the intelligence tests, are purposely designed to avoid discriminations between boys and girls. The test-makers make them that way, and the test-buyers want them that way. When a test-maker finds tasks which discriminate 11-year-olds from 10-year-olds fairly systematically, he discards those tasks which 11-year-old girls do better than 11-year-old boys, so that the resulting tests are "nondiscriminating." Since the test-makers seem to find this is a common weakness of test items which do distinguish 11-year-olds from 10-year-olds, I am inclined to suspect that the tests have a built-in bias favoring the boys. This should be investigated.

The last point, and perhaps the most important, refers to those who showed that the organoid syndromes are associated with poverty and a poor physical environment. As members of a society characterized by several generations of upward social mobility and dramatic improvement in the environment, we are impressed, I presume, by our general knowledge that many children are being born into middle-class homes whose grandparents were born into subsistence-level homes. Hence, we have a bias toward euthenical theories, I think with good reason, in spite of the absence of good statistical data covering several generations. Yet it is also clear that the reduction of disease which accompanies social progress also facilitates economic advance. It is also clearly true that civilization brings with it new problems and new environmental hazards.[8–10]

Although each of these three propositions is undoubtedly correct, yet, for the world's population as a whole, the proposition that poor living conditions favor the development of the organoid syndromes outweighs the other two. Most would agree that this is true of the peoples of Latin America, Africa, and Asia. It is worth considering the possibility that it is true for the United States as well. In a study in Onondaga County, New York,[11] a remarkably disproportionate number of the mentally retarded and suspected mentally retarded came from the small number of people living in the census tracts with the lowest standard of living.

This leads me to end my remarks by suggesting that if you wish to find the part of the population with a high incidence of the organic and organoid syndromes, look for the population with high paranatal mortality rates. I think this will generally turn out to be the case, but I also believe it should be investigated directly.

To summarize a rather discursive set of remarks, I would say, first, that the organoid syndrome is exhibited in a group of cases some of which have clearly suffered brain damage, some of which are clearly disordered because of psychosocial disturbances, and many of which cannot be placed definitively in either category but may be due to either set of causes.

Second, genetic, euthenical, and Social Darwinist mechanisms all occur; certain families do, in fact, carry deleterious genes, certain families are handicapped in upward social mobility by cases of brain damage, and improving social environments reduce the risk of many sources of brain damage. This last leads to a reduced *incidence* of new cases but, because improved social environment also aids in the survival of handicapped people, the *prevalence* of some conditions is probably raised by improved environment. (But who is appraising this phenomenon quantitatively?)

Third, of these three mechanisms, the most promising approach to the prevention of congenital brain syndromes is an attack on unfavorable maternal, fetal, and infant environments. The current incidence, I believe, is due largely to preventable causes. Perhaps infant mortality rates are a function of the same factors.

I have been asked to discuss the relationship between this view and the concept of a "continuum of damage ranging from death to minimal damage" associated with the names of Hilda Knobloch, Benjamin Pasamanick, and Abraham Lilienfeld. These investigators have provided us with a large proportion of the available information on the relationships I have discussed. I believe the available evidence suggests that it is a mistake to believe that the nature of the damage experienced by the organism is solely a function of the time, intensity, and duration of the agent's action; the nature of the agent also seems to make a difference. Some causes and some consequences are more specifically related. Other causes show a capacity to produce a graded response that may more or less appropriately be named "a continuum." I am urging attention to the fact that certain common causes cluster, are not independently distributed but are more likely to come into play together. Thus, infections and poor nutrition work hand in glove, not independently of each other.

At the same time I put great stock in refining our knowledge regarding specific relationships. However, when you sum up the available knowledge regarding specific agents acting in specific ways and group together the wide variety of phenomena occurring in the organic brain syndromes and the organoid syndromes, you end up with largely the same general conclusions regarding the very large effect which is arising from unfavorable environment.

So regardless of which way one prefers to look at the problem—as a "continuum" or as a clustering of specifics—one is bound to view the present period as one in which the social application of existing knowledge provides a substantial challenge. One also is led to the conclusion that opportunities for social change offer opportunities for improving our knowledge. Thus, systematic control of infections and systematic improvement of nutrition might conceivably go on in some areas as though they were controlled trials. My personal opinion is that this can be done only if the local government sees the advantages of it and if collaborating scientists are available to work where the experiment is politically feasible. I do not think research workers can create these situations.

A final reference to the problems of developing countries may not be out of order. Professional leaders from developing countries sometimes ask whether industrialization and compulsory education are bound to bring to the surface a large problem of mental retardation or whether one can build on American and European experience to make this unnecessary. I believe we are in no position to make a categorical statement on this issue; we can make what we know of our own experience available and point to probable consequences of different policies, but I think we are dead wrong if we suggest that we know how to do a good job or that our methods are particularly desirable, even if they are feasible, in developing countries.

REFERENCES

1. Frost, W. H.: "Snow on Cholera: Introduction," The Commonwealth Fund, New York, 1936.
2. Goddard, H. H.: *The Kallikak Family*. The Macmillan Co., 1919.
3. Lombroso, C.: Der Verbrecher (Homo Delinquens), transl. by M. O. Fraenkel. Verlagsanstalt und Druckerei Actien-Gesellschaft, Hamburg, 1890.
4. MacMahon, B., and Sowa, J. M.: "Physical Damage to the Fetus," in *Causes of Mental Disorders: A Review of Epidemiological Knowledge, 1959*. Milbank Memorial Fund, New York, 1961.
5. *Mental Disorders: A Guide to Control Methods,* Program Area Committee on Mental Health, American Public Health Association, New York, 1962.
6. Gruenberg, E. M.: Epidemiology of Mental Subnormality. Chapter for the American Association on Mental Deficiency. University of Illinois. In press.
7. Record, R. G., and Smith, A.: Incidence, mortality, and sex distribution of mongoloid defectives, *Brit. J. Prev. Soc. Med., 9*:10–15, 1955.
8. Gruenberg, E. M.: Public health and the people's health, *Public Health Rep., 72*:47–50, 1957.
9. Sigerist, H. E.: *Civilization and Disease.* Cornell University Press, 1945.
10. Fox, T. F.: "Priorities," in *Population Trends in Eastern Europe, the USSR, and Mainland China,* Proceedings of the Thirty-sixth Annual Dinner Meeting of the Milbank Memorial Fund, New York, 1960.
11. Mental Health Research Unit, Technical Report, New York State Department of Mental Hygiene, 1955.

DISCUSSION

Dr. Gruenberg's attempt to distinguish what he called eugenical, euthenical, and general socio-developmental factors in the occurrence of cerebral dysfunction in children led to a discussion of some of the ways in which these factors might interact in the production of specific disabilities. It was pointed out that a considerable body of evidence suggests that damaging hereditary traits are transmitted from generation to generation and tend to produce families in which a high frequency of persons manifest defective central nervous system organization. It was noted, however, that the fate and functional status of such people in any population depend to a very considerable extent upon the nature of the society in which they live. If the society emphasizes individual striving and upward economic mobility, such people may be biologically stigmatized if they are unable to rise at the same rate as others. Even individuals who are themselves of entirely adequate genetic composition but who have a seriously handicapped family member may, in certain societies and under certain conditions, be placed at serious disadvantage.

One logical extension of these considerations is that the incidence of disorders that may involve familial inheritance may itself be determined by the social conditions under which the individuals live. It may well be that a given disease entity comes to social notice only when the society makes demands upon the person which make obvious his deficiencies in functioning. This phenomenon leads one to distinguish between the presence of an underlying defect and its manifestation as a handicap.

This way of viewing the problem seems to have particular importance for those countries that are currently becoming industrialized. Industrialization requires people with specific technical skills and necessarily results in some forms of compulsory public education. One of the consequences of universal compulsory education is the identification of numbers of people who cannot fit into the new environment or respond adequately to the new demands for learning. It is to be expected, therefore, that the noted incidence of mental deficiency, brain damage, and a wide variety of syndromes associated with behavioral inadequacies will show continuous increases as social modernization proceeds. Individuals who, despite damaged brains, could in their former, more simple social circumstances behave adequately and meet the demands made upon them come in the new and more complex circumstances to be stigmatized by the society because they cannot engage in normal work or social roles without special help. Thus there is an increase in dependency and, because it takes place within the decaying framework of the old social and familial structures, no adequate system of incorporating dependent individuals in the community yet exists. Conditions of developing industrialization thus show clearly that the functional problem associated with brain damage most frequently results from the interaction of the eugenical, euthenical, and social conditions.

Dr. Gruenberg expressed the belief that the developing countries provide special opportunities for studying the causes and consequences of defective brain development. As social laboratories, they provide exceptional possibilities for exploring effective patterns of management. He pointed out that despite the widely held view that a stable and highly organized situation is essential to serious epidemiologic investigation, the developing countries provide special opportunities for study precisely because of their fluidity. The interaction between such phenomena as patterns of nutrition, patterns of child rearing and socialization, patterns of social demands and their timing, and the effect of these influences upon children with both normal and aberrantly developing nervous systems may all be studied at close range. To be effective, such studies must have the fullest cooperation and interest from the people who are indigenous to the area being studied. The role of societies such as our own would be to provide both financial support and the necessary technical knowledge. It is through such cooperative interaction that maximal use may be made of present opportunities for expanding our understanding of mechanisms of development through the study of communities in which social change is proceeding at an extremely rapid pace. Studies of this kind, conducted effectively, can result both in the enhancement of social progress in the community and in the advance of scientific understanding of problems attending abnormal brain development.

In addition to the general philosophical and methodological considerations provoked by Dr. Gruenberg's remarks, several specific epidemiologic questions were raised. The first of these dealt with the problem of sex differentials in the incidence of disturbances of brain function in children. It was pointed out that in almost any of the disorders with which we are concerned, the ratio of males to females is greater than one. For some reason male children seem to be more vulnerable to brain insult than females. Several possible mechanisms were advanced to account for the differences. The first, for which it was agreed that there is little evidence, was that the male is a genetically inferior organism lacking in certain of the chromosomal complements that characterize the female. It was pointed out that although such genetic factors may play some role, their mechanism is at present quite inaccessible and that, from a practical point of view, it might be most productive to turn to more specific and approachable differences between male and female infants.

It was suggested that one possible basis for the sex differential is the indication that head circumference is greater in male infants than in female infants of the same general body weight. These larger-headed infants may have more difficulties in delivery and this may result in some increased risk. However, the magnitude of the reported size difference is so small that it was not felt that this factor is likely to be the most significant one. Moreover, it was pointed out that the sex ratio appears to differ markedly for various syndromes. Some disorders affect four or five times as many boys as girls. This high differential was reported for those disorders having as their principal manifestation disturbances in language and symbolic functioning. In other entities the male-female ratio can be as low as 1.2:1 and in still others there may be no sex difference. It was suggested that, although we have no ready explanation for them, differential sex ratios provide certain opportunities for the study of factors in the development of the syndrome associated with brain damage.

The final specific topic in this discussion was the concept of a continuum of reproductive damage, advanced by Pasamanick and Knobloch. It was the consensus of the group that this view has considerable value in that it shifts the focus from specific etiologic factors to certain of the broader public health problems that probably underlie a wide variety of syndromes. This approach may lead to modifications of some factors in the general environment—for example, poor conditions of housing and nutrition or inadequacies in medical and obstetrical care—which, if improved, would probably contribute markedly to the diminution of the number of new cases of children with damaged nervous systems. It was emphasized, however, that although concern with specific etiology might be suspended temporarily, it must never be lost sight of. Rather we must continue to concentrate our efforts on the task of identifying the specific factors that contribute to specific types of disorder. The general concern with environmental health, though contributive, could have only a negative outcome in the long run if it diverted our attention from the study of specific interrelations among agent, disease, and factors determining functional outcome.

A SELECTIVE BIBLIOGRAPHY ON BRAIN-DAMAGED CHILDREN

The Entity and Its Description

Clinical and Special Diagnosis

Characteristic Mechanisms and Natural History

Etiology—Clinical, Experimental, Epidemiologic

Treatment, Education, and Management

Reviews, Overviews, and Theories

A Selective Bibliography on Brain-damaged Children

THE PREPARATION of a bibliography for a subject area has at least two purposes. The first is to facilitate the task of both the research worker and the practitioner by identifying the basic reports, materials, and conceptualizations that represent our present state of knowledge. The second is to provoke new inquiry by indicating regions of strength and weakness, of concern and neglect, and of agreement and disagreement. It is to be hoped that the following compilation and annotation of representative references can assist research both through the stimulation of exploration into relatively neglected aspects of the subject and through the more effective integration of ongoing investigation with the existing body of knowledge. Hopefully, too, it can be of more immediate practical usefulness by contributing directly to the effectiveness of clinical diagnosis and treatment as well as to educational practice and social planning.

The degree to which these objectives have been achieved by the present bibliography can be judged only by its users. But their judgment is likely to be more valid if they are aware of the selective and organizational criteria employed by the editors.

From the outset it was decided to be drastically selective and to limit the bibliography to materials dealing directly with children with cerebral dysfunction and, more particularly, with their behavioral characteristics. Despite the relevance of animal experimentation, of inquiries into the functioning of adult patients with central nervous system impairment, and of more general sociological and developmental study for the understanding of both the causes and consequences of cerebral dysfunction, references to such materials were systematically excluded if they did not bear directly on the problem.

The focus of the bibliography is therefore both sharp and narrow. It was made still sharper by the criterion that, to be maximally useful, references must be in the English language and must have appeared in journals or other sources readily available in university libraries.

Despite these successive restrictions, hundreds of references remained to be classified. Since many of them were either redundant or merely confirmatory, it was decided to limit the number of items still further by selecting for inclusion that report, among several, which was most representative and most informative.

The selection of a specific item does not, of course, imply that the editors have no quarrel with it and that its inclusion is equivalent to a reasoned critical endorsement of the methodology and viewpoint adopted by its authors. On the contrary, we disagree strongly with the findings and views expressed in a number of the papers included in the bibliography, but we feel justified in including them because they are representative of the kinds of problems which have been of interest to workers in this field and of the ways in which these problems have been approached. Within its limits, therefore, we hope that the bibliography reflects accurately the current state of our knowledge concerning children with cerebral dysfunction.

As is to be expected, an annotated bibliography for so rapidly expanding an area of research resembles the map of Africa in the days of Livingstone and Stanley. Well-explored regions are represented by an increasing wealth of detail but *terra incognita* either by blank spaces or by episodic recordings, the interrelations among which are obscure or absent. Although it fails to satisfy a desire for completeness or offends the esthetic sense by its lack of balance, such a map almost inevitably excites the creative imagination.

Like the task of selection, the task of annotation and abstracting of the items finally chosen was not without its difficulties. An abstract should capture the essence of a report. But what is this essence? A moment's reflection makes it clear that not only the interpretation of the report but, indeed, its very reading depends on who the reader is and what he looks for. The expert in an area may read with an eye toward what he considers crucial methodological nuances. The interested bystander searches for the conclusion which he can generalize. In terms of our map analogy, the expert on a locality might prefer a scale in yards—his distant neighbor, a scale in miles.

The abstracter must therefore make a judgment: How specific shall he be? Shall he report all the variables, such as age, sex, IQ, social class, personal characteristics, test used, or only the main ones? In this case a double standard was used. For the most part, all the variables reported were abstracted. However, in a number of instances this standard was not followed literally either because the variables were not reported completely (this happened most often in the realm of social variables) or because the report was flooded with overly specific details. The effort was made to follow the spirit of the author's intent —an admittedly subjective criterion.

In reporting results, a similar problem arose: How specific and technical a language should be used to record the findings? A compromise between technical specificity and general intelligibility was sought. For some papers technical accuracy seemed crucial; for others, intelligibility seemed more important.

In assessing a large number of references, the bibliographer is likely to develop a certain sense of irritation and dissatisfaction. In part, this reaction is personal and best repressed, but these negative feelings stem also in part from certain persistent deficiencies in the reported work. Since such deficiencies affect the evaluation of the work being reported, they ought to be noted.

One such deficiency derives from the vagueness of the clinical entity with which we are concerned. In different studies children described as "brain-damaged," "with organic [*sic*] brain damage," "organic," "exogenously retarded," "with cerebral dysfunction," etc. have ranged from individuals of relatively normal intelligence and behavior but some dyskinesia to severely defective individuals with psychotic behavior and marked motor impairment. The specific samples of children studied are often inadequately described, and the degree of comparability between reports presumably concerned with the variety of patients is undeterminable. Behavioral measures, too, have varied widely, and different studies, presumably of the same psychological functions, have utilized techniques so different as to measure independent functional entities. Thus, of two studies concerned with perception, one uses drawing tasks (from which indices of perception are inferred) and the other a tachistoscopic identification of visual design. Resulting differences in findings are then irrationally argued as representing contradictions.

At another level, important and oft-repeated methodological deficiencies occur. Excellent clinical description is accompanied by crude and erroneous statistics or by none at all, and by unnecessarily inelegant physiologic, genetic, or psychologic examination. In contrast, highly sophisticated psychologic, epidemiologic, and genetic explorations are defective in neurologic or pediatric skill or sophistication. Viewed against the bibliography as a whole, these difficulties appear to be of major proportions and constitute a most cogent argument for the pooling of research skills and for interdisciplinary training. Its deficiencies notwithstanding, however, we believe that the bibliography is useful and that it reflects accurately the state of published knowledge concerning cerebral dysfunction in children.

In order to facilitate use, references have been classified into six major divisions as follows:

1. The entity and its description.
2. Clinical and special diagnosis.
3. Characteristic mechanisms and natural history.
4. Etiology—clinical, experimental, epidemiologic.
5. Treatment, education, and management.
6. Reviews, overviews, and theories.

Within each section references have been arranged alphabetically.

1. THE ENTITY AND ITS DESCRIPTION

Baxter, D. W., and Bailey, A. A.: Primary reading epilepsy, *Neurology, 11*:445–449, 1961. Two cases of primary reading epilepsy are reported (CA 19, CA 15). Patients with primary reading epilepsy complain of a sensation of jaw-snapping or jaw-opening when reading. Such symptoms are most likely to develop when the patient reads aloud or when the reading material requires concentration. A generalized seizure is likely to occur if he persists in reading once the myoclonic jaw movements occur. These patients do not have seizures in any other circumstances, and their neurologic examinations are normal.

Bender, L.: "Post-Encephalitic Behavior Disorders in Childhood," in *Encephalitis: A Clinical Study,* ed. J. Neal. Grune & Stratton, 1942. After reviewing follow-up studies reported in the literature, Bender recounts her experiences with 55 children studied between 1934 and 1940 (all born after 1919). These children constituted .14 percent of admissions to the Bellevue Hospital service, indicating the rarity of this disorder. The primary manifestations are psychopathic personality type of reaction with hyperkinesis not modifiable by insight or psychotherapy, typical psychometric patterns and motility disturbances. A number of cases are presented to illustrate that motility and impulse disturbances progress, whereas disturbance in perceptual patterns does not.

Bender, L.: Psychological problems of children with organic brain disease, *Amer. J. Orthopsychiat., 19*:404–441, 1949. Psychological problems arise in the organically "sick" child because (1) motor disorders make for prolonged dependency on the mother; (2) perceptual or intellectual problems lead to frustrations, misinterpretations of reality, and bizarre behavior patterns in efforts to make contact with the world; and (3) disturbed patterning of impulses leads to distortion in action patterns with compulsive features. Anxiety due to physiologic disorganization but secondary to frustration is basic. The method of treatment is prolonged mothering, avoidance of isolation, and specific aids for motor, perceptual, and interpersonal disabilities. Strong drive to normality is present.

Bender, L.: *Psychopathology of Children with Organic Brain Disorders.* Charles C. Thomas, 1959. In this series of essays summarizing the work at Bellevue Hospital, Bender is concerned with the ways in which organic children adapt to their damage. Following an examination of the psychological implications of motor development, which is concerned with the function of mobility in maintaining posture and with actions to achieve security and explore the world, considerations of the psychology of organic disturbances of the cerebellum are presented to show the close relationship between physiological and psychological development. Sections on the psychiatric implications of organic brain disorders, personality problems of the child with a closed head injury, body-image problems of the brain-damaged child, and a summary round out the book. The influence of Schilder (*Ment. Hyg., 15*:480–486, 1931; *19*:539–446, 1935; Proceedings of Fourth Institute on Exceptional Children, Wood School, *4*:38–59, 1938) is fully acknowledged. Much of Bender's previous work (*Amer. J. Orthopsychiat., 10*:287–292, 1940; *17*:68–79, 1947; *22*:335–355, 1952; *Ment. Hyg., 24*:617–630, 1942; *Arch. Pediat., 59*:772–783, 1942; *Confin. Neurol., 3*:320–331, 1941) constitutes the basis of the book. Total evaluation of developmental levels and the special needs, particularly severe anxiety, are stressed. Treatment involves support, planned program for patterning impulses, drugs, and psychotherapy.

Blau, A.: Mental changes following head trauma in children, *Arch. Neurol. Psychiat., 35*:723–769, 1937. Twenty-two children who showed mental changes following head trauma are reported. The cases are classified into post-traumatic acute psychosis, post-traumatic chronic behavior disorder, post-traumatic epilepsy with secondary deterioration, and secondary intellectual deterioration. The symptomatology of the organic behavior disorder in children is discussed, and it is suggested that the disorder may be the result of a localized lesion of the prefrontal association areas. The varieties of mental changes in children are reviewed from a historical standpoint.

Bradley, C.: "Organic Factors in the Psychopathology of Childhood," in *Psychopathology of Childhood,* eds. P. Hoch and J. Zubin. Grune & Stratton, 1955. After outlining some of the reasons for the neglect of organic factors by psychiatry, Bradley states that hyperactivity and deviant psychological test performances are the most general response to brain injury in children. Some neurophysiological theories are offered: Jasper on abnormal discharges, Strauss on deficiency of inhibition of higher cortical centers, Kahn and Cohen on brain-stem lesions, Blau on frontal lobes. A description of the secondary symptoms, including perseveration, etc., is offered. Considerations in the use of the neurologic examination, the EEG, and treatment procedure round out the chapter.

Cohn, R.: Delayed acquisition of reading and writing abilities in children: a neurological study, *Arch. Neurol., 4*:153–164, 1961. Forty-six children, aged 7 to 10, were selected from a county school system because of specific reading and writing difficulties. Profiles of language development, somatic receiving and expressive systems, personal spatial organization, and social adaptation were recorded. Two control groups of 100 normal children and 24 children with reading problems who were able to function in a normal school setting were used. Tests showed the experimental group to be inferior in language as well as in most of the other areas. More than 50 percent showed EEG abnormalities in comparison with 10 percent of the controls. Defects persisted two years later when 29 were re-examined. Maturational lag was also noted when behavior functions were plotted longitudinally. Hyperactivity is a consequence of disorganization of motor patterns rather than a reaction to social rejection. Delay in grasping graphic language symbols therefore reflects a general disturbance in biological function.

Doll, E. A.: Neurophrenia, *Amer. J. Psychiat., 108*:50–53, 1951. Neurophrenia denotes abnormal behavior resulting from central nervous system impairment. The term was introduced because of a number of objections to the term "cerebral palsy," which refers only to neuromuscular consequence of cerebral impairment, refers to only one point of anatomy, and does not specify the time of onset or etiology. A description of the symptomatology at this stage must be impressionistic. There are disturbances in neuromuscular coordination, receptivity, behavior patterns, and emotions. Because of variability in behavior, its interpretation on standard instruments is hazardous.

Green, J. B.: Association of behavior disorder with an electroencephalographic focus in children without seizure, *Neurology, 11*:337–344, 1961. Behavior disorders associated with abnormal electroencephalograms in 10 children divided into three groups are reported. The first group ($N = 5$) were characterized by hyperactivity, short attention span, and probable intellectual deficit. The second group ($N = 3$) were children of normal intelligence with varied behavior problems. The third group ($N = 2$) had paroxysmal headaches. A spike focus in a temporal or occipital area was identified in all but one case. None of the children had a history of seizures at the time of initial study. Most were referred by a school psychologist after testing "suggested an organic mental disorder." The children were strikingly similar in behavioral characteristics to children with psychomotor seizures. Anticonvulsant medication was prescribed in each case but was of little help in the first group, some help in the second, and very helpful in the third.

Hanvik, L. J., Nelson, S. E., Hanson, H. B., Anderson, A. S., Dressler, W. H., and Zarling, V. R.: Diagnosis of cerebral dysfunction in children as made in a child guidance clinic, *Amer. J. Dis. Child., 101*:364–375, 1961. Independent ratings of brain damage were made on 150 children (CA 7–14) by two electroencephalographers, a psychologist, and a pediatrician. Each used his own methods without knowledge of the findings of the others. A psychiatrist made an over-all judgment based on all the available data. The diagnosis of brain damage apparently varies with the diagnostic tool. Although there appears to be an underlying agreement between the EEG and the psychologist's rating ($r = .40$) and between the medical examination and the psychological examination ($r = .35$), the relationship is not strong enough to permit reliance on a single tool. The final diagnosis of brain damage was made in 59 percent of the cases. Different rates of diagnosis of brain damage characterize the three disciplines.

Ingram, T. T. S.: A characteristic form of

overactive behavior in brain damaged children, *J. Ment. Sci., 102*:550–558, 1956. Histories and clinical findings of 25 children showing overactive behavior are presented. Distractibility, short attention span, urge to chew and touch objects, lack of affective relationships, aggression, absence of fear, and failure to respond to punishment are characteristic. Neurological findings indicate the presence of cortical damage in most cases (*e.g.,* 18 were hemiplegic and 13 had epilepsy). Phenobarbitone increased behavior symptoms but decreased epilepsy. Amphetamine and primidone controlled behavior symptoms. All had histories suggesting brain damage: 13 at birth (anoxia) and 12 due to trauma, 10 of these 12 having been less than three years old at the time of illness. Histories and neurological findings implicate temporal lobes in most cases.

Jacob, W.: Helping teachers recognize some mentally retarded types, *Train. Sch. Bull., 48*:160–165, 1951. The brain-damaged child who is retarded by noninherited causes and who shows recognizable symptoms is discussed. Pathologically, psychologically, and intellectually, the symptoms and abilities of these children reveal either no obvious defects or wide swings of ability. Mental age is inadequate as a basis for judging these children, and the IQ is discouraged as a measure. Usual concepts of teaching the mentally retarded do not fit needs of the brain damaged. Experimentation with various teaching methods is urged.

Knobel, M., Wolman, B., and Mason, E.: Hyperkinesis and organicity in children, *Arch. Gen. Psychiat., 1*:310–321, 1959. On the basis of a "syndromic approach" to the acting-out child, careful measurements from a variety of sources, including history of pregnancy, birth and early development, EEG's, psychological tests, neurological examinations, and psychiatric interviews, were obtained from 40 children referred to a child guidance center. Hyperkinesis and hypokinesis were defined by a symptom check list. The determination of organicity was made by combining neurological, psychological, and EEG tests. Hyperkinesis was not related to organicity. The findings are considered in terms of newer developments in neurophysiology. Ritalin appears useful. A previous report appeared in *Dis. Nerv. Syst., 20*:80–85, 1959.

Laufer, M. W., and Denhoff, E.: Hyperkinetic behavior syndrome in children, *J. Pediat., 50*:463–474, 1957. A specific and common behavior disorder in children, the hyperkinetic syndrome is characterized by hyperactivity, short attention span, impulsiveness and distractibility, explosiveness, variability, and poor school work. A laboratory procedure—the photo-Metrazol EEG—offers a means of explaining the mechanism and confirming the existence of this syndrome. The syndrome responds to amphetamine and requires psychological guidance for the parents. It may require psychotherapy for the child. It tends to disappear by adulthood.

Lenneberg, E. H.: Understanding language without the ability to speak, *J. Abnorm. Soc. Psychol., 65*:419–425, 1962. Present theories of language acquisition assert that babbling, hearing oneself vocalize, and imitation are the cornerstones of speech development. These involve the motor skills necessary for speech. The case presented here, which is typical of a large category of patients, is one in which an organic defect prevented the acquisition of the motor skill necessary for speaking a language (anarthria), but in which there was evidence of the acquisition of grammatical skills. This case, considered together with language deficit in certain mongoloids, clearly shows that babbling, hearing oneself talk, and imitation are neither sufficient nor necessary factors in the acquisition of grammar. Present theories are, therefore, inadequate.

Morris, D. P., and Dolier, E.: Childhood behavior disorders: subtler organic factors, *Texas State J. Med., 57*:134–138, 1961. On the basis of 12 cases, clinical histories, diagnostic techniques, and a therapeutic program are outlined for the minimal and relatively unrecognized dysfunctions of the nervous system which may cause behavior deviations. These deviations occur at all levels of intelligence. Their understanding by all concerned is difficult because these handicaps are not obvious. It is helpful to interpret the nature of the handicap to the child himself.

Paine, R. S.: Minimal chronic brain syndromes in children, *Develop. Med. Child Neurol., 4*:21–27, 1962. In response to a recent debate over the concept of "syndrome of brain damage" in children, 41 children (CA 4–12) seen in a private neurologic practice because of poor school work, overactivity, clumsiness, poor speech, or emotional problems are presented. Of these, 31 showed abnormal neurological signs, whereas 9 of the remaining 10 were excessively clumsy. It is suggested that there is a syndrome of minimal brain damage, with subclinical manifestations in each of the four areas—motor, mental, sensory, and convulsive.

Strecker, E. A., and Ebaugh, F. G.: Neuropsychiatric sequelae of cerebral trauma in children, *Arch. Neurol. Psychiat.*, *12*:443–453, 1924. During a one-year period, 30 children (CA 3–16) with histories of head injury were referred. Immediately after onset, major problems were cerebral concussion, headache, and vertigo. Neurologic disturbances occurred in very few of the cases. The post-traumatic behaviors were characterized by "traumatic constitution" —*i.e.*, explosive outbreaks ($N = 15$)—and "traumatic defects"—*i.e.*, amnesias, mental deterioration, etc. ($N = 15$) Psychologic findings indicated fatiguability, *e.g.*, poor digit span. These disorders resemble post-encephalitic disorders of children, not the adult traumatic sequelae. They are related to delinquency. Prognosis: 6 are improving, the rest are not. Treatment: surgery in acute stage. Drugs are useless. Environmental manipulation helps.

Walker, E. F., and Katz, D. L.: Brain-damaged children: the problem of relations in the family group, *Calif. Med.*, *88*:320–323, 1958. From a larger sample of brain-damaged children, 16 who had minimal brain damage and responded to drugs are presented for detailed study. Although no motor abnormality was present, diagnosis could be made from the history, EEG, psychological tests, and repeated observations. Behavior is a composite of the brain damage and of the child's response to his environment, which continually thwarts him. Only one set of parents showed accepting attitudes. Two weeks after the children had been placed on a drug regime which helped them, improvement in attitudes was noted in 11 of the 16 sets of parents. The parents were able to shift their concern from their own problems to those of the child.

Weir, H. F., and Anderson, R. L.: Organic and organizational aspects of school adjustment problems, *J.A.M.A.*, *166*:1708–1710, 1958. Of 181 school children with severe school adjustment problems, electroencephalographic and neurological evidence of brain damage was found in a large percentage of cases (75% abnormal EEG). The use of tranquilizing drugs was helpful in reducing tension. The significance of the problem is seen by the fact that 5 percent of the children in the school system (Rockford, Ill.) fail in any given year. The physician is urged to become interested in this area.

Woods, G. E.: The early diagnosis of cerebral palsy, *Cereb. Palsy Rev.*, *22*:10–14, 1961. This is an account of the clinical signs of cerebral palsy manifested in the young infant. The paper is discussed by J. P. Duarte, J. Hariga, and B. Epstein.

2. CLINICAL AND SPECIAL DIAGNOSIS

Allen, R. M., and Collins, M. G.: Suggestions for the adaptive administration of intelligence tests for those with cerebral palsy, *Cereb. Palsy Rev.*, *16*:11–14, 1955. Three types of tests may be used to obviate the handicaps in cerebral palsy. Type I, which is discussed most extensively, includes techniques that assume an understanding of verbal directions but do not absolutely require motor manipulation. Type II involves developmental assessment rather than formal testing. Type III tests call for a constant shift in the nature of the instructions. The Ammons, Columbia Mental Maturity Scale, Progressive Matrices, and Leiter International Performance Scale are examples of Type I tests. Where motor involvement prevents the patient from performing, the examiner may point to alternative items one at a time. Detailed considerations in the practical uses of these instruments with cerebral-palsied persons are cited. The report is of interest to those concerned with technical problems of psychological evaluation.

Allen, R. M., and Jefferson, T. W.: *Psychological Evaluation of the Cerebral Palsied Person.* Charles C. Thomas, 1962. This brief manual includes testing procedures and suggestions for their use with individuals with cerebral palsy. Various tests that do not penalize the individual for his handicap are described, as well as procedures for gathering behavioral information (Gesell scales and Vineland Social Maturity Scale). Issues and procedures in personality and vocational assessment are discussed. The literature pertinent to the application of specific techniques to cerebral-palsied individuals is surveyed. Tips on "how to" test are presented throughout.

Arthur, B.: Comparison of the psychological test performance of brain damaged and normal children in the mental age range from five to six, University of Michigan, *Diss. Abst.*, *19*:6, 1958. Thirty children, aged 5 to 6, with a history of brain damage and positive evidence of central nervous system damage were compared on the Stanford-Binet with 30 controls. All the intelligence, perception, and motor tests discriminated between the two groups. Results indicate that there is a separation of intelligence and perception at an early age. Patterns of success and failure on intelligence tests can be used to diagnose the presence of brain damage. (Original not seen.)

Avakian, S. A.: The applicability of the Hunt-Minnesota Test for organic brain damage to children between the ages of ten and sixteen, *J. Clin. Psychol.*, *17*:45–49, 1961. Eighteen boys with a history of head injury, encephalitis, or convulsions, attending an institution for delinquent boys, were compared with a control group matched for age, grade, and IQ, attending a parochial or public high school. The control group exceeded the brain-injured groups ($p = .01$) on the Hunt-Minnesota Test. Using a cut-off point of 60, it was possible to classify correctly all the brain-injured but one and all the controls but one. The Hunt-Minnesota is therefore recommended for children from 10 to 16 years of age.

Ayres, A. J., *The Ayres Space Test*, Western Psychological Services, 1962. This manual presents a rationale and norms for testing space perception, particularly in disabled persons, including the cerebral palsied. The test has been standardized within a factor analytic framework derived from Guilford's work. It may prove useful in studying brain-injured children.

Beck, H. S., and Lam, A. L.: Use of the WISC in predicting organicity, *J. Clin. Psychol.*, *11*:154–158, 1955. Three groups of children—a "definitely organic" group ($N = 27$, CA 10), a "suspected organic" group ($N = 48$, CA 10), and two nonorganic groups ($N = 40$, CA 11) received the Wechsler Intelligence Scale for Children with the following results: (1) organics tend to score lower on the full-scale WISC than nonorganics (58 vs. 74; $p = .01$); (2) organics do less well on the performance than on the verbal scale whereas nonorganics do not; (3) the possibility of organicity increases as the IQ drops; (4) there is no typical organic pattern on the WISC; (5) 31 of 42 children with IQ's below 80 who, as a result of tests, were suspected of organic disease were found to have confirmatory neurological signs. All the children had been referred for eligibility for special classes in a southern Illinois public school system.

Bender, L.: *A Visual Motor Gestalt Test and Its Clinical Use*, American Orthopsychiatric Association, 1938. This classic monograph has gone through nine printings. Gestalt psychology, with its emphasis on perception and the total situation, supplies a theory for a specific test involving the copy of forms which permits observation of a wide range of phenomena and clinical populations. Particular concern with processes of maturation in the growing child, the primitive, and the retarded child is emphasized along with the interplay between vision and movement. The second half of the monograph is concerned with the clinical application of the test in studying aphasia, brain damage, schizophrenia, manic depressive psychosis, mental deficiency, malingering, and psychoneurosis. Both the theory and technique have made important contributions.

Bender, L.: Goodenough test in chronic encephalitis in children, *J. Nerv. Ment. Dis.*, *91*:277–286, 1940. The theory that drawings of a human figure are related not only to intellectual development but to the maturation of the body image is presented. Children who have been known to be suffering from chronic encephalitis draw below the level expected from an intelligence test. Six cases are used to illustrate this. "However, the test is not always reliable in the nonspecific types of encephalitis or traumatic conditions of the brain, due probably to localization problems." The test is "a reflection of a specific disability. . . ." It illustrates the "importance of mobility in the perception of one's own body. . . ."

Berko, M. J.: Mental evaluation of the aphasic child, *Amer. J. Occup. Ther.*, *5*: 241–246, 1951. The concept of IQ for this type of child is useless for all but statistical purposes. Examples of how testing is altered to fit a number of difficulties in this type of child are recorded. They include ways of dealing with propositional difficulties, disorders in categorical behavior and abstract ability, apraxia and agnosia, and initiatory delay and confusion. These difficulties often simulate mental retardation and can be distinguished from retardation by (1) the presence of absurd responses not in keeping with the intelligence level, (2) "digging out" the logic behind the absurdity, and (3) motor performance on Strauss-type tests.

Berko, M. J.: Measurement of behavioral development in cerebral palsy, *Cereb. Palsy Rev.*, *15*:5–6, 1953. Fifty cerebral-palsied children undergoing habilitative training at the Institute of Logopedics received the Vineland Social Maturity Scale and the Gesell Developmental Schedules at the onset and close of a 23-week training period. The subjects (CA 16 months to 27 years) were classified on a four-point scale on the basis of grossness of defect. The findings show that social maturity was roughly 60 percent below normal. The Vineland appears to be highly related to the degree of physical handicap. 38 of the subjects gained in social quotients following habilitation. The group as a whole gained .68 of a year as opposed to an elapsed period of .44 of a year. The amount of gain is highly correlated with the original social quotient ($r = .94$). The Gesell was broken down into separate areas. Results paralleled the Vineland.

Berko, M. J.: Some factors in the mental evaluation of cerebral palsied children, *Cereb. Palsy Rev.*, *14*:6–7, 1953. The consequences of the motor and sensory problems for socialization are illustrated. Inadequate socialization may penalize the cerebral-palsied child as much as his actual handicap. Emotional habit distortions similar to those of the aphasic child should be recognized. Perceptual deviations also occur. The following test modifications are therefore suggested: (1) evaluate the highest level of performance, (2) evaluate specific areas of ability and disability, and (3) evaluate in quantitative terms. The value of these suggestions is seen by the fact that test-retest of 50 cerebral-palsied children following one year of treatment at the Institute of Logopedics showed an average IQ gain of four points. This is presumed to be due not to an actual rise in intelligence but to increased ability to perform specific tasks.

Berko, M. J.: Some factors in the perceptual deviation of cerebral palsied children, *Cereb. Palsy Rev.*, *15*:3–4, 1954. Repeated failure on the Seguin Formboard task has been noted in examination of more than 300 cerebral-palsied children. In a comparison of 20 cerebral-palsied children with matched controls (CA 9, MA 7–8), 19 of the 20 cerebral palsied made 90 errors on the first trial of the Seguin, whereas 4 of the controls made 8 errors. In copying a diamond, only 2 of the cerebral-palsied group and 18 of the controls were able to copy it successfully on the first trial. The errors appear to resemble those found in younger normal children—*e.g.*, deviation in perception of the diagonal. Inadequate experience with perceptual phenomena account for this lag. Methods of remedying it are suggested.

Berko, M. J.: The measurement of intelligence in children with cerebral palsy: the Columbia Mental Maturity Scale, *J. Pediat.*, *47*:253–260, 1955. After a discussion of some of the psychological problems of the brain-injured child and the difficulties they pose in psychometric evaluation, a detailed account of the Columbia Mental Maturity Scale is presented. Although designed for use with brain-injured children, the CMMS has many problems. In a sample of 30 cerebral-palsied children (CA 7; IQ 68; MA 6), only 9 achieved a CMMS score within +4 to −4 points of the Stanford-Binet, whereas 21 did not. Those who showed a greater discrepancy had more signs pathognomonic of brain injury—*e.g.*, confusion, overconcreteness, etc. CMMS, therefore, must be interpreted cautiously.

Berko, M. J.: A note on psychometric scatter "as a factor in the differentiation" of exogenous and endogenous mental deficiency, *Cereb. Palsy Rev.*, *16*:20, 1955.

Forty-six retarded children (CA 9.3; MA 4.5; IQ 48) classified as "aphasic" by both a speech examiner and a psychologist were compared with matched nonaphasic controls. On the basis of the number of errors between the last consecutive item passed and the upper limit of each child's total performance, the aphasics showed an average of 12.54 misses and the controls 6.78 misses ($p = .006$). Berko concludes that psychometric scatter can therefore differentiate the brain-injured from the non-brain-injured retardate.

Blau, T. H., and Schaffer, R. E.: The Spiral Aftereffect Test (SAET) as a predictor of normal and abnormal electroencephalographic records in children, *J. Consult. Psychol.*, *24*:35–42, 1960. The SAET was administered to 46 children (CA 10–12, Gr. 4) who showed abnormal EEG's and a matched group of 20 children who showed no abnormal signs. Ratings of EEG abnormality were made by a single judge, who rerated the records reliably ($r = .77$). In addition, the Bender Gestalt, Draw-A-Person, and the Wechsler Intelligence Scale for Children were administered. All measures distinguished the groups. The SAET predicted the normal EEG 100 percent of the time and the abnormal EEG 86 percent of the time. It is more accurate than any other measure. The SAET appears to be a useful measure of cortical dysfunction. Limitations of EEG data are discussed.

Blum, L. H., Burgemeister, B., and Lorge, I.: Trends in estimating the mental maturity of the pre-school child, *Except. Child.*, *17*:174–177, 1951. This brief report on the testing of the motor-handicapped child describes the development of the Columbia Mental Maturity Scale.

Burgemeister, B., Blum, L. H., and Lorge, I.: Columbia Mental Maturity Scales: Ages Three to Twelve. Kit of 100 test cards, with manual; untimed (15–30 minutes). World Book Co., 1952. This test was standardized on 957 normal children, ages 3 to 12, who also took the Stanford-Binet (Form L). It is designed to test the intelligence of motor- and/or speech-impaired children. Stimuli are generally within the range of experience of handicapped children. No verbal response is necessary, and the test score is convertible to mental age and IQ scores. The task consists, essentially, in selecting a stimulus different from others that are alike.

Canter, A.: The use of the Columbia Mental Maturity Scale with cerebral palsied children, *Amer. J. Ment. Defic.*, *60*:843–851, 1956. Of 30 children (CA 5–17) attending a cerebral palsy center, 4 could not comprehend test instructions. Data on 24 indicate that 50 percent are retarded on the basis of the CMMS. The CMMS ranked children on intelligence about as well as other tests; however, IQ attainment was influenced by perseveration and the speech handicap. Because the CMMS may also be related to severity of disability, and because it relies very heavily on visuo-perceptual functions, its usefulness may be limited. Eight revisions are suggested to make it clinically useful.

Chorost, S. B., Spivack, A., and Levine, M.: Bender Gestalt rotations and EEG abnormalities in children, *J. Consult. Psychol.*, *23*:559, 1959. This is a brief report on 68 adolescents at Devereux Schools. Of these, 51 had rotations on the Bender Gestalt; 17 did not. Of those who showed rotations, 69 percent had abnormal EEG's; of those who did not, 47 percent had abnormal EEG's. Although the difference is significant ($p = .05$), it does not support Hanvik's conclusion that Bender rotations are diagnostic of brain injury. Diagnostic efficiency and scientific validity are not equivalent.

Clawson, A.: *The Bender Visual Motor Gestalt Test for Children*, Western Psychological Services, 1962. This manual on the use of the BVMGT for children describes the administration of the test, the development of visual motor function in the normal child, and the significance of BVMGT factors with normal and disturbed children. A chapter on the BVMGT and cerebral disorders, along with a case record, is included.

Costello, G. C.: Aphasic cerebral palsied children's wrong answers on Raven's Progressive Matrices, *J. Clin. Psychol.*, *15*:76–79, 1953. Ten cerebral-palsied children were matched with 10 children who had had poliomyelitis on age (9 years) and Matrices Scores. Data show differences in frequencies in the selection of a particular type of wrong answer. The cerebral-palsied children are more evasive.

Crowell, D. H., and Crowell, D. C.: Intelligence test reliability for cerebral palsied children, *J. Consult. Psychol.*, *18*:276, 1954. Test-retests on 61 cases with two to six examinations per child were obtained at an average interval of 30 months. Half the group scored within five points on test-retest and 75 percent scored within ten points. Test-retest correlation was +.92 with a standard error of ±11. The tests may therefore be considered highly stable for clinical purposes.

Cruickshank, W. M., Bice, H. V., and Wallen, N. E.: *Perception and Cerebral Palsy*. Syracuse University Press, 1957. To test the proposition that perceptual functioning is disrupted in brain-injured children, spastic (211) and athetoid (114) cerebral-palsied children (CA 6–16, IQ above 75, able to use at least one hand, intelligible speech, and minimum MA 6) were matched with 110 controls and tested on the following tasks: tactual motor test, marble-board test, Syracuse Visual Figure-Background Test, two-disc tests, and a maze. In general (1) the nonhandicapped group performed more adequately than both cerebral-palsied groups, and (2) the tests did not correlate highly with each other, arguing against the notion of a generalized perceptual impairment. Some of the limitations are discussed. The study presents in detail many of the technical problems in scoring tests.

D'Asaro, M. J., and John, V.: Rating scale for evaluation of receptive, expressive and phonetic language development in the young child, *Cereb. Palsy Rev.*, *22*:3–5, 1961. Items were drawn from the Gesell Inventory, the Cattell, and the Stanford-Binet pertaining to language areas and administered to infants in two well-baby clinics representing different socioeconomic levels in Los Angeles. Data were gathered by interviews with mothers as well as by actual observation ($N = 108$; CA 6 weeks to 68 months). Preliminary findings indicated the expected pattern of adequate grading of difficulty in items. In addition, 34 language-handicapped children were examined. The severely retarded showed a lag in both expressive and receptive items, whereas the emotionally disturbed showed higher receptive and lower expressive items.

Davids, A., Goldenberg, L., and Laufer, M. W.: The relation of the Archimedes Spiral Aftereffect and the Trail Making Test to brain damage in children, *J. Consult. Psychol.*, *21*:429–439, 1957. Fifteen cerebral-palsied children (CA 10, IQ 98) were matched with 29 emotionally disturbed non-brain-damaged children and 24 normal children attending public school. The brain-injured children performed less well than either of the other groups, who resembled each other in their productions. This was true also for Trail A of the Trail Making Test but not for Trail B, where the emotionally disturbed children performed at the same level as the brain-damaged group. Both the SAET and the TMT appear useful in detecting the presence of brain damage in children.

Denhoff, E.: Needs in the field of psychologic appraisal of children with cerebral palsy, *New Eng. J. Med.*, *243*:524–527, 1950. The basic need is to develop simple methods that can indicate the educability and prognosticate the ultimate level of mental attainment. Medical history and examination, formal psychologic tests, and observational techniques by teachers and parents all have equal status in the analysis of the whole child.

Doll, E. A.: Mental evaluation of children with expressive handicaps, *Amer. J. Orthopsychiat.*, *21*:148–154, 1951. Some issues in the evaluation of children with expressive handicaps are raised and illustrated by clinical examples. There is often a tendency to confuse a factual observation with the explanation that is offered for the defective performance. We may, therefore, err in assuming that a child who is penalized by a physical handicap would pass a test item if he were physically intact. In practice, we keep in mind both the actual performance and the handicap and carefully seek out the influence of the handicap as the examination proceeds. The clinician should carefully catalogue the complaint and its history. The Vineland Social Maturity Scale is useful for this. In severely handicapped children to whom the numerous assumptions which underlie a standard psychometric test do not pertain, it is often necessary to rely on clinical observations.

Dunn, L. M., and Harley, R. K.: Comparability of Peabody, Ammons, Van Alstyne, and Columbia test scores with cerebral palsied children, *Except. Child.*, *26*:70–74, 1959. A comparison of these tests—each of which requires only "yes," "no," or pointing responses—on a sample of 20 cerebral-palsied children in Nashville public schools shows that all appear useful for predicting school success.

Fisher, G. M.: Differences in WAIS verbal and performance IQ's in various diagnostic groups of mental retardates, *Amer. J. Ment. Defic.*, *65*:256–260, 1960. Examination of the protocols of 508 institutionalized retardates who had received all the subscales of the Wechsler Adult Intelligence Scale indicates that diagnostic groups comprising individuals with central nervous system infection and other organic nervous diseases have significantly higher verbal IQ than performance IQ. There is no difference between verbal and performance IQ's in other varieties of mental subnormality.

Frostig, M., LeFever, D. W., and Whittlesey, J. R. B.: A developmental test of visual perception evaluating normal and neurologically handicapped children, *Percept. Motor Skills*, *12*:383–394, 1961. The developmental test discussed includes five areas of visual perception: (1) eye-motor coordination, (2) constancy of form, (3) figure-ground relationships, (4) position in space, and (5) spatial relationships. The test was standardized on a sample of 434 normal children, ages 3½ to 8. It was administered also to 71 children diagnosed as neurologically handicapped or suspected of neurological handicaps (criteria not cited), all of whom had learning difficulties. Perceptual disturbances were found in nearly all of the clinical sample. Analysis of the scatter among the five subtests showed that perceptual difficulties were not uniform. Specific training based on the test results produced clinically observed changes in perceptual ability and subsequent improvement in academic performance.

Gallagher, J. J., Benoit, E. P., and Boyd, H. F.: Measures in intelligence in brain damaged children, *J. Clin. Psychol.*, *12*: 69–72, 1956. Forty institutionalized, mentally defective brain-injured children (CA 7–14) received the Stanford-Binet, Columbia Mental Maturity Scale, and the Leiter International Performance Scale. Although the tests intercorrelate ($r = .85+$), the CMMS was 9 points higher than the Stanford-Binet and the LIPS was 3 points lower. These differences are significant. Caution in the use of the CMMS and LIPS is suggested.

Gibbs, F. A., Gibbs, E. L., Carpenter, P. R., and Spies, H. W.: Electroencephalographic abnormality in "uncomplicated" childhood diseases, *J.A.M.A.*, *171*:1050–1055, 1959. EEG's were obtained from 1298 children admitted to a hospital with diagnoses of measles, mumps, chicken pox, rubella, or scarlet fever. The tracings were studied in relation to clinical evidence of encephalitic processes accompanying these diseases. The body temperature in itself was not a factor, and normal EEG's were obtained in a number of patients whose rectal temperatures exceeded 40° C. (104° F.). Of 717 patients with measles, 37 had evidence of encephalitis and all had abnormal EEG's; of the remaining 680 patients with measles but without clinical evidence of encephalitis, 344 (51%) had abnormally slow EEG's during the acute or immediate-past acute phase of their illness. The probability of brain involvement was greatest at age 3 for measles and chicken pox and at age 2 for mumps. Of the five diseases studied, rubella was the least likely, and measles the most likely, to be accompanied by evidence of encephalitis. In three cases, impairment of intellectual ability and general behavior was noted in spite of a return of the EEG to normal. The number of patients in whom the brain is affected by these diseases is far greater than the number with clinically obvious encephalitis.

Gurevitz, S., and Klapper, Z. S.: Techniques for and evaluation of the response of schizophrenic and cerebral palsied children to the Children's Apperception Test (C.A.T.), *Quart. J. Child Behav.*, *3*:38–65, 1951. Ten schizophrenic children (Bellevue Hospital, N.Y.) and 18 spastic hemiplegic cerebral-palsied children (clinic, Hospital for Special Surgery, N.Y.) were matched for age (5–12) and IQ (normal) and compared on the Children's Apperception Test. The records were compared on 47 characteristics that were derived impressionistically (no reliability data are offered). For the schizophrenic children major trends appeared, moving from close adherence to formal stimuli to departure from them in the form of confabulations. Hostility and anxiety predominated. For the cerebral-palsied children, the major finding was the affectless quality. Only a few consistent trends were noted in analyses of emotional processes. Further research is suggested.

Haeussermann, E.: Evaluating the developmental level of cerebral palsied pre-school children, *J. Genet. Psychol.*, *80*:3–23, 1952. The reasons for trying to find special tests and the requirements of these tests are described. A number of original items are included: presentation of concrete, life-sized objects; large, clear pictures; large pegs of wood in matched pairs of different colors; toy wooden milk bottles; wooden blocks of matched shapes, etc. The administration of these items, their interpretation, and some specific problems in testing cerebral-palsied children are described.

Haeussermann, E.: Estimating developmental potential of pre-school children with brain lesions, *Amer. J. Ment. Defic.*, *61*:170–180, 1956. Whereas an earlier report attempted to describe techniques for circumventing the physical limitations of the cerebral-palsied child, this report is concerned with the deviations in mental, emotional, sensory, and sensory-motor functioning of children with brain lesions. The aims, methods, and underlying principle of using a structured interview with parallel objective and subjective evaluation are described, with illustrations—*e.g.*, testing for body image. An inventory of a child's total functioning and a description of the intactness or nonintactness of the areas of functioning are presented.

Haeussermann, E.: *Developmental Potential of Pre-school Children*. Grune & Stratton, 1958. This manual is concerned with the problem of evaluating the educational potential of handicapped children. Basing her approach on a quarter of a century of experience, the author proposes that the evaluation take the form of a structured interview rather than a standard psychometric test. The purposes of educational evaluation are outlined and a method involving novel stimuli and details of administration is presented in great detail. Instructions regarding what to look for are scattered through the text. The philosophy of the method is "to shift the burden of proof . . . from the child who is being examined to the items which test the level of his comprehension." Although norms and validity data are not presented, the style of examination is different from standard American methods of psychological examination. In addition, the stimuli are designed to minimize the effects of physical handicaps.

Haines, M. S.: Test performance of preschool children with and without organic brain pathology, *J. Consult. Psychol.*, *18*: 37, 1954. A comparison on the Merrill-Palmer test of 100 brain-injured children with 100 foster-home children showed no differences. Children ranged from 3 to 7 years and were matched on the basis of Stanford-Binet intelligence (low average to average). The Merrill-Palmer is therefore not sensitive as a diagnostic tool for brain injury. The author thinks that the negative finding occurs because differentiation of abilities increases with age. Tests at earlier ages may not be sensitive to special deficits.

Halpin, V.: Rotation errors made by brain-injured and familial children on two visual motor tests, *Amer. J. Ment. Defic.*, *59*: 485–489, 1955. Fifteen institutionalized brain-injured children were matched with 15 familial retardates on age (7–13) and IQ (40–72) and administered the Bender Gestalt test and the Goldstein-Scheerer Stick Test. In addition to control for maturational factors in manipulating a pencil, the Bender Gestalt figures were broken down into two elements and the children were asked to put them together. The findings are: (1) brain-injured children show more breakdowns of gestalts on the Bender but not more rotations; (2) they show more breakdowns and rotations on the stick test ($p = .05$); (3) the simplified Bender shows the same results as the original; (4) rotation on the bender is unrelated to rotations on the stick test. The theory is: rotation is a complex, multidetermined phenomenon. Failure to replicate expected findings may be due to the low MA (6 years) used in this study.

Heilman, A.: Intelligence in cerebral palsy: a new interpretation of research studies, *Crippled Child*, *30*:11–13, 1952. Basing her opinion on a review of recent studies, the author feels that intelligence estimates should be revised downward. The need for further research to chart distribution of intelligence among cerebral-palsied children is stressed.

Hohman, L. B.: Intelligence levels in cerebral palsied children, *Amer. J. Phys. Med.*, *32*:282–290, 1953. Much therapeutic effort has been wasted because it has been assumed that cerebral-palsied children are of normal intelligence but fail to test at this level because of their multiple handicaps. The proponents of this view have never been able to document it. After examining the records of 600 cerebral-palsied children, who probably constitute a representative sample (author's statement) in the state of North Carolina, the author concludes that the picture "is a dismal one. . . . At least half of the children are retarded, and 75 percent are below average. These findings are quite stable and pertain at all age levels. Efforts and expenditures of funds might be better spent on the 15 percent of the brighter children rather than on all cerebral palsied."

Hohman, L. B., and Freedheim, D. K.: Further studies on intelligence levels in cerebral palsied children, *Amer. J. Phys. Med.*, *37*:90–97, 1958. Examination of 1003 cases between 7 months and 16 years of age shows "a tragically" high incidence of retardation. The total number who are educable is probably much less than 40 percent, because among those who have high IQ's many are incapacitated by physical handicaps. We must take a sober look at the limitations inherent in this population.

Hohman, L. B., and Freedheim, D. K.: A study of IQ retest evaluations on 370 cerebral palsied children, *Amer. J. Phys. Med.*, *38*:180–187, 1959. From a sample of 1000 cerebral-palsied children seen at Duke University Hospital, test-retest data were available at intervals ranging from 6 months to 5 years. The tests were standard individual intelligence tests, prorated so as not to penalize children with severe motor difficulties. From data based on the re-examination of 370 children, the following conclusions are drawn: (1) The levels of IQ on test-retest are the same in more than 75 percent of the cases; in the remainder, there is a shift up or down ten points. (2) Dividing the cases by initial IQ level showed that the smallest change occurred in the 90+ and 50− IQ groups, with the largest shift in the 50–70 range; division of the total sample by age at initial testing indicated fewer shifts in children above age 6. (3) In spite of the relatively large percentage of cases in which IQ shifted more than 10 points, only 30 of 248 cases tested after a one-year interval required a reclassification. The methods used to evaluate the cerebral-palsied child are adequate. (4) Whereas for normal children there is an expected error of ±5 points, for cerebral-palsied it is closer to ±10 because of the handicaps.

Holden, R. H.: Improved methods in testing cerebral palsied children, *Amer. J. Ment. Defic.*, *56*:349–353, 1951. "This paper has attempted to illustrate a more flexible use of present standardized intelligence tests in order to determine most adequately the intellectual level of a physically handicapped, brain-injured child. . . . Two new tests, Raven's Progressive Matrices and the Ammons Full Range Picture Vocabulary Test, need further evaluation to assess their usefulness in determining the intellectual level of physically handicapped brain-injured children and adults."

Holden, R. H.: The Children's Apperception Test with cerebral palsied and normal children, *Child Devel.*, *27*:5–8, 1956. Eight cerebral-palsied children (CA 9; MA 7; IQ 73) were compared with 7 normal and 3 neurotic children (CA 7; MA 7; IQ 101) on the CAT. The cerebral-palsied described 61 percent of the cards and made up thema for 39 percent, whereas the controls described 28 percent and made up thema for 72 percent ($p = .01$). Results are interpreted to indicate that CAT is a useful tool for detecting brain injury and that the differences arise because the cerebral-palsied group shows more concrete than abstract behavior.

Irwin, O. C.: A manual of articulation testing for use with children with cerebral palsy, *Cereb. Palsy Rev.*, *22*:1–24, 1961. This manual attempts to present a reliable, valid, and objective measuring instrument for evaluating the articulatory status of the cerebral-palsied child. Altogether, 1155 children, drawn from a nationwide sample, were used to standardize four short consonant tests and a vowel test, which were reported on separately. The present study is a replication on 147 cerebral-palsied children (CA 3–16) of all five tests treated as an integrated unit. Data on validity and reliability, copies of the test forms, and a demonstration are presented. The results are examined in terms of differences due to sex, CA, MA, IQ, type of cerebral palsy, severity of disability, and proper placement of consonants and vowels. (Data on the separate tests have been reported in *J. Speech Hearing Dis.*, *21*:446–449, 1956; *Cereb. Palsy Rev.*, *12*:18, 1957; *19*:8–10, 1958; *19*:12–14, 1958; *20*:7–9, 1959; *21*: 3–4, 1960.)

Katz, E.: A survey of degree of physical handicap, *Cereb. Palsy Rev.*, *15*:10–11, 1954. The paper presents a graphic form for recording the more obvious disabilities in various categories of functioning. Six areas of functioning are included: (1) vision, (2) hearing, (3) speech, (4) sitting balance, (5) arm-hand use, and (6) walking. Each of these areas is rated on a four-point scale ranging from minimally to severely handicapping. The survey is useful for rapid or large-scale screening.

Katz, E.: Can the mental abilities of cerebral palsied be measured? *Calif. J. Educ. Res.*, *6*:3–8, 1955. This article deals with modifying some of the test items on the Stanford-Binet Scale to make them feasible for cerebral-palsied children. All the items can be grouped according to six major categories: (1) "pointing," (2) "picture vocabulary," (3) number, (4) memory, (5) drawing, and (6) bead stringing. Additional sequences of major items might include three-hole form board, block building, comprehension, and vocabulary. Pointing and picture vocabulary are distributed throughout the range of mental age. This scheme may be useful in making decisions about which items can be used to test the child without penalizing him for his handicap. It may help in correlating behaviorial deficit with brain damage.

Katz, E.: Success on Stanford-Binet Intelligence Scale test items of cerebral palsied children compared with non-handicapped children, *Cereb. Palsy Rev.*, *16*:7–11, 1955. Experience with the traditional Stanford-Binet indicates that it tends to underestimate the child's ability when scored and interpreted literally. On the other hand, it provides valuable information when the items are interpreted separately. It was found that when 62 cerebral-palsied children (CA 2–6, IQ average) were compared with 873 nonhandicapped controls on the basis of what percentage passed each item (age 2 to 6), no statistically significant difference was found in 36 of the 48 test items studied. The controls were superior in the remaining 12 items. Test items involving pointing, picture vocabulary, and number found the two groups equal. Memory and drawing items yielded slight differences between the groups. Motor coordination items yielded major differences.

Katz, E.: The "pointing modification" of the Revised Stanford-Binet Intelligence Scales, Forms E and M, Years II through VI: a report of research in progress, *Amer. J. Ment. Defic.*, *62*:698–707, 1958. This is a proposed procedure for adapting this test for the young cerebral-palsied child. The examiner carries out some of the tasks and the child indicates by voice or gesture whether the procedure has been properly accomplished. In some instances, some changes in the test material must be made to obtain a meaningful response. It will be necessary to standardize the modified test items so that more difficult items may be assigned higher mental age levels, whereas easier items may be assigned lower mental age levels.

Kogan, K. L.: A method of assessing capacity in preschool cerebral palsied children, *J. Clin. Psychol.*, *13*:54–56, 1957. The Children's Picture Information Test was designed for use with preschool cerebral-palsied children. It is based on a multiple-choice task of 34 sets of items. Correlating the results of 50 children with those achieved on the Stanford-Binet yielded an r of .82. The sample ranged in age from 2 to 7 with IQ's from below 50 to 110. Administering the test to 10 severely handicapped children yielded mental ages from 2 to 5, indicating that the test is sensitive to individual differences within a cerebral palsy population.

Kogan, K. L.: Repeated psychometric evaluations of preschool children with cerebral palsy, *Pediatrics*, *19*:619–622, 1957. Test scores based on the Cattell Infant Intelligence Scales or the Stanford-Binet are reviewed for 31 children with cerebral palsy who had two or more examinations administered according to standard instructions within a three-year period. The average shift from one examination to another was 6.5 IQ points. The age at initial examination was 2 to 6 years; the average IQ was 73. It is likely that the changes in test scores are attributable to chance and that the intelligence quotient is no less consistent for disabled children than it is for normal children.

Kogan, K. L.: Standardization of the children's Picture Information Test, *J. Clin. Psychol.*, *16*:405–411, 1959. The Children's Picture Information Test was administered to 400 children divided equally into 8 six-month age-interval groups ranging from 2½ to 6 years. The groups were selected so that they approached as closely as possible an optimal distribution of sex, age in months, and parents' occupation. Both mean and median total scores increased from each age group to the adjacent higher age group. Discrimination between adjacent age groups was significant between ages 2½ and 5½. CPIT performance was not related to sex or parents' occupation. For 50 subjects selected from the standardization population, the *r* between CPIT and Stanford-Binet was .89. For 59 handicapped children (type not cited), the *r* was .80. Test-retest reliability for 50 subjects was .93. Normalized standard scores are presented. It is suggested that the test is useful for evaluating cerebral-palsied children.

Koppitz, E. M.: Diagnosing brain damage in young children with the Bender Gestalt test, *J. Consult. Psychol.*, *26*:541–547, 1962. The Bender Gestalt test was administered to 384 public-school children aged 5 to 10 years and was scored according to a scheme devised by the author. 103, diagnosed as brain damaged (based on medical criteria not cited), had no serious physical, motor, or mental retardation, and the remaining 281 subjects, matched for age and sex but not IQ, served as controls. The total Bender scores, as well as individual items, can differentiate significantly between subjects with and without brain damage. The diagnostic value for each given deviation on the Bender varies according to the subject's age. Most brain-damaged subjects do poorly, regardless of their IQ. Good Bender records are very rare among brain-damaged subjects and occur almost exclusively among children with at least average intelligence.

Kralovitch, A. M.: A study of differences on the Cattell Infant Intelligence Scale between matched groups of organic and mongoloid subjects, *J. Clin. Psychol.*, *15*: 198–199, 1959. Twenty-eight brain-injured children (CA 8) were matched with mongoloids for age, sex, social class, and length of residency at the North New Jersey Training School at Totowa. Both groups achieved mental age scores between 1 and 1½ years. Differences were most optimal at MA 5–8 months. Brain-injured children tend to be less competent in motor skills.

Krout, M. H.: Is the brain-injured a mental defective? *Amer. J. Ment. Defic.*, *54*:81–85, 1949. The psychologist should first employ a standard global intelligence test. If the results are below average, medical examination for the presence of physical handicaps is suggested. "Then he might proceed to discover the presence or absence of organic brain involvement." Then will follow the selection of a "true intelligence" test and projective techniques.

Lacey, H. M.: Pre-conditions for the psychological evaluation of young cerebral palsied children, *Cereb. Palsy Rev.*, *23*:12–14, 1962. An adaptive approach to appraising intellectual abilities, which considers the factors outside the test that influence the results, is presented. Variables such as personality and physical disability are examined along with the specific influences of set, motivation, and fatigue as well as previous experience with testing. Other variables considered are the examiner, the test items and instructions, and extrinsic factors such as the testing room and the presence of the parent during the testing.

Maisel, R. N., Allen, R. M., and Tallarico, R. B.: A comparison of the adaptive and standard administration of the Leiter International Performance Scale with normal children, *Cereb. Palsy Rev.*, *23*:3–4;16, 1962. To test the theory that special adaptations of a test to eliminate the effects of impairment due to a disability yield the same results as the full scale, the LIPS was administered to 46 normal children (CA 5–11). Sixteen participated in a reliability study, 30 received half the items of the LIPS under normal conditions, and half pointed to the correct response. Results indicate that the modified version yields the same findings as the original.

McCarthy, J. J.: A test for the identification of defects in language usage among young cerebral palsied children, *Cereb. Palsy Rev.*, *21*:3–5, 1960. A test for the identification of language defects is being developed at the Institute for Research on Exceptional Children, University of Illinois. Each of the 9 subtests is designed to measure a single ability derived from Osgood's theory of communication. The resulting profile should be useful in remediation. A number of doctoral studies (Sievers, Gallagher, and McCarthy) indicate that the test has promise.

Mecham, M. J.: Measurement of verbal language development in cerebral palsy, *Cereb. Palsy Rev., 21*:3–4, 1960. A test for language development derived from interviewing parents of cerebral-palsied children had been applied previously to mentally defective and to normal children. The rationale, norms, reliability, and validity of the test are reviewed. Data on application of the test to cerebral-palsied children are presented. In general, scores are related more to mental age than to motor handicaps.

Quast, W.: The Bender Gestalt: a clinical study of children's records, *J. Consult. Psychol., 25*:155–162, 1961. On the basis of presenting complaints, 50 children in a psychiatric treatment hospital who were suspected of being brain-damaged were compared with 50 children suspected of being emotionally disturbed. The children were matched on socioeconomic status and age (10–12). Although the emotionally disturbed group was brighter (IQ 100 vs. 82), it had previously been demonstrated that IQ did not affect performance on the Bender Gestalt. A priori selection of 17 attributes normally not occurring after age 8 showed 10 of these to differentiate the groups at the .01 level. False positive "organic" signs occurred in but one discriminating attribute. The 10 attributes had low positive correlations, suggesting a variety of defects rather than a unitary defect.

Richards, T. W.: Movement in the fantasy of brain-injured (cerebral palsied) children, *J. Clin. Psychol., 14*:67–68, 1958. Lundin's Projective Movement Sequence was administered to 32 cerebral-palsied children (CA 4–20) and 32 controls matched for age, sex, and IQ. The groups were essentially similar.

Richards, T. W., and Hooper, S.: Brain injury at birth (cerebral palsy) and perceptual responses during childhood and adolescence, *J. Nerv. Ment. Dis., 123*:117–124, 1956. Thirty-two cerebral-palsied children were matched with controls on age (11 years) and verbal IQ (WISC 97). The cerebral-palsied group were drawn from a treatment center in Biloxi, Miss., and the controls came from similar social and economic backgrounds in New Orleans. On the Rorschach test, the cerebral-palsied children were less productive quantitatively and qualitatively and had fewer responses and poorer form level. They exhibited greater caution and less spontaneity, seeing parts of people rather than whole people, and less overt movement. Five Piotrowski signs were given by more than half the cerebral-palsied group and one-fourth of the controls. "Blind" identification is accurate, but there is a tendency to consider dull control children as brain-injured and bright brain-injured children as normal.

Richards, T. W., and Lederman, R.: A study of action in the fantasy of physically handicapped children, *J. Clin. Psychol., 12*:188–189, 1956. Of 66 handicapped children (42 boys and 24 girls, CA 13, IQ 96) attending the Illinois Children's Hospital School in Chicago, 14 were cerebral palsied. Data on controls are not cited. On the Levy Movement Inkblot test, the cerebral-palsied group showed less activity, less energy, and less cooperation in their movement projections.

Richardson, E. J., and Kebler, F. J.: Testing the cerebral palsied: a study comparing the Stanford-Binet, Raven's Progressive Matrices, and the Ammons Full Range Vocabulary tests for use with cerebral palsied children, *Except. Child., 21*:101–103;108–109, 1954. Advantages of using these tests are discussed; data are presented from a study of 32 cerebral-palsied children. Although the correlations are sufficiently high to warrant use of either of these tests separately (with a preference for the Ammons), the most acceptable procedure, in view of the results, is to give each child both tests.

Rosvold, H. E., Mirsky, A. F., Sarason, I., Bransome, E. D., Jr., and Beck, L. H.: A continuous performance test of brain damage, *J. Consult. Psychol., 20*:343–351, 1956. Evidence from EEG studies and Hebb's theories suggests that brain-damaged people would perform poorly on tests requiring sustained attention or alertness. A continuous performance test (CPT) was devised, requiring the subject to press a key every time the letter *X* or the letter *X* preceded by *A* was viewed on a revolving drum. Three groups were tested: adults of normal intelligence, adult retardates, and children of normal intelligence. Each group was subdivided into brain damaged and non-brain damaged. There were 19 brain-damaged children (CA 9, IQ 102) and 26 non-brain-damaged children. The test correctly identified 84 to 90 percent of the brain-damaged children and 77 percent of the controls. It was slightly less discriminating among the adults. The test is "sufficiently reliable and yields sufficiently large differences between subgroups to suggest that they might . . . be useful as a clinical instrument."

Rowley, V. N.: An analysis of the WISC performance of brain damaged and disturbed children, *J. Consult. Psychol., 25*: 553–560, 1961. When 30 brain-damaged children seen in a pediatric clinic were matched with respect to sex, CA, and full-scale IQ with 30 emotionally disturbed children seen in a psychiatric clinic, no differences in intelligence-test patterns were uncovered. The minimum IQ was 83.

Rowley, V. N., and Baer, P. E.: Visual retention test performances in emotionally disturbed and brain-damaged children, *Amer. J. Orthopsychiat., 31*:579–583, 1961. The Visual Retention Test performances of 25 nondefective, emotionally disturbed children (CA 12, IQ 92) were compared with those of a brain-damaged group (mostly postinfection in origin) who were matched for age and IQ. Four percent of the emotionally disturbed children and 28 percent of the brain-damaged made grossly defective performances in comparison with the norms for chronological and mental age. When compared with the norms, however, the emotionally disturbed children showed an unduly high proportion (8) who performed at the borderline level. Defective performance is therefore due not to emotional disturbance but to brain damage.

Sarason, S. B., and Sarason, E. K.: The discriminatory value of a test pattern with cerebral palsied defective children, *J. Clin. Psychol., 3*:141–147, 1947. In a previous study, a psychometric profile that discriminated good and bad emotional adjustment in familial retardates was thought to be similar to a test profile that purported to distinguish brain-damaged from non-brain-damaged people. The group with the profile suggestive of brain damage had abnormal EEG's. In this study of 17 cerebral-palsied children, 8 had psychometric profiles indicative of brain damage: *i.e.,* the Stanford-Binet score was higher than the Kohs blocks and the form level of the Rorschach test was variable. Six of these 8 had abnormal EEG's. In contrast, where the Kohs blocks was higher than the Stanford-Binet and the Rorschach form level was adequate, 7 of the 9 cases had normal EEG's. The former group probably had cortical damage, the latter subcortical damage. The study illustrates the importance of qualitative analysis of test data and the relationship of EEG and behavior.

Shaw, M. D., and Cruickshank, W. M.: The Rorschach performance of epileptic children, *J. Consult. Psychol., 21*:422–425, 1957. The Rorschach test was administered to 25 epileptic children in institutions and matched controls in institutions (CA 14, IQ 81). There were no differences between the groups. The failure to confirm the alleged indicators of epilepsy on the Rorschach test may be due to the use of rigorous controls and statistical comparisons rather than subjective impressions; or it may have resulted from confining the study to one homogeneous category of epilepsy instead of lumping together all types of patients regardless of etiology.

Sievers, D. J.: A study to compare the performance of brain-injured and non-brain-injured mentally retarded children on the differential language facility test, *Amer. J. Ment. Defic., 63*:839–847, 1959. The Differential Language Facility Test is derived from Osgood's theory of communication and was standardized on normal children in nursery school. Mental retardates with MA from 2 to 6 years who were diagnosed as brain injured on the basis of (1) infections, (2) birth history, (3) toxins, (4) hydrocephalus, (5) postnatal influences, and (6) epilepsy were compared with familial retardates in a state school. The 100 controls exceeded the other groups in over-all language ability. This appeared to increase with mental age. They were also higher in subtests requiring expression without semantic meaning. The non-brain-injured retarded were higher than the brain-injured on subtests involving the making of semantic connections between visual objects. The findings, in the main, support those of McCarthy, who compared normal with cerebral-palsied children, but contradict those of Gallagher, who did not group his subjects according to MA levels.

Truss, C. V., and Allen, R. M.: Duration of the spiral after-effect in cerebral palsy: an exploratory study, *Percept. Motor Skills, 9*:216–218, 1959. "In this exploratory study of the duration of the spiral after-effect, it was found that mean reported duration was quite variable among both normal and organic (CP's) S's, and seemed to depend, in part, upon motivation and choice of criterion of termination of the after-effect." Use of the ratio of the durations following 30 ten-second exposures eliminated significant differences found between groups using mean duration of the after-effect, as the ratio appears to be substantially independent of the criterion. The intrasubject variability in duration of the after-effect for ten-second exposures was significantly greater for organics than for normals.

3. CHARACTERISTIC MECHANISMS AND NATURAL HISTORY

Achilles, R. F.: Communicative anomalies of individuals with cerebral palsy, *Cereb. Palsy Rev., 16*:9–10, 1955; *17*:19–26, 1956. Definition and detailed analyses of speech problems is presented. 90 athetoids are compared with 61 individuals with other types of cerebral palsy. Tables are presented on 12 anomalies, including breathing, laryngeal, tongue, mandibular function, teeth and palate, face and head, neck and trunk, vision, hearing, aphasia, and general factors. Athetoids present a somewhat greater number of deviations than other types of cerebral palsy. The study was based on a survey of children's records (CA 2–22).

Asher, P.: A study of 63 cases of athetosis with special reference to hearing defects, *Arch. Dis. Child., 27*:135;475–477, 1952. Of 63 cases of athetosis, there was a history of neonatal jaundice in 34. Of 24 jaundice cases who were tested, 22 had hearing defects whereas only 4 of the 18 nonjaundiced had such defects. Deafness may often be mistaken for mental deficiency. Clinical estimates of intelligence of athetoids are less accurate than of spastics. This study was carried out at the Birmingham (England) Children's Hospital.

Barnett, C. D., Ellis, N. R., and Pryer, M. W.: Learning in familial and brain injured defectives, *Amer. J. Ment. Defic., 64*:894–900, 1960. From six previously conducted learning studies (oddity problem, object quality discrimination, mirror drawing, rotary pursuit, image learning, and serial verbal learning), subjects were re-evaluated to separate the organics (defined on the basis of family history of normal intelligence coupled with a significant incident that may have contributed to the condition) from familial defectives (defined on the basis of family history of mental deficiency, no known developmental incident, and no organic signs). The groups averaged MA 7 years and CA 17 years, with the organic group excluding the grossly physically impaired. The groups were then subjected to the Yerkes double alternation problem. Familials were significantly superior on the serial verbal learning and Yerkes alternation. An attempt to reconcile some disparate findings from earlier studies is presented, along with a survey of the literature.

Barsch, R. H.: The concept of regression in the brain-injured child, *Except. Child., 27*:84–89;93, 1960. The brain-injured child lives in a perceptually unstable world. Under stress he tends to regress. A brief survey of more than 200 records shows that regression may be induced by many situations. Examples of regressed behavior are cited. During periods of regression, the child is not encouraged to learn anything new but, rather, to fall back on safe, familiar habits and easy tasks. Regression may be manifested in many ways. Suggestions for developing a continuum of sensitivity to stress are offered in the form of a five-point rating scale based on degrees of sensitivity to change.

Barsch, R. H.: Explanations offered by parents and siblings of brain-damaged children, *Except. Child., 27*:286–291, 1961. 119 children (CA 4–12) attending a cerebral palsy clinic in Milwaukee were divided into four groups on the basis of four areas of primary defect: behavior, symbol formation, immaturity, and sensori-motor ability. Most of the parents of all groups used the term "brain injury" freely, except where the child's functioning level was near normal. Some parents used the term "cerebral palsy" even where such a diagnosis had not been made. The nature and severity of the disturbance did not affect the parent's explanation. Siblings tend to adopt the explanation of the parents. Their explanations generally don't pose a problem in the eyes of the parents.

Barsch, R. H.: Rearing practices of parents of children with cerebral palsy in toilet training, *Cereb. Palsy Rev.*, *23*:12–16, 1962. Demographic data on 51 parents of cerebral-palsied children are presented. Comparing the findings on toilet-training practices with those reported by Sears *et al.* (R. Sears, E. Maccoby, and H. Levin, *Patterns of Child Rearing*, Row, Peterson and Co., 1957), it was found that mothers of cerebral-palsied children begin toilet training later and take more time (*e.g.*, only 23 percent report success after one year). Mothers expect little from the child and are encouraged in this by professionals. No ingenious approaches or special techniques to bypass the handicapping conditions are reported. Most mothers do not view toilet training as a particular or unique problem. Fathers play a secondary role. Nocturnal bedwetting is controlled at a rate close to normal (Sears *et al.*). Bowel and bladder training is seen as an anxiety-laden area for parents of cerebral-palsied children.

Barsch, R. H., and Rudell, B.: A study of reading development among 77 children with cerebral palsy, *Cereb. Palsy Rev.*, *23*:3–13, 1962. Seventy-six patients of the Cerebral Palsy Clinic of Milwaukee (CA 5–16) who were attending school were evaluated on a comprehensive battery of reading tests. Six percent read above their age or grade level, 25 percent were at their level, and 69 percent were below their level (by at least 1 year). Various relationships between type of reading problem and medical, psychological, and educational variables are presented. Major findings indicate that inarticulation was a factor in only 25 percent of this group; in 75 percent, reading level was directly related to IQ; more than half the group were managing in the development of a basic sight vocabulary and were acquiring a system for new words. Hemiplegics did better than other groups.

Beck, H. S.: The incidence of brain injury in public school special classes for the educable mentally handicapped, *Amer. J. Ment. Defic.*, *60*:818–822, 1956. The incidence of brain injury in classes for educable mentally handicapped was estimated in two ways to determine whether both methods would give the same results: (1) by examining the number of cases referred for neurological examinations in the whole southern area of Illinois, taking the number actually examined and the incidence of brain-injury diagnosis resulting from this procedure, and (2) by taking a single complete EMH population in one school district and obtaining neurological evaluations on all the children. Of 252 children in the former group, 60 percent were estimated to be brain injured. Of 45 in the second group, 67 percent were brain injured. Thus, both methods indicate that between 60 and 70 percent of children in EMH classes are brain injured. In the organic group, the ratio of boys to girls is 2:1, in the nonorganic group, 1:1.

Beck, H. S.: Comparison of convulsive organic, non convulsive organic, and non organic public school children. *Amer. J. Ment. Defic.*, *63*:866–875, 1959. Neurological workups were available on 160 children (CA 9–10) examined by a school psychologist in southern Illinois. The children, referred for placement in classes for the educationally handicapped, had a mean IQ of 62 and were divided into three groups: (1) convulsive-organic ($N = 60$) on the basis of history of seizures or EEG findings; (2) non-convulsive-organic ($N = 71$) on the basis of evidence of brain damage but without seizures; and (3) nonorganic ($N = 29$). They were compared on the WISC, Bender Gestalt test, developmental history, and Strauss behavior check list. The CO group (IQ 59) showed fewer WISC gains on retest, more variability, and more frequent poor maternal health during pregnancy. The NCO group (IQ 60) showed fewer decreases in verbal IQ on retest and more increases in performance IQ on retest. The group also used fewer colors in drawing a house, had more unrecognizable Bender Gestalt figures, stood alone later, and had more feeding problems during infancy. The NO group (IQ 72) had higher performance than verbal tests, better Bender Gestalt drawings, better muscular coordination, and fewer developmental problems. The author claims that the CO group resembles the type of child described by Strauss. Developmental data and teacher ratings are included, even though their reliability is not established, on the grounds that "it is better to make the best of a poor situation than sit back and do nothing while waiting for the ideal situation."

Belmont, L., and Birch, H. G.: The relation of time of life to behavioral consequence in brain damage: I. The performance of brain-injured adults on the marble board test, *J. Nerv. Ment. Dis., 131*:91–97, 1960. In a study of marble-board behavior of 20 hemiplegics who sustained brain injury late in life and a group of children with early damage (studied originally by Werner), it was found by the method of pseudo-comparison (*i.e.,* comparison of each experimental group with its control by using the difference between each brain-damaged group and its control) that the brain-injured children showed a greater deficit in a visual construction task than the brain-injured adults. The brain-injured children tend to be more incoherent in their approach. Time of life, therefore, does have a bearing on the effects of brain damage.

Bender, L., and Silver, A.: Body image problems of the brain-damaged child, *J. Soc. Issues, 4*:84–89, 1948. The body image develops from (1) biologic laws of growth and (2) integration of new experiences, physical and psychological, arising from one's self and from relationships and attitudes of others, into a gestalt. This image is continually being modified at various levels of development, perception, or integration, and may be altered by either organic or psychologic events. The body image of the brain-damaged child is disturbed by tonus pulls, equilibrium problems, perceptual and integrative difficulties, and social inadequacy. His physical disability is very real. It is by recognizing the disability and by understanding his body-image needs and satisfying them that improvement in the prognosis of the brain-damaged child can be made possible.

Bensberg, G. J., Jr.: A test for differentiating exogenous and endogenous mental defectives, *Amer. J. Ment. Defic., 54*:502–507, 1950. Thirty-one exogenous retardates were matched with an equal number of endogenous retardates (MA 88 months, CA 20 years) in a study designed to replicate the classic marble-board study of Werner and Strauss. For the most part, their findings were confirmed. The brain-injured group was less accurate and made more jumps than the control. However, both scores were related to mental age in both groups, indicating that test interpretation must be qualified by norms if it is to be used to diagnose the presence of brain injury.

Bensberg, G. J., Jr.: The relation of academic achievement of mental defectives to mental age, sex, institutionalization, and etiology, *Amer. J. Ment. Defic., 58*:327–330, 1953. "Records of 274 male and 230 female mental defectives who had been administered the American School Achievement Test and Revised Stanford-Binet were investigated to find the influence of variables which might influence achievement. . . . Females matched with males on the basis of CA and MA were found to achieve significantly higher than the males, both in arithmetic and reading. No differences in achievement were found between patients of the same ages who had attended the institution school for five years or longer and those who had attended public schools prior to commitment. No differences in achievement were found between brain-injured defectives and familial defectives."

Berger, A.: Inhibition of the eyelid reflex in three etiologic groups of mentally retarded boys as compared with normals, *Train. Sch. Bull., 51*:146–152, 1954. Data and results of a study attempting to differentiate between normal children and individuals whose mental retardation is due to brain damage, inheritance, and/or psychogenic factors are presented. It was assumed that a well-integrated and undamaged central nervous system is necessary to inhibit the eye-blink reflex and that those with organic damage would have the greatest difficulty in inhibiting the reflex. None of the differences between retarded groups was significant, except for a comparison of the organic and familial groups in partial inhibition.

Berko, M. J., and Berko, F. G.: Implications of language difficulties in the cerebral palsied adult, *Cereb. Palsy Rev., 14*:11, 1953. Motor speech deficit is one aspect of a total language problem which also includes distortions in experiencing the world. Distortions in experiencing visual stimuli occur in approximately 40 of 100 cerebral-palsied children and adults seen by the author. Defects in visual perception include geometric agnosia, figure-background disturbances, and defects in perceptual integration. The importance of these defects in reading and real life situations is illustrated.

Bijou, S. W., and Werner, H.: Language analysis in brain-injured and non-brain-injured mentally deficient children, *J. Genet. Psychol.*, *66*:239–254, 1945. Nineteen brain-injured boys (CA 14, IQ 68) who were matched with non-brain-injured controls received 57 vocabulary words. The brain-injured boys had a superior vocabulary, both qualitatively and quantitatively. It is concluded that the inferiority of brain-injured subjects on grouping and sorting tasks is due not to an inferiority in concept formation but to pathological dynamisms which appear in unstructured situations.

Birch, H. G., and Belmont, L.: The relation of time of life to behavioral consequence in brain damage: II. The organization of tactual form experience in brain-injured adults, *J. Nerv. Ment. Dis.*, *137*:489–495, 1960. Twenty adult hemiplegics did less well than 20 non-brain-damaged physically handicapped patients on a task of tactual reproduction in the face of background interference. When the data were compared with those on children originally reported by Werner, it was discovered that the brain-injured child shows a relatively greater deviance from the control than the adult hemiplegic. This may be owing to a mild impairment in the adult control group due to aging.

Birch, H. G., and Demb, H.: The formation and extinction of conditioned reflexes in "brain-damaged" and mongoloid children, *J. Nerv. Ment. Dis.*, *129*:162–169, 1959. Conditionability and rate of extinction of conditioned galvanic skin reflex of two groups of brain-injured children, a group of mongoloid, and a small group of normal children, were studied. The brain-injured hyperactive children ($N = 10$; IQ 59; CA 10) required a larger number of paired presentations of light and shock to reach the criterion for conditioning than did a group of nonhyperactive children ($N = 8$; IQ 57; CA 10). Mongoloid children required a longer conditioning period than either group. While no differences in number of extinction trials existed, qualitative approaches emerged. The hyperactive group gave little evidence of internal inhibition and even increased their activity level, whereas half the children in the other groups demonstrated internal inhibition by falling asleep. Conditioned-reflex theory can explain the results which indicate that the population of brain-injured children is not homogeneous.

Block, W. E.: Personality of the brain injured child, *Except. Child.*, *21*:91–100, 1954. In a comparison of 20 spastics with 18 athetoids of normal intelligence by means of a battery of projective tests, case histories, and functional evaluation scales, no significant differences were found.

Boles, G.: Personality factors in mothers of cerebral palsied children, *Genet. Psychol. Monogr.*, *59*:159–218, 1959. Sixty mothers of cerebral-palsied children were matched with 60 mothers of nonhandicapped children. They were matched on 10 variables and were subdivided so as to represent mothers of younger and older children, and mothers of Catholic, Jewish, and Protestant faiths in equal amounts. On the basis of self-administered attitude questionnaires designed specifically for this study, mothers of cerebral-palsied children proved more overprotective and had more marital conflicts. Mothers of older children in both groups were more guilty, rejecting, and unrealistic. Mothers of younger cerebral-palsied children were more withdrawn. Catholic mothers in both groups were more guilty, unrealistic, and socially withdrawn than Jewish mothers. Jewish mothers provide significantly more social opportunities than Catholic or Protestant mothers. Detailed discussion of the intercorrelations of the seven characteristics examined on the questionnaire is presented.

Bortner, M., and Birch, H. G.: Perception and perceptual-motor dissociation in cerebral palsied children, *J. Nerv. Ment. Dis.*, *130*:49–53, 1960. Twenty-eight cerebral-palsied children (CA 8–18, IQ 64) received the block-design test. On three consecutive designs where the subject had failed, he was presented with a correct copy of the model, his own incorrect version, and a standard inaccurate copy. In 79 percent of the 89 failures, the correct copy was selected. Furthermore, copying the design took 88 seconds, whereas discriminating it took 12 seconds. This indicates discrimination ability may be intact although synthetic, integrative processes are impaired in brain-injured persons.

Breakey, A. S.: Ocular findings in cerebral palsy, *Arch. Ophthal., 53*:852–856, 1955. Fifty-six of 100 unselected patients showed ocular defects. Abnormalities of muscle balance were most prominent. Management by treatment and surgery is described.

Burks, H. F.: The effect of brain pathology on learning, *Except. Child., 24*:169–172, 1957. In this review of recent work in brain physiology and his own work with children with reading disabilities, the author is concerned with faulty pattern-making attempts of the brain due to poor physiological integration. In earlier studies of 137 school problem children of the acting-out type in comparison with 94 controls, he found that the group with abnormal EEG's showed perceptual academic problems, whereas the normal EEG group showed difficulties in emotional-social areas, although both were poor readers. The former showed defects on verbal intelligence scales, the latter on tasks requiring attention. The hypothesis is offered that the former group suffers from a cortical disturbance and the latter suffers from disturbance of the diencephalon, which is related to disturbance in the reticular activating system. Evidence for this hypothesis, including the negative findings on the EEG of the subcortical group, is presented.

Byrne, M. C.: Speech and language development of athetoid and spastic children, *J. Speech Hearing Dis., 241*:231–240, 1959. Language development and articulation skills in 74 cerebral-palsied children (CA 2–7), all of whom were considered educable, were evaluated. An equal number of spastics and athetoids, with disability ranging from mild to severe and intelligence from retarded to above average, were used. Most used oral language; the rest depended on gestures. The children developed first the skills appearing earliest in normal children. All were delayed in achieving proficiency in speech and language items. Spastics achieved higher scores than athetoids, but the differences were not significant. Methods of testing are described.

Cassel, M., and Riggs, M.: Comparison of three etiological groups of mentally retarded children on the Vineland Social Maturity Scale, *Amer. J. Ment. Defic., 58*:162–169, 1953. Sixty boys at Vineland Training School (CA 9–15, IQ 40–76) were divided into three groups—definitely organic, definitely familial, and unexplained—and their competence evaluated on the Vineland Social Maturity Scale. Familials were relatively competent in all areas. Organics were relatively incompetent in all areas. The unexplained cases had a well-defined pattern of competence in some areas but not in others. Organics were particularly poor in visuo-motor items and items pertaining to organizing the social environment. The unexplained group did poorly in items requiring effort, dependability, responsibility, and contribution to the community.

Cassel, R. H.: The effect of mental age and etiology on two factors in the formboard performance, *J. Clin. Psychol., 5*:398–404, 1949. Eight endogenous and 15 exogenous boys (CA 11, MA 5) received a modified formboard test where all the objects were (1) circular, to maximize the effects of speed and minimize the effects of form perception, and (2) permitted to drop through the bottom of the Witmer formboard so that each person would continue to have the same number of choices as the problem-solving progressed. Findings indicate that: (1) formboard performance consists of two independent factors—motor speed and form perception; (2) differences at higher age levels are due primarily to motor speed; (3) the endogenous group performs better on total formboard score, form-perception score, and motor-speed score; (4) form perception is related to maturation in the endogenous group but not clearly related to MA in the exogenous group. Conclusion: mental retardation is not a homogenous condition.

Child Neurology and Cerebral Palsy; Little Club Clinics in Developmental Medicine, No. 2, London Medical Advisory Committee of the National Spastics Society, 1960. This collection consists of 42 brief papers that were presented at the Second National Spastics Society International

Study Group at Oxford. Topics range from spinal cord and polymyographic studies, metabolism of the developing brain, the first-year neurology and development, paresis, and nonmotor defects in cerebral palsy to the results of treatment in cerebral palsy to parents, patients, and doctors. Although the vast majority of the participants came from England, a number from the United States, continental Europe, and South Africa participated also.

Cobrinik, L.: Performance of brain-injured children on hidden-figure tasks, *Amer. J. Psychol.*, *72*:566–571, 1959. Normal and cerebral-palsied children were compared on a variety of hidden-figure tasks. Normals exceeded brain-injured in all tasks. Performance for both groups improves with age. Those with severe motor impairment do less well. IQ is not related to the ability to detect hidden figures. Impaired performance on hidden-figure tasks is probably related to the extent, rather than location, of brain damage. The hidden-figure tasks were developed especially for this study. They may be useful devices for studying some types of figure-ground disturbances.

Cohen, P., and Hannegan, H. M.: "Aphasia" in cerebral palsy, *Amer. J. Phys. Med.*, *35*:218–223, 1956. In a large number of cases at a cerebral palsy clinic, 22 had language difficulties resembling aphasia in adults, which may be called "aphasoid" or aphasia-like. Most were athetoids whose brain damage was the result of kernicterus. No constant EEG pattern was found. Characteristic appearance, gait, eye difficulty, and emotional pattern are described.

Cotton, C. B.: A study of the reactions of spastic children to certain test situations, *J. Genet. Psychol.*, *58*:27–44, 1941. Twenty-six spastic cerebral-palsied children were matched with normal controls (CA 9, MA 9) and compared on (1) a series of 13 sorting situations, (2) a completion test involving concrete, pictorial, and verbal materials, (3) a light-pattern memory test, and (4) a string pattern test. The spastics differed from the controls by showing: (1) a wider range of individual differences in type of response within any one test situation, with bizarre responses present; (2) a greater tendency toward more concrete types of response with less ability to shift toward the more abstract forms of behavior; (3) a greater tendency toward stereotyped responses no matter what the nature of the test situation. "There seems to be evidence that these children are affected by their cortical injuries in somewhat the same fashion as are cases of brain injury after maturity."

Cruse, D. B.: "The Effects of Distraction upon the Performance of Brain-injured and Familial Retarded Children," in *Readings on the Exceptional Child*, by E. P. Trapp and P. Himelstein. Appleton-Century-Crofts, 1962. No differences appeared when 24 brain-injured retardates were compared with non-brain-injured retardates (CA 14, MA 6) in a visual-reaction experiment under distraction and non-distraction conditions. However, when the brain-injured group was subdivided into two groups, one with determinate and known etiology ($N = 18$) and the other with indeterminate etiology ($N = 6$), the former had significantly longer mean reaction times. Although brain-injured children with known etiology appear to be more distractible than either familial retardates or children with indeterminate etiology, there seems to be little difference in their ability to benefit from a minimization of environmental distractions. The findings confirm those of Gallagher. (*Monogr. Soc. Res. Child Develop.*, *22*:2, Serial No. 65, 1957. See also Bensberg, G. J., and Cantor, G. N., *Amer. J. Ment. Defic.*, *62*:634–637, 1957).

de Hirsch, K.: Two categories of learning difficulty in adolescence, *Amer. J. Orthopsychiat.*, *33*:87–91, 1963. There are at least two categories of intelligent adolescents with severe learning difficulties who are usually grouped together when in fact they are different. In Group A, the academic difficulty is related to ego impairment and is a manifestation of a severe character disorder indicating primary learning disabilities. In Group B, scholastic dysfunction is secondary to residual language deficiencies, and psychological problems as well as difficulties in school are the result, rather than the cause, of the disability. The differences between the groups and their methods of management make accurate diagnosis mandatory.

Denhoff, E., and Holden, R.: Family influence on successful school adjustment of cerebral palsied children, *Except. Child., 20*:5–8, 1954. A follow-up study of 33 children attending school after receiving evaluation and treatment in a preschool setting indicates that two-thirds were making an adequate adjustment to regular class, special class, or home teacher. One-third were not. Good adjustment appears to be related more to family acceptance than to intelligence or severity of disability. Indications for type of school placement and a check list of the characteristics of the "good" family are listed as a guide to clinical management.

Doll, E. A.: "Behavioral Syndromes of CNS Impairment," in *The Exceptional Child,* eds. J. F. Magary and J. R. Eichorn. Holt, Rinehart & Winston, 1961. An attempt is made to contrast the behavior symptomatology of cerebral palsy, exogenous mental deficiency, and neurophrenia. In neurophrenia, behavior is "organically driven. Posture and movement reveal awkwardness rather than orthopedic handicap. Intellectual functioning reveals deficiency or disharmony. Disturbances in speech, language, visual and auditory perception, rhythm, laterality, attention, emotions, conduct, learning, social competence, concept formation, retention, effort, and the integrity of behavior, are manifested." Neurophrenia simulates exogenous mental deficiency but is more amenable to therapeutic management, although all areas of functioning are affected. For the time being, the concept of neurophrenia remains at a level of clinical observation and the methods of management are still experimental.

Dolphin, J. E., and Cruickshank, W. M.: The figure-ground relationship in children with cerebral palsy, *J. Clin. Psychol.,* 7:228–231, 1951. Thirty cerebral-palsied children (CA 10; MA 9.5; IQ 93) were compared with matched controls on two tests of figure-background relationship, one an embedded figure test and the other a multiple-choice embedded figure test. The cerebral-palsied were inferior in both tasks. The findings confirm those of Werner and Strauss and appear to result from the phenomenon of forced responsiveness to extraneous stimuli and overmeticulousness in brain-damaged children.

Dolphin, J. E., and Cruickshank, W. M.: Pathology of concept formation in children with cerebral palsy, *Amer. J. Ment. Defic., 56*:386–392, 1951. Thirty cerebral-palsied children (CA 10; MA 9.5; IQ 93) were compared with matched controls. Cerebral-palsied children were inferior in responding to the Picture Object Test, designed to measure differences in concept formation.

Dolphin, J. E., and Cruickshank, W. M.: Visuo-motor perception in children with cerebral palsy, *Quart. J. Child Behav., 3*:198–209, 1951. Thirty cerebral-palsied children (CA 10; MA 9–15; IQ 93) were matched with controls and were given the marble-board test. The cerebral-palsied children were inferior in their method of approaching a problem. Background of the test was a distracting element, which constantly interfered with construction of patterns by the cerebral-palsied. Their approach was more incoherent than constructive or global. Qualitative differences were more striking than quantitative. A second experiment, using mosaic patterns to be copied from a marble board, yielded essentially the same results. Clinical observation: The cerebral-palsied children made bizarre designs and the controls tended to oversimplify designs.

Dolphin, J. E., and Cruickshank, W. M.: Tactual motor performance of children with cerebral palsy, *J. Personality, 20*:466–471, 1952. Thirty cerebral-palsied children (CA 10; MA 9.5; IQ 93) were matched with controls on a figure-ground test of tactual motor performance. The cerebral-palsied children did less well. Differences in responses were still greater when a highly structured background was used.

Eames, T. H.: The relationship of birth weight, the speeds of object and word perception, and visual acuity, *J. Pediat., 47*: 603–606, 1955. Summarizing previous studies in this series (*J. Educ. Res., 38*:506, 1945; *Amer. J. Ophthal., 29*:57, 1946; *Amer. J. Ophthal., 38*:850, 1954; *Brit. J. Ophthal., 37*:312, 1953; *Amer. J. Ophthal., 21*:1370, 1938), the author states that prematures ($N = 158$) show more visual problems when tested at ages 5 to 9 than controls ($N = 439$), and visual acuity is related to speed of perception. In a comparison of 25 pupils (prematures) whose birth weight was under 5.5 lb. with controls ($N = 25$) whose birth weight was over 5.5 lb. on visual acuity (Snellen method) and speeds of object and word perception as measured by a tachistoscope, the interrelationships among these variables was much higher for the premature group than for the control group. Prematurity must, therefore, be considered as a possible handicap to learning, although "It must be stated that there are individual differences in response to prematurity just as there are in diseases, learning, and memory."

Elkan, D.: Development of the aphasic child: a case study, *Volta Rev.*, *57*:71–72, 1955. This is the case history of a 5½-year-old boy, believed to have had poliomyelitis at the age of 3. Methods used in teaching him to talk are presented. Although sensory and motor centers appeared greatly impaired, some residual hearing was present.

Feldman, I. S.: Psychological differences among moron and borderline mental defectives as a function of etiology: I. Visual-motor functioning, *Amer. J. Ment. Defic.*, *57*:484–494, 1953. Fifty-four exogenous retardates were matched with 54 endogenous retardates in a state training school (CA 10–37, Mean 23, IQ 53). The criterion for exogenous retardates was the presence of neurological signs. Exogenous retardates performed less well on the Pascal Suttel scoring scheme for the Bender Gestalt. Performance on this task was correlated with MA for both groups to a significant extent. Although both groups do less well than normals, the exogenous group showed more perseveration, failure to complete difficult designs, and failure to overlap figures. The Bender Gestalt may, therefore, "prove to be more predictive than Strauss criteria" for the presence of brain injury and prognosis. An incidental finding: First-born in both groups did less well than non-first-born.

Flores, P. M., and Irwin, O. C.: Status of five front consonants in the speech of cerebral palsied children, *J. Speech Hearing Dis.*, *21*:238–244, 1956. In teaching consonants *p, b, m, d,* and *t* to cerebral-palsied children, verbal stimulation elicits more correct responses than pictorial stimulation in the medial position than at the beginning and end of a series. In comparing the positions for ease of eliciting responses, the initial, the medial, and the final were of increasing difficulty.

French, E. L.: A system for classifying the mentally deficient on the basis of anamnesis, *Train. Sch. Bull.*, *47:* Supplement p. 40, 1950. "The usefulness of the new classification system for research is indicated by the findings that groups classified by it as familial and nonfamilial show significant differences in measures from the Heath Rail-Walking Test, the Cassel modification of the Witmer Formboard Test, and the Ellis Designs Test. These differences are in the same directions as differences formally reported on the basis of diagnosis of endogenous and exogenous. . . ."

Gallagher, J. J.: A comparison of brain injured and non-brain injured mentally retarded children on several psychological variables, *Monogr. Soc. Res. Child Develop.*, *22*:2, Serial No. 65, 1957. After a careful review of the literature on the perceptual, intellectual, and personality characteristics of brain-injured children, a study is presented wherein 24 brain-injured retardates at a state school in Illinois (CA 7–14, IQ 35–76) were matched with a control group of nonretardates. No differences were found in learning ability. The brain-injured group was slightly inferior in some perceptual tasks (*e.g.*, marble board) but not others (memory for designs). In language, the brain-injured group was superior in verbal imitative responses but poorer in making associations and integrating verbal concepts. The brain-injured group was more hyperactive, fearful, and less popular. Conclusion: Some differences between the groups exist, but not enough to warrant drastically modified educational programs. In short, on the whole, similarities outweigh differences.

Guibor, G. P.: Some eye defects seen in cerebral palsy, with some statistics, *Amer. J. Phys. Med.*, *32*:342–347, 1953. In general, the eyes respond to cortical injury in the following ways: (1) horizontal conjugate deviation without limitation of movement, (2) horizontal conjugate deviation with limitation of movement, (3) nasal turning of one or both eyes, and/or (4) temporal turning of one or both eyes.

Motor defects of the eyes occurred in 75 percent, subnormal vision in 25 percent, and the eyes turned inward toward the nose in 51 percent of cerebral-palsied persons. Treatment of 142 patients over a nine-year period has been less successful than with patients with similar eye defects who did not have cerebral palsy.

Guibor, G. P.: Cerebral palsy: a practical routine for discerning oculomotor defects in cerebral palsied children, *J. Pediat.*, *47*:333–339, 1955. More than half of cerebral-palsied patients have ocular defects. Early treatment develops vision and may improve general motor ability, especially in patients with athetosis or ataxia. A series of simple tests for the nonspecialist are described, with indications as to when referral to the specialist is desirable.

Halpin, V. G., and Patterson, R. M.: The performance of brain-injured children on the Goldstein-Scheerer test, *Amer. J. Ment. Defic.*, *59*:91–99, 1954. Fifteen "brain-injured" institutionalized children (CA 10; MA 5–8; IQ 54) were matched with 15 familial retardates on a test battery including the Arthur Point Scale, Goodenough Draw-A-Man, and Vineland Social Maturity Scale. In a number of dimensions of performance, both groups scored the same on the Goldstein-Scheerer tests; however, a number of differences were observed. The brain-injured group had particular difficulty on the stick test, mostly in breakdown of the gestalts and increased rotations ($p = .05$). The findings are analyzed in a careful, detailed way that raises a number of interesting points, *e.g.*, the possibility that the brain-injured child fails a task for a reason different from the familial, and why some brain-injured do well and others do not.

Hardy, W. G.: Aphasia in children, *J. Ontario Speech Hearing Assoc.*, *1*:1–4, 1960. Aphasia in children may include impaired hearing together with problems of learning and memory. Auditory discrimination, pattern perception, and the EEG should be investigated. Several hypotheses concerning cerebral functioning are offered. Diagnostic teaching is useful. Diagnostic testing is always in order.

Harrower-Erickson, M. R.: Personality changes accompanying organic brain lesions: III. A study of pre-adolescent children, *J. Genet. Psychol.*, *58*:391–405, 1941. Three 12-year-old boys with established brain lesions were examined preoperatively. The Rorschach record was interpreted "blindly," *i.e.*, without any other data. Two of the boys were examined postoperatively. They appeared improved on all tests. The cases are presented in detail to illustrate the correlation of psychological and anatomical data and also to demonstrate the usefulness of psychological tests, particularly the Rorschach, in studying brain-damaged individuals.

Hohman, L., Baker, L., and Reed, R.: Sensory disturbances in children with infantile hemiplegia, triplegia, and quadriplegia, *Amer. J. Phys. Med.*, *37*:1–6, 1958. Forty-seven children (CA 6–16) of average-to-superior intelligence were studied on 13 sensory tasks. 72 percent showed sensory defects. The major defect appears to be of the cortical parietal lobe variety (loss of form sense, two-point discrimination, and position sense). Sensory losses in other modalities may also be present (hemionopsia, light touch, sharp and dull, hot and cold, measuring ability, wet and dry, rough and smooth). When losses occurred in parietal modalities, cortical modalities showed losses also. Other findings: Very small areas of the hand may be involved, although the rest of the hand is intact. Fifteen cases showed underdevelopment of the involved side. This fits Penfield and Roberts' theory that damage to the parietal lobe before the second year leads to a shortened extremity.

Holden, R. H.: Motivation, adjustment, and anxiety of cerebral palsied children, *Except. Child.*, *24*:313–317, 1958. Two studies were carried out at a preschool cerebral palsy center (CA 3–6). I. 35 preschool children were rated by a psychologist, a nursery school teacher, an occupational therapist, and a physical therapist on five-point scales of motivation, adjustment, and anxiety. Results: 15 were rated low in motivation. 12 of these (80%) were poorly adjusted and highly anxious. Well-motivated children, however, are evenly distributed on both ends of the adjustment and anxiety scales. Reliability of the scales was high, with 94 percent agreement within one point in a sample of 10 cases. II. The 10 most motivated and 10 least motivated (unbeknown to the judges) were rated on improvement. A high relationship between judgment of progress and motivation is indicated ($r = .79$). Judges agreed on progress in 17 of the 20 cases.

Hood, P. N., and Perlstein, M. A.: Infantile spastic hemiplegia: II. Laterality of involvement, *Amer. J. Phys. Med., 34*:457–466, 1955. In a sample of 334 left and right hemiplegics, there were no differences in rate of language and motor development and intelligence. This is in sharp contrast to the bulk of the previous literature which is reviewed. Right hemiplegics tend to have a greater birth weight than left hemiplegics.

Hopkins, T. W., Bice, N. V., and Colton, K. C.: *Evaluation and Education of the Cerebral Palsied Child: New Jersey Study,* Council for Exceptional Children, 1954. A detailed summary of medical and psychological findings as well as educational procedures developed in New Jersey from 1936 to 1951 is presented. Data and comparisons of physical and psychological characteristics of the four major types of cerebral palsy are examined on a large number of cases ($N = 1406$, CA 1–21). The teaching methods and counseling carried out at the A. Harry Moore School in Jersey City are discussed. The findings by individual psychological tests and special problems and their administration are presented.

Hunt, B., and Patterson, R. M.: Performance of brain-injured and familial mentally deficient children on visual and auditory sequences, *Amer. J. Ment. Defic., 63*:72–80, 1958. Both types of mentally defective children were tested on the perception of visual and auditory sequences and ability to arrange materials in both types of sequences. Results indicate that teaching methods should be altered to facilitate the use of cues from the area least handicapped. Children should be classified on the basis of disability as well as by mental and chronological age.

Kahn, E., and Cohen, L. H.: Organic driveness: a brain stem syndrome and an experience, *New Eng. J. Med., 210*:748–756, 1934. Cases are presented in which hyperkinesis due to surplus of inner impulsion is the predominating feature. This is termed "organic driveness." Its association with neurological signs referrable to the brain-stem indicates the locus of its genesis in this region. Restlessness, clumsiness, and explosive motor release of voluntarily inhibited activity are secondary to the hyperkinesis. "Organic driveness" is found in various encephalopathies, notably encephalitis epidemica, but its incidence in various degenerative diseases of the nervous system, as well as the probable existence of constitutional types, is emphasized. Various differentiating criteria from the hyperactivity of hypomanic and euphoric individuals are discussed. It is in accordance with his personality make-up that the hyperkinesis and the "organic driveness" are experienced by the individual. This classic paper is followed by a discussion which questions the evidence for implicating the brain stem, the lack of autopsy material, the possibilities of cortical damage touching off release phenomena, and the role of personality in adapting to the driveness.

Kastein, S., and Hendin, J.: Language in development in a group of children with spastic hemiplegia, *J. Pediat., 39*:476–480, 1951. "A thorough study of 67 case histories of children with spastic hemiplegia seems to indicate that the development of language is based on the mental potential rather than on the severity or side of impairment (lesion) or handedness. Among the cases with average intelligence or above, the incidence of right and left hemiplegia is equal."

Kelloway, P., Crawley, J. W., and Kagawa, N.: A specific electroencephalographic correlate of convulsive equivalent disorders in children, *J. Pediat., 55*:582–592, 1959. A study of 550 patients (from birth to 16 years of age) showing the EEG pattern known as 14 and 6 per second positive spikes has shown that this pattern is a particular correlate of convulsive equivalent disorders in children and provides objective laboratory evidence to support such a diagnosis. The high incidence of paroxysmal attacks of headache, abdominal pain, and behavioral and autonomic disturbance may be considered the basis of a specific clinical syndrome. It has its greatest incidence between ages 4 and 15 but may occur at any age. Prognosis for spontaneous remission and response to anticonvulsant drugs is good.

Kelly, E. M.: Educational implications in the public school special class of the endogenous-exogenous classification, *Amer. J. Ment. Defic.*, *54*:207–211, 1947. Two groups of 13 special-class children (CA 10–12), divided into exogenous vs. endogenous, received the Vineland Social Maturity Scale and were described by their teachers. There were some differences in profiles between the groups; however, the data were not submitted to statistical tests, so that it is difficult to tell whether these differences are significant. In the teachers' descriptions, the picture fits that suggested by Doll.

Keller, J. E.: "The Use of Certain Perceptual Measures of Brain Injury with Mentally Retarded Children," in *Readings on the Exceptional Child,* by E. P. Trapp and P. Himelstein. Appleton-Century-Crofts, 1962. In an attempt to replicate earlier findings of Werner and Thuma (1942), from which they concluded that brain-injured boys are unable to perceive apparent motion and have low critical flicker-frequency thresholds, all the boys ($N = 100$) at the Wayne County Training School (CA 11–14, IQ 48–102) were reexamined on these measures. Since 42 percent of the boys at Wayne County Training School showed positive neurological signs on Strauss's previous examination and the Werner-Thuma studies showed clear-cut differences between groups, it was expected that a bimodal distribution would occur. It was found that (1) the original techniques could not be replicated, so that modifications had to be made in the apparent motion apparatus; (2) in contrast to Werner and Thuma's findings, all subjects saw apparent motion; (3) the variation in critical flicker-frequency thresholds was considerably less than Werner and Thuma reported; (4) the two measures (CFF and apparent motion) are not correlated. Explanation for the failure to replicate are offered.

Kennard, M. A.: The characteristics of thought disturbances as related to electroencephalographic findings in children and adolescents, *Amer. J. Psychiat.*, *115*:911–921, 1959. A multidisciplinary examination of 200 children (CA 7–16) in a mental hospital revealed that organic brain disorders, as indicated by history and behavioral patterns, have a strong positive association with EEG abnormality (83%). Although this is to be expected, it is surprising in view of the absence of neurological signs in most of the cases. Thought disorders in children with no sign of organic brain disturbance were accompanied by EEG abnormality in 40 percent of the cases compared with 23 percent of non-thought disorders.

Klapper, Z. S., and Werner, H.: Developmental deviations in brain-injured (cerebral palsied) members of pairs of identical twins, *Quart. J. Child Behav.*, *2*:288–313, 1950. "Three pairs of identical twins . . . were studied to investigate the effect of birth injury to the brain on development. . . . Seven test situations were employed, comprising standardized tests of intelligence and personality, and special tests designed for the diagnosis of developmental deviations of various psychological functions. . . . In spite of great variability, the modifications of behavior found in the cerebral-palsied twins are essentially of the same type described in previous studies of brain-injured children without motor handicap. . . . Findings concerning such modifications, and the part they play in the total clinical picture, are pertinent to any attempt at prognosis. . . ."

Knott, J. R.: EEG and behavior, *Amer. J. Orthopsychiat.*, *30*:292–298, 1960. This paper is a survey of the application of the EEG since its discovery in 1929 to a number of clinical problems, including the study of individual differences in personality, psychiatric diagnosis, and intelligence. A number of studies suggest that EEG disturbances occur in children diagnosed as having primary behavior disorder. Recent work on learning indicates that the integrity of an organism's behavior depends on the intactness of a critical zone in the midbrain area. Need for more careful analysis of behavior, as well as correlation with biochemical changes in the brain, are indicated.

Lamm, S., and Fish, M. L.: Intellectual development of the cerebral palsied child as a factor in therapeutic progress, *Amer. J. Ment. Defic.*, *59*:452–458, 1955. A study of 99 cerebral-palsied children at a clinic ($N = 73$) and public school ($N = 26$) confirms findings of others that approximately three-fourths have IQ's below 90. Progress, as measured by ratings of individual staff members (reliability of the scales not cited), appears to be related to IQ in the clinic group ($p = .01$) but not in the school group. In 5 high-IQ children who showed no progress, psychiatric problems predominated. Unlike other studies, the IQ levels of the spastic and athetoid group do not differ; also, an unusually high percent (88) of athetoids showed progress.

Lending, M., Slobody, L. B., Stone, M. L., Hosbach, R. E., and Mestern, J.: Activity of glutamic-oxalacetic transminase and lactic dehydrogenase in cerebrospinal fluid and plasma of normal and abnormal infants, *Pediatrics, 24*:378–387, 1959. The activity of the enzymes glutamic oxalacetic transminase (GOT) and lactic dehydrogenase (LDH) in the cerebrospinal fluid and plasma was studied in 54 normal, full-term, newborn infants from 2½ to 240 hours of age and in 20 newborn infants suspected to have intracranial pathology. The normal range of activities of these enzymes is described. In infants with suspected intracranial pathology, average GOT activity of cerebrospinal fluid was 82 percent higher than in the normal newborn infant, and plasma GOT activity had an 18-percent mean increase over normal. In the cerebrospinal fluid of the abnormal infants, LDH activity had a mean increase of 309 percent over normal, and plasma LDH activity an increase of 11 percent over normal. Enzyme determinations in cerebrospinal fluid, particularly LDH, may be useful in the study of newborn infants suspected of intracranial pathology.

Lesky, J.: Aphasia in childhood, *J. Ontario Speech Hearing Assoc., 2*:5–7, 1960. A three-fold classification is used: (1) "acquired" after speech and language has been developed, (2) "developmental" owing to a delay in conceptual organization related to speech, and (3) "pure" or "congenital" where the localized lesion is probably bilateral or subcortical. Symptoms that act as a guidepost in diagnosis are listed. Treatment of congenital aphasia involves the entire family over a period of time. Left untreated, the child will level off with an odd word or two, or jargon. Developmental aphasics will learn to talk in concrete terms but show gaps in comprehension. Start therapy early using a visual, kinesthetic, and tactile multidisciplinary approach. If no progress follows after a year of treatment, the child should be treated as if he were deaf.

Linde, T.: Accent on assets—two problems in psychology and cerebral palsy: Part one. Individual personality, *Cereb. Palsy Rev., 23*:3–4;11, 1962. Four areas of adjustment problems are presented along with anecdotal material from the United Cerebral Palsy Association of Milwaukee. These are: frustration, guilt, inferiority, and idolization. They lead to anxiety. It is important to distinguish between objective inability to adjust and that stemming from deep social bias. The rehabilitation worker can clarify and give information in regard to the objective inability and point out the asset components. Stress on asset over comparative-valuing systems is suggested.

Linde, T.: Accent on assets—two problems in psychology and cerebral palsy: Part two. Social interaction, *Cereb. Palsy Rev., 23*:5–7;19, 1962. What makes people evaluate one another favorably or unfavorably? The answer is: positive and negative expectancies based on experiences. This finding in social psychology is applied to cerebral-palsied people with illustrations.

Luria, A. R.: An objective approach to the study of the abnormal child, *Amer. J. Orthopsychiat., 31*:1–17, 1961. Failure in school may be due to emotional conflict, feeblemindedness (*i.e.*, "brain injury" in the intrauterine period), malnutrition, and partial defects. It is, therefore, important to diagnose correctly the reasons for school failure. Vigotsky's principle of a "zone of potential development,"—*i.e.*, the possibility of enhancing a child's performance through helping him—is diagnostically useful. A method for studying the distinctions between hearing, listening, and thinking is presented. This is based on a technique for measuring the constriction of a blood vessel in response to a stimulus. Semantic generalization is a useful technique also. The psychometric approach is unrewarding. Arthur Benton, as a discussant, indicates that there may be differences between Russian and American psychologists; *e.g.*, the former pay more attention to the asthenic child, the latter to the emotionally disturbed. Americans are more similar to Russian psychologists in their wish for objective methods and their objections to single-score psychometric approaches than Luria indicates.

Mark, H. J.: Two symptoms pathognomonic for congenital cerebral communication disorders in children, *J. Pediat.*, *55*:391–396, 1959. Failure to make "expected responses" to sound, irrespective of intensity level and total absence of speech, are almost always pathognomonic of central nervous system dysfunction. Failure to respond may be called a disturbance in orienting or alerting responses to social stimuli. It is pathognomonic at all age levels. Sometimes it is not noticed until 18 months, because failure of the auditory system to serve more complex communication functions may even disorganize previously learned auditory functions. Absence of speech is secondary to inability to comprehend spoken language in the thousands of children seen at the Johns Hopkins Hearing and Speech Center. It is on an organic, not a psychogenic, basis and is different from peripheral hearing impairment. Little is known about the prognosis in these two conditions.

Mark, H. J., and Hardy, W. G.: Orienting reflex disturbances in central auditory or language handicapped children, *J. Speech Hearing Dis.*, *23*:237–242, 1958. There seems to be a relationship between disorganized learning processes and orienting reflex disturbances in children with central auditory or language disorders due to brain injury present since birth. A study of 36 children suggests that orienting reflex disturbances may not appear until as late as 3 or 4 years of age. The inability of the auditory system to serve more complex communicative functions gives rise to disorganized learning processes. This, in turn, explains the extinction of a previously present orienting reflex. Hence, the disturbance may not be manifest soon after birth.

Mark, H. J., and Pasamanick, B.: Asynchronism and apparent movement thresholds in brain-injured children, *J. Consult. Psychol.*, *22*:173–177, 1958. Ten brain-injured children (pyramidal trait involvement but no ophthalmological pathology) were compared with 10 controls equated for age, IQ, and sex. The brain-injured were slower and more variable in reporting (1) when two flashing lights (which were not simultaneous) were not seen as simultaneous (asynchronism), (2) apparent movement, and (3) peripheral two-point thresholds. Although the differences were statistically significant (.01), they were not sharp enough to be used as a diagnostic tool.

McMurray, J. G.: Rigidity in conceptual thinking in exogenous and endogenous mentally retarded children, *J. Consult. Psychol.*, *18*:366–370, 1954. In a large institution for mental retardates, 15 exogenous were matched with 15 endogenous on age (10–20), IQ (40–70), and sex. Each received a modified form of the Wisconsin Card-Sorting Test. The exogenous showed evidence of greater rigidity by manifesting more perseveration and by requiring more time and a greater number of responses to sort to a correct principle.

McPherson, M. W., and Fisch, R. L.: Affect in the etiology and maintenance of mental deficiency, *J. Clin. Psychol.*, *11*:55–60, 1955. "This study was designed to determine the characteristics, incidence, and possible etiological sources of mental defectives' evasive attempts to respond to difficult items on the Wechsler-Bellevue Scale, Form I. . . . Children with the lower MA's evidenced evasion consistently more frequently than did the subjects with higher MA's. . . . There is evidence to suggest that the phenomenon might reflect an attitude of learned negativism. The relatively low incidence of evasive responses suggests that experimental antecedents of this type will elucidate only one type of mental deficiency."

Mednick, S. A., and Wild, C.: Stimulus generalization in brain damaged children, *J. Consult. Psychol.*, *75*:525–528, 1961. Cerebral-palsied children ($N = 18$) showed less stimulus generalization than a matched control group on a task requiring a voluntary response along a visual-spatial dimension. This explains the "concrete" behavior of the brain-injured child from a learning-theory standpoint. Implications for training are suggested.

Murphy, M. M.: Comparison of developmental patterns of three diagnostic groups of middle-grade and low-grade mental defectives, *Amer. J. Ment. Defic.*, *61*:164–169, 1956. Forty mongoloids (CA 15) were compared with 40 familial retardates (CA 16) and 38 brain-injured (CA 14). IQ's were in the 20's. Unlike higher grade defectives, all groups showed equal verbal and motor development. The average developmental levels of the brain-injured and mongolian groups were quantitatively similar and inferior to the familial group, but the mongolian group was qualitatively similar to the familial group. Results appear to support Benda, who classifies mongolism as exogenous because of damage to the pituitary gland during the fetal period.

Myklebust, H. R.: Aphasia in children, *Except. Child., 19*:9–14, 1952. Aphasia is described along with its common causes. For special education, it is recommended that children be classified separately and trained through the use of appropriate remedial methods and techniques.

Nelson, C. D.: Subtle brain damage: its influence on learning and language, *Element. School J., 61*:317–324, 1961. The hyperactive, "driven" child with brain damage has been well described. Often overlooked is the child with subtle damage that is manifested by learning and adjustment problems. A number of language tasks and examples of how the "subtly brain-damaged" child responds to them are mentioned: (1) sequence difficulties, (2) familial language disòrder, (3) confused cerebral dominance, (4) perseveration, (5) writing and spelling disturbances, (6) poor sound discrimination, (7) difficulty in abstract behavior. Cautious observations using the team approach is stressed.

Nelson, T. M.: A study comparing visual and visual-motor perceptions of unimpaired, defective, and spastic cerebral palsied children, *J. Genet. Psychol., 101*:299–332, 1962. With a two-dimensional diamond as a stimulus, subjects were required to match the target in 8 purely visual situations and 3 visual-motor situations. Quality of response varied with chronologic and mental age for all groups and tasks except in the cerebral-palsied group ($N = 16$; CA 5–12; MA 3–11) where the r between visual performance and CA was —.11 for the spastic group. The tasks could be graded in order of difficulty for all groups. When the groups were equated for MA, the defective group ($N = 20$; CA 6–12; MA 3–9) exceeded the others on higher level visual tasks and the spastics were the poorest. These findings suggest that: (1) quality of purely visual performance is dependent on neurophysiologic maturation within the visual pathway, (2) mechanisms of the visual pathway seem involved in spastic cerebral palsy and cause a developmental lag, and (3) characteristics of responses to flat copy reflect a host of variables, making them poorly suited for clinical situations.

Nielson, H. N.: *Visual-Motor Functioning of Cerebral Palsied and Normal Children.* Ejnar Munksgaards Forlag, Copenhagen, 1962. Twenty hemiplegic and 20 paraplegic spastic cerebral-palsied children, ages 6–15 years, were matched with 40 controls on MA, sex, parents' social status (not defined), and IQ. All but 6 of the spastics and 6 of the controls had IQ's above 90 (this is an atypical sample of spastic children). On the Bender Visual Motor Gestalt Test, the Goldstein-Scheerer Test, and the Rey Labyrinth Test, the experimental group performed less well. The Bender and Rey tests were most discriminating in the higher IQ ranges, because both groups showed deviant performance in the lower ranges. Differences were also greatest between 6 and 8 years, implying a slower rate of maturation in the spastic children or a tendency to compensate with age. The lag may be manifested in school achievements (17 of 24 spastics on whom data were available were classified as slow learners). Interrelationships between tests was low: 40 percent of the spastics and 73 percent of the controls showed no abnormal signs. There is no typical brain-injured child. EEG findings correlate with the Bender.

Oki, T., Sakai, T., Kisu, M., and Higashi, H.: A comparative study concerning the psychological traits of children with organic brain damage and subnormal oligophrenia, *Jap. J. Child Psychiat., 1*:126–134, 1960. The Bender Gestalt test was administered to 17 organic, oligophrenic children, 17 subnormal children, and 135 normal children. Visual-motor function of the oligophrenic children was found to be inferior and their marks fluctuated depending on the figures offered. "There was a striking disintegration of the contents of their copied figures. Their understanding of the figures was sporadic and fragmentary, lacking coherence as a whole. In addition, their order of drawing was found to be extremely incoherent."

Osborn, W. J.: Associative clustering in organic and familial retardates, *Amer. J. Ment. Defic., 65*:351–355, 1960. Familial and organic retardates (CA 10–30) were matched with normals (MA 5–11, IQ 45–70) and compared with respect to their functioning on the associate clustering task. In recalling the content of 32 pictures, the three groups showed no differences in clustering effects. There were qualitative differences, however, in the manner in which the retardates developed their total scores, suggesting inefficiencies in functioning which may be related to inappropriate learning habits. Both groups of retardates showed more variability than the normals.

Paak, E. B.: Measures of ability in a preacademic group of brain-injured children, *Amer. J. Ment. Defic., 59*:220–225, 1954. To solve the problem of "where to start" in educating the brain-injured child whose IQ range is 40 to 60, CA 8 to 10 years, and MA 4 to 6 years, an academic inventory was devised. An "abilities check list" comprising 15 titles (*e.g.*, visual matching and visual discrimination followed by specific observation), is described. More than half the article consists of the items and record sheet.

Pascal, G. R., and Zax, M.: Double alternation performance as a measure of educability in cerebral palsied children, *Amer. J. Ment. Defic., 59*:658–665, 1955. Hunter's classical double alternation problem, originally devised for animals, has been adapted for cerebral-palsied children. It has been suitable in overcoming many difficulties due to expressive handicaps. For a sample of 24 children studied intensively by three observers over a one-year period, a correlation of .64 between the test and the observations was obtained. Biserial correlation of passing or failing the problem was .74. Performance was not related to CA.

Perlstein, M. A., Gibbs, E. L., and Gibbs, F. A.: The electroencephalogram in infantile cerebral palsy, *Amer. J. Phys. Med., 34*:377–397, 1955. In an EEG study of 1217 consecutive cases, it was observed that seizures occur in nearly half the cases. The incidence and nature of the seizures are described for the varieties of cerebral palsy. Very abnormal EEG's occur in 90 percent of the cases having seizures and 44 percent not having seizures. Differences of EEG patterns with age, laterality of clinical findings, and a sample of unselected epileptics are described in detail.

Perlstein, M. A., and Hood, P. N.: Infantile spastic hemiplegia, *Amer. J. Phys. Med., 34*:391–407, 1955. A study of 334 spastic hemiplegics (CA 1–20) revealed that: (1) The ratio of right to left hemiplegia was 5:4; the two groups were equal in intelligence and age of acquiring speech. (2) Negroes did not differ from whites except in a greater incidence of postnatal acquisition and seizures which may be due to socioeconomic factors. (3) The incidence of seizures was much greater than that previously reported in the literature, occurring more often in acquired cases and in those with lower IQ. (4) The onset of walking and talking was related to IQ, but they were not related to each other.

Perlstein, M. A., and Hood, P. N.: Infantile spastic hemiplegia: intelligence, *Pediatrics, 15*:676–682, 1955. A study of 334 patients was made with respect to age distribution, race, sex, presence of seizures, side of involvement, and time of onset in regard to intelligence.

Perlstein, M. A., and Hood, P. N.: Infantile spastic hemiplegia: intelligence and age of walking and talking, *Amer. J. Ment. Defic., 61*:534–542, 1957. In 334 infantile spastic hemiplegics, the mean IQ was 77, with 28 percent achieving scores below 65. There was a delay of 9 months in walking and 6 months in sentence acquisition. Sex and side of hemiplegia did not affect the results. Individuals with acquired hemiplegia had the same intelligence as congenital hemiplegics, although they tended to walk and talk a little faster. Seizures occurred in 43 percent of the cases and were associated with lowered intelligence and delay in walking and talking. Mental deficiency appears to be more important than seizures in delay in motor and language development.

Pond, D. A.: Psychiatric aspects of epileptic and brain-damaged children, *Brit. Med. J., 2*:1377–1382;1454–1459, 1961. These two lectures were delivered before the Royal College of Physicians, London. The first discusses current concepts, prevalence, intelligence and personality, drug effects, and treatment of epilepsy. The second lecture covers the brain-damaged child, including criteria for the presence of brain damage. Data from a survey of 58 cases are presented to illustrate the nature of the evidence for brain damage, intelligence, social class and environment, age of onset, and the relationship between personality traits and parental attitudes. The effects of environmental events prior to brain damage and findings from animal studies are presented. The latter are necessary because of the poverty of our methods of studying the brain in people. A careful, critical survey of the literature is woven into the discussion.

Robinson, C. L.: "An Analysis of Understanding and Cooperation as it Depends upon Communication Between the Meeting Street School and Parents of Children Enrolled There." Master's thesis, Boston University, 1951. The role of communication in promoting parents' understanding of the cerebral-palsied child and his needs was studied. Aims were to determine (1) parents' understanding of goals of the nursery school, (2) degrees of cooperation given by parents to the school, (3) extent of relation between levels of understanding and degrees of cooperation, (4) areas where there is misinformation or lack of information, and (5) effectiveness of existing communication methods.

Rudel, R. G., Teuber, H. L., Liebert, R., and Halpern, S.: Localization of auditory midline and reactions to body tilt in brain-damaged children, *J. Nerv. Ment. Dis.*, *131*:302–309, 1960. A comparison of 72 cerebral-palsied children (CA 5–17) matched with controls for age and sex for whom data were available from a previous study revealed that in setting a sound source to the midline while the body is tilted, brain-damaged children lagged behind normal children. In setting the auditory midline, differences emerged only in adolescence. On the other hand, a starting position error was noted in brain-damaged persons at all ages. The extent of the starting position error is apparently related to extent of neurologic impairment. Similarities and differences between this study and prior work on brain-damaged adults are reviewed.

Sato, C.: Musical aptitude of cerebral palsied children, *Cereb. Palsy Rev.*, *22*:3–8, 1960. In a study of 107 cerebral-palsied children on a standard test of musical aptitude (the Tanaka test) it was found that, although "their expressions in music are full of errors and their quality is poor, their aptitude is by no means inferior." The findings and their relationship to the disability, the methods and problems of test administration, and a number of questions about the musical aptitudes of the children are discussed in detail.

Sato, C.: The change of voice in cerebral palsied boys, *Cereb. Palsy Rev.*, *23*:7–11, 1962. A study of the vocal pitch range of 26 cerebral-palsied boys (CA 13–21) over a period of several years revealed that vocal pitch range became lower in 15 cases, narrower in 3 cases, did not change in 3 cases, rose in 4 cases, and was not determinable in 1 case. Cerebral-palsied children have narrower and lower pitch ranges than normal children, and their ranges do not descend conspicuously. Although athetoids with difficulties in phonation begin to change at normal ages, it takes a longer time for their voices to become steady. Changes in countenance appear at about the same time as change in voice.

Sato, C.: A study on rhythm patterns of cerebral palsied children, *Cereb. Palsy Rev.*, *22*:7–11, 1962. Two tests were administered to 125 cerebral-palsied children (first to sixth grade) in a Tokyo school for physically handicapped children: (1) a time reproduction test, *i.e.*, reproducing a beat to two musical phrases, and (2) a speed adaptation test, *i.e.*, reproducing the beat when a phrase was speeded up. Success on both tests was achieved only by mildly handicapped children with high intelligence. No athetoids succeeded in both tests. Success on the test appears to be related to improvement through training. Different patterns of success and failure on the combinations of tasks point to important correlations in rhythm patterns. Scoring scheme, methodology, and results are presented.

Satter, G., and Cassel, R. H.: Tactual kinesthetic localization in the mentally retarded, *Amer. J. Ment. Defic.*, *59*:652–668, 1955. A comparison of three groups of 20 retardates (CA 14, IQ 60) classified as to etiology by the Riggs and Cassel method with a group of 20 normals showed that (1) brain-damaged retardates made most errors in six tactile localization tasks in different parts of the body, whereas the normals made the least; (2) the brain-damaged group was not more variable in its judgment, contrary to hypotheses derived from supposed effects of distractibility.

Schulman, J. L., Thorne, F. M., and Caspar, J. C.: Studies on distractibility: a progress report, *Train. Sch. Bull.*, *59*:142–149, 1963. Four new tasks presumed to be sensitive to distractibility, defined as an ability to attend to a moving unpredictable target, are described: (1) the clock test, (2) the box test, (3) the card test, and (4) the tone test. Two pilot studies were performed on 40 retarded children (CA 6–16, IQ 40–79) and 19 retarded children (CA 5–7, IQ 43–89). The former group was chosen on the basis of the teacher's ratings of most and least distractible. All four tests appear highly reliable ($r = .74$ to $.91$). They also are significantly related to one another ($p = .01$) and to the teacher's ratings ($p = .01$). The ratings appear to be related to CA and MA in the former group ($p = .01$) but not in the latter group. Further studies of the efforts of a distracting stimulus and correlations with other behavioral signs of brain damage are indicated.

Sievers, D. J., and Rosenberg, C. M.: The differential language facility test and electroencephalograms of brain injured mentally retarded children, *Amer. J. Ment. Defic.*, *65*:46–50, 1960. The EEG tracings of 50 brain-injured mentally retarded children (CA 12; MA 4; IQ 36) were grouped into four categories: (1) grand mal, (2) grand mal and petit mal, (3) hypothalamic, and (4) slowing. The scores of the four groups on the Differential Language Facility Test were compared. There were significant differences among groups on the two tests that involved the audio-vocal on the integrational and grammatical levels. The grand mal mixed with the petit mal group was significantly lower than the slowing group on both tests. On one subtest, the slowing group was also significantly higher than the hypothalamic group. On the other subtest, the grand mal mixed with petit mal group also had a significantly poorer performance than the hypothalamic group. The grand mal pure group and the slowing group were significantly different.

Sleeper, M. D.: "Correlation of Body Balance and Space Perception in Cerebral Palsied Individuals." Master's thesis, University of Southern California, 1962. Thirty-eight cerebral-palsied individuals (CA 10–43) received (1) the Ayres Space Perception Test, (2) a test of perception of verticality, and (3) a test of body balance. The Ayres test correlated with perception of the vertical ($r = .47$, $p = .01$). Neither of these measures correlated with a test of body balance.

Solomons, H. C.: "A Developmental Study of Tactual Perception in Normal and Brain Damaged Children." Doctoral (education) dissertation, Boston University, 1957. One hundred and sixty normal children (IQ 108, CA 5–9) were compared with 49 brain-injured children, of whom 19 had motor involvement (IQ 96) and 30 were free of any physical handicap (IQ 100). Test stimuli were varied by size, weight, texture, and form. In normal subjects there was a steady decline in errors with increasing age, except for the nine-year level. Normal subjects exceeded the nonhandicapped brain-injured group, which, in turn, exceeded the handicapped brain-injured group. The weight test did not discriminate between the groups and was the least reliable of the measures.

Spivack, G., and Levine, M.: The spiral aftereffect and reversible figures as measures of brain damage and memory, *J. Personality*, *25*:767–778, 1957. Thirty-two brain-damaged boys (CA 11–21) were compared with 35 emotionally disturbed boys (CA 11–19) with primarily neurotic and characterological diagnoses. The emotionally disturbed boys perceived the spiral aftereffect more often and for a shorter duration. They also showed more rapid reversals on reversible figure tasks, reversible faces, and the Necker Cube. On recall of a memory paragraph, they were also superior on both immediate and delay. On the whole, although the significant differences appear, discriminating power of the spiral aftereffect is lower than other reports in the literature have indicated. Furthermore, there appears little relationship among the aftereffect, reversible figures, and memory.

Stephenson, G. R.: "Form Perception, Abstract Thinking and Intelligence Test Validity in Cerebral Palsy." Doctoral dissertation, Teachers College, Columbia University, 1957. Thirty-six cerebral-palsied children, 20 of whom were retarded and 16 nonretarded (CA 5–18), were matched for age and educational achievement as rated by teachers. The group received a test battery of two language tests—the Ammons Full Range Vocabulary Test and the Non-Vocal Scale of Mental Functioning (constructed specially for this research) —and two nonlanguage tests involving the perception of visual form—the Columbia Mental Maturity Scale and the Raven Progressive Matrices. Over-all performances were the same for both groups. The cerebral-palsied group was significantly inferior in nonlanguage tasks ($p = .001$), although the groups were equal when items were subdivided into concrete and abstract for both language and nonlanguage tasks. Inferior form perception in cerebral-palsied children confirms previous findings. The negative findings with regard to the abstract-concrete dichotomy contradict previous research.

St. Hilaire, T. F.: A study of abstract thinking in cerebral palsied children, *The Bulletin, Georgetown University Medical Center, 2*:206–220, 1957. A review of the literature on the mental evaluation of cerebral-palsied children since the work of Sachs in 1926 is presented. The work of Lord, Doll, Gesell, Phelps, McIntire, Myer and Simmel, and Sarason and Sarason form the background for this study. 73 cerebral-palsied children under treatment at the Washington, D.C., Society for Crippled Children received the Stanford-Binet. The children averaged 6.4 years of age (3–14), with an average mental age of 4.5 (2–12). They were subdivided into seven groups on the basis of medical diagnoses. 43 also received the Merrill Palmer. All the items on both of these scales were rescored by two judges on a four-point scale of abstract–not abstract, as defined by Goldstein and Scheerer. Although 30 of the 73 children had IQ's below 70, many children were able to make plus scores on items that were rated as abstract and were above their mental age. Cerebral-palsied children did better in abstract thinking than equated groups of familial defectives. Differences between types of cerebral palsy on the various measures are discussed.

Strauss, A. A.: Ways of thinking in brain-crippled deficient children, *Amer. J. Psychiat., 100*:639–647, 1944. Brain-injured children relate ideas on the basis of unusual or nonessential details. Their most serious thinking handicap is in the function of selectivity, or the inability to discriminate the essential from the nonessential. The ability to pursue a goal is impaired because of this. Such children may recognize reality very well and stick closely, even meticulously, to the facts but, because of their specific disorders, they may actually evade the proper solution of a problem or escape into fantasy.

Strauss, A. A., and Kephart, N. C.: Behavior differences in mentally retarded children measured by a new behavior rating scale, *Amer. J. Psychiat., 97*:1117–1123, 1940. A comparison of 40 familial with 40 brain-injured mentally retarded children (CA 16, IQ 60) on a behavior rating scale filled out by teachers showed that the brain-injured group was more impulsive, erratic, restless, furious, daydreaming, and socially unacceptable. No evidence of cross-validation is presented.

Strauss, A. A., and Kephart, N. C.: *Psychopathology and Education of the Brain Injured Child: Vol. II. Progress in Clinic and Theory*. Grune & Stratton, 1955. This book is an attempt to present newer views on brain functioning since publication of the original Strauss and Lehtinen volume in 1947. It is concerned with the child of normal IQ. Theories of brain function stressing concepts such as servomechanisms, homeostasis, and scanning functions are emphasized. The relationship of embryology to brain injury is explored. In describing the psychopathology of perception, language, concept formation, and behavior, theories of normal development in these areas are sketched. Essays on testing the brain-injured child, including a description of various aspects of mental functioning and how they can be measured by the marble board and the Ellis Design Test, are presented along with a discussion of educational principles and practices.

Strauss, A. A., and Lehtinen, L.: *Psychopathology and Education of the Brain Injured Child*. Grune & Stratton, 1947. This classic has undergone 10 reprintings since its initial publication. It is based on a series of researches and influenced by Gestalt psychologists, particularly the work of Goldstein on brain-injured soldiers after World War I, and attempts to delineate disturbances in the brain-injured retarded child. Although defects of the neuromotor system may be present or absent, disturbances in perception, thinking, and emotional behavior—singly or in combination—are characteristic. These disturbances can be demonstrated by specific tests, which are described. The findings lend support for distinguishing between the exogenous and the endogenous retarded child, although the studies carried out at the Wayne County Training School are not confined to the retarded. The second half presents the general principles in the education of the brain-injured child, including teaching arithmetic, reading, and writing. Modifications of classroom procedures to reduce hyperactivity are suggested.

Strauss, A. A., and Werner, H.: Disorders of conceptual thinking in the brain-injured child, *J. Nerv. Ment. Dis.*, *96*:153–172, 1942. The materials used in these studies consist of two sorting tasks and a picture object test. In grouping objects, brain-injured children formed more groups than non-brain-injured children. They also used more uncommon responses and more singular or unique combinations. Selection tended to be on the basis of unspecific or vaguely conceived qualities, unessential or accidental details or functional relationships, or *ad hoc* constructions. In the picture object test, which involves the relationship between life situations as represented in pictures and small objects, brain-injured children used more objects. They deviated from the standard meaning of these objects. They organized objects in circumscribed, small units with conspicuous formalistic and oversystematic arrangements. Whereas the non-brain-injured child saw this task as a problem of grouping, the brain-injured child saw it as a concrete, alive situation with a past and a future, stressing the dynamic, functional properties of the objects. In the discussion, observations are made about the forced responsiveness to stimuli, the pathological fixation, the motor disinhibition, and the dissociation (*i.e.*, incoherence in patterned behavior). The clinical descriptions and interpretations are extremely rich.

Strauss, A. A., and Werner, H.: Experimental analyses of the clinical symptom "perseveration" in mentally retarded children, *Amer. J. Ment. Defic.*, *47*:185–192, 1942. Twenty endogenous children who were matched with 20 exogenous retarded children on MA and IQ were presented with two tasks: reproducing tone rhythms and recognizing drawings of objects upon brief tachistoscopic exposure. The groups did not differ in immediate or single perseverations (*i.e.*, repetition of a response that immediately preceded the wrong one); however, the exogenous group showed more repetitive perseveration (*i.e.*, repeating the wrong response several times) and delayed perseveration (*i.e.*, repeating a response that had been presented two or more trials earlier). Exogenous children also continued to perseverate even when strikingly different test objects were presented.

Strauss, A. A., and Werner, H.: Comparative psychopathology of the brain-injured and the traumatic brain-injured adult, *Amer. J. Psychiat.*, *99*:835–840, 1943. Characteristics of the behavior of brain-injured children and the experiments that elicit them are described. Among the characteristics are (1) forced responsiveness to stimuli, (2) fixation and perseveration, (3) instability or fluctuation, (4) meticulousness and pedantry, and (5) substitute activity, a term that describes the response of the brain-injured child who constructs a figure on the marble-board test not by immediate perception but by counting the holes. Most of these behaviors and experimental situations have been described in other studies in this series.

Sugar, O.: Congenital aphasia: an anatomical and physiological approach, *J. Speech Hearing Dis.*, *17*:301–304, 1952. Because it is possible to remove one hemisphere in children without inducing aphasia, one must postulate that both hemispheres are implicated in aphasic children. The term should refer to disability in speech in children intellectually and physically capable of talking. As it occurs in adults, aphasia implies a loss of a learned function; this type does not affect children permanently and could not be said to occur as a congenital condition.

Taterka, J., and Katz, J.: Study of correlations between electroencephalographic and psychological patterns in emotionally disturbed children, *Psychosom. Med.*, *17*: 62–73, 1955. The Rorschach, Bender Gestalt, Figure Drawings, and EEG were administered to 195 children suffering from schizophrenia or primary behavior disorder

(CA 5–12) and a control group consisting of 44 children matched for age and sex and free of emotional disturbance. Conclusions: (1) 78 percent abnormal EEG in childhood schizophrenia suggests an organic component. 73 percent abnormal EEG in the primary behavior group also suggests a cerebral defect or lag; (2) the EEG is not related to specific traits; (3) the more abnormal the EEG, the greater the problems in perception; (4) gross distortions in visual-motor gestalten appear related to foci and asymmetrics in the EEG, mostly in the occipital area; (5) alpha percentage is related to accuracy of form perception on the Rorschach; and (6) results support Schilder's theory that organic damage to the brain causes perceptual and motor disturbance.

Taylor, Edith M.: *Psychological Appraisal of Children with Cerebral Defects.* Harvard University Press, 1959. On the basis of many years of clinical experience, Dr. Taylor outlines a number of portraits of children with different types of central nervous system damage at different ages. She describes the testing techniques and their clinical implications in detail. Follow-up data on 244 cerebral-palsied children 3 to 12 years after the initial evaluation shows that intelligence remained the same in 73 percent of the cases. Disagreement tended to be related to delayed language development, hearing problems, or precocious verbal fluency. Detailed test protocols are presented. The influence of Gesell and Piaget are freely acknowledged.

Teuber, H. L., and Rudel, R. G.: Behavior after cerebral lesions in children and adults, *Devel. Med. Child Neurol., 4*:3–20, 1962. Review of animal experiments suggests that brain injuries sustained early in life have less effect than comparable lesions incurred at later ages. In contrast, neurological observations suggest that certain forms of early brain damage in children may have disproportionately serious consequences for later life. The apparent contradiction may be resolved if one grants that results might differ according to (1) the kind of task involved and (2) the age at which the child is tested. These perceptual tasks have been devised to show such differential effects. On one task (constant error in auditory localization with the body tilted), the performance of brain-damaged children was essentially the same as that of normal children until age 11, but it became increasingly different thereafter. On the second task (starting position error in the same test), brain-damaged children did consistently worse than controls at all ages. On the third task (self-righting in a tilted chair until the vertical position is reached) brain-injured children did less well than controls until the age of 11. After this, differences washed out. The brain-injured children ($N = 72$) used in this study were cerebral palsied. Actuarial characteristics are reported elsewhere.

Thelander, H. E., Phelps, J. K., and Kisk, E. W.: Learning disabilities associated with lesser brain damage, *J. Pediat., 53*: 405–409, 1958. Any interference with the integrity of the central nervous system may give rise to deviations in intellectual development. The most easily recognized are speech and hearing problems, usually detected when a child enters school. More subtle defects are in the areas of expressive speech, understanding oral commands, writing, hearing, control of hyperactivity, and emotional control. Emotional and social maladjustment may result if defects are not recognized and managed. Five case histories are presented.

Tizard, J. P., Paine, R. S., and Crothers, B.: Disturbances of sensation in children with hemiplegia, *J.A.M.A., 155*:628–632, 1954. This is a report on 106 patients with hemiplegia. The possible presence of impaired sensation in the affected arm is significant when considering physical therapy and orthopedic surgery. Impairments included most frequently are total or partial ostereognosis or diminished two-point discrimination.

Tolman, N. G., and Johnson, A. P.: Need for achievement as related to brain injury in mentally retarded children, *Amer. J. Ment. Defic., 62*:692–697, 1958. "Organic" children appear less able to compete than familials. They are relatively more accepting of rejections by their parents. Intense frustration of a need over long duration impairs need for achievement rather than enhances it, a common finding following brief experimental frustration. Observed differences between groups appears to be more a function of parental management than etiology.

Toman, J. E. P.: Physiological triggering mechanisms in childhood epilepsy, *Amer. J. Orthopsychiat.*, *32*:507–514, 1962. What causes seizures? They cannot occur in a normal brain without the prerequisite of some prior pathological substratum of an organic type. Where such a pathological foundation exists, the relatively normal aggregations of nerve impulses, as well as variations in the cerebral internal environment within normal physiological limits, may act as habitual triggering mechanisms in seizures. The concept of the normally triggered focus of pathology implies a high degree of specialization of function in brain areas, including the anatomical substratum of conditioned reflexes. It is well recognized that prodromata and various types of minor seizures may have a high degree of localizing value for the diagnostician. There has, however, been little exploration of the diagnostic value of data on triggering mechanisms. Sufficient knowledge of such mechanisms in any particular patient may suggest psychotherapeutic maneuvers to help avoid the triggering circumstances. Drugs and psychotherapy help.

Torok, N., and Perlstein, M. A.: Vestibular findings in cerebral palsy, *Amer. Otol. Rhinol. Laryngol.*, *71*:51–67, 1962. Vestibular function was tested in 403 cerebral-palsied children and in 115 children with various other neurologic conditions. Possible spontaneous vestibular manifestations, such as spontaneous nystagmus, and vestibular stimulation by rotation and by 10 cc. water at 20° C. were observed. Hyposensitivity, partial or total, and hypersensitivity were the vestibular abnormalities noted most often. Hypersensitivity was most common in hemiplegic children. Hearing and vestibular abnormalities were much greater in athetoid than in spastic children. Hearing losses were more common than vestibular abnormalities in cases of Rh incompatibility. In cases of neonatal jaundice other than those associated with Rh incompatibility, vestibular abnormalities were twice as common as hearing losses. Abnormal vestibular function was present in 45 of the 73 deaf or severely hard-of-hearing children.

Weatherwax, J., and Benoit, E. P.: "Concrete and Abstract Thinking in Organic and Non-organic Mentally Retarded Children," in *Readings on the Exceptional Child*, by E. P. Trapp and P. Himelstein. Appleton-Century-Crofts, 1962. (Also *Amer. J. Ment. Defic.*, *62*:548–553, 1957.) The assumptions of Strauss that there is a difference between organic and nonorganic children in thinking, and that the organic fails a task because he thinks concretely rather than because he fails to verbalize his thinking processes, are questioned. 25 children with visible neurological impairment (CA 13, IQ 50) were matched with 25 controls. Each subject was shown 12 pictures (comprising four categories of three items each) separately and then asked to recall the pictures as a whole. An index of clustering, *i.e.*, succession of two words in the same category, was taken as the measure of associative grouping or level of abstract thinking. Results showed that both groups could think abstractly to the same degree. By subdividing both groups into two on the basis of training on a similar task, it was possible to demonstrate that the factor of verbal habit training, rather than organicity, is crucial.

Werner, H.: Abnormal and subnormal rigidity, *J. Abnorm. Soc. Psychol.*, *41*:15–24, 1946. Is rigidity a uniform trait, or are there different kinds of rigidity varying in quality with particular organismic conditions? Non-brain-injured, retarded children may be rigid because of lack of differentiation, whereas brain-injured children may be rigid because of disintegration, incoherence, etc. A series of experiments provides evidence for the different types of rigidity. These include (1) reproduction of tone rhythms, (2) apprehension of tachistoscopic pictures, (3) reproduction of briefly exposed dot patterns, and (4) reproduction of words. Brain-injured children show different patterns of rigidity. The repetitive and delayed forms of perseveration which they demonstrate are probably the result of involuntary isolation of certain elements of the task. These isolated elements may become self-contained and detached from the continuity of the series to such an extent that they may be repeated over and over again or jump suddenly into prominence in spite of the incongruity of such behavior.

Werner, H., and Bowers, M.: Auditory motor organization in two clinical types of mentally deficient children, *J. Gen. Psychol.*, *59*:85–99, 1941. Twenty-five endogenous retardates and 26 exogenous retardates were tested on their ability to reproduce 17 melodic patterns. The endogenous responded as normal children. Their errors may be seen as a retrogression to a simpler, more primitive organization. Errors of the exogenous type are generally uncommon in normal development, with incoherence rather than globality. These characteristics correspond to previous findings in the visuo-motor area. The findings may, therefore, be presumed to cut across sense modalities.

Werner, H., and Carrison, D.: Animistic thinking in brain-injured mentally retarded children, *J. Abnorm. Soc. Psychol.*, *39*:43–62, 1944. Eighteen pairs of retarded children, differing in regard to the presence or absence of brain damage, were matched on MA and IQ. In one experiment, when asked whether inanimate objects, natural events, plants, and animals were living or dead, the brain-injured group referred to a larger range of objects as living than the non-brain-injured group. In a second experiment, brain-injured children attributed capability of feeling, knowing, being mean, etc. to a larger number of objects than the controls, corroborating the results of the first study. Animistic thinking is due to an inability to separate living from nonliving objects. In normal development, egocentrism of the young child, who sees the world as being entirely like himself, is the course of animistic thinking. To the brain-injured child, who is influenced by external stimuli to an inordinate degree, the difference between the outside world and the self must be of less import.

Werner, H., and Strauss, A. A.: Causal factors in low test performance, *Amer. J. Ment. Defic.*, *45*:213–218, 1940. On the marble-board and similar tests, mentally deficient children of the exogenous type responded in an incoherent, discontinuous manner. A second type of marble-board test, in which the holes formed a definitely structured background, showed that interference of the background was actually a condition for incoherent organization. Marble-board and tachistoscopic tests (9 cards having black and white drawings of objects, *e.g.*, hat, cup, bottle, etc. embedded in clearly structured homogenous backgrounds consisting of jagged or wavy lines were shown for 1/5 second and each child was asked to tell what he saw) demonstrated an impairment of primitive perceptive functioning—the differentiation of figure from ground—in exogenous children.

Werner, H., and Strauss, A. A.: Pathology of figure ground relation in the child, *J. Abnorm. Soc. Psychol.*, *36*:58–67, 1941. Three groups of children were studied: normals ($N = 30$, CA 7–10), endogenous ($N = 25$; MA 11; IQ 60–90), and exogenous ($N = 25$; MA 8–12; IQ 55–95). They were first presented with cards with black and white drawings of common objects embedded in clearly structured backgrounds consisting of jagged lines, etc. The brain-injured children responded more frequently to the background material than to the foreground, in contrast to the other groups. Second, only the two retarded groups were presented with a geometric figure consisting of heavy circular dots embedded in a configuration of smaller dots. The figures were exposed tachistoscopically for half a second and the child was asked to pick out the one most like the test card from among 3 cards. One card contained only the background. The second contained the correct background and the wrong foreground. The third contained the correct foreground and the wrong background. 52 percent of the brain-injured group responded to the second card (background) whereas only 28 percent of the familials did. Third, the two groups were asked to construct patterns on a marble board similar to the one presented by the examiner. The board had background patterns designed to confuse the subject. 84 percent of the brain-injured showed interference from the background and only 15 percent of the familials did. Finally, when two retarded groups were presented with three geometric figures (a square, an oval, and a triangle) in a test of kinesthetic perception, differences occurred. The brain-injured group had difficulty with figures composed of spherical rubber tacks which were placed against a background of flat enamel tacks. These difficulties were less pronounced when the figures were presented in the form of a raised wood solid upon a smooth surface board.

Werner, H., and Thuma, B. D.: Critical flicker frequency in children with brain injury, *Amer. J. Psychol.*, *55*:394–400, 1942. Exogenous retarded children showed lower critical flicker frequency than endogenous retarded children. The difference was greater at the lower brightness levels than at the higher. The results can be explained by the impairment of the normal mechanism of integration and by lesions that interfere with the interaction of regions of the nervous system, leading to the isolation of neural events. This isolation may be due to perseveration or prolonged aftereffect of stimulation as a consequence of the inhibitory action of the cortex on the lower centers. The lower CFF in the exogenous group may be due to a perseveration of the aftereffects of successive flashes, which might be expected to yield fusion at a lower rate of stimulation.

Werner, H., and Thuma, B. D.: A deficiency in the perception of apparent motion in children with brain injury, *Amer. J. Psychol., 55*:58–67, 1942. In this series of four experiments comparing 20 endogenous and 20 exogenous children (CA 12, MA 9) on a series of tasks to determine the child's ability to perceive apparent motion, the following findings resulted: (1) When the time of exposure of two straight-line figures was varied by means of a tachistoscope, the brain-injured children did not see apparent motion of the figure; all but one of the non-brain-injured were able to perceive such motion. (2) When subjects were asked to judge a band of light moving through a sector of a circle, the brain-injured children needed a much slower speed of rotation before the motion itself became obvious, but they were able to perceive real motion. (3) When presented with two alternating figures by the use of a tachistoscope—the first was a stick man standing on one foot and the second was an arrow pointing diagonally upward—most of the endogenous children reported some sort of motion, such as dancing or jumping of the man or angular or linear displacement of the arrow. However, only 17 percent of the brain-injured reported this, indicating that the failure to see movement in the parallel line situation was not due to interference of strong independent movements of the two figures but to the rare occurrence of seeing movement with tachistoscopic exposure. (4) Two figures were presented alternately to the subjects, one a black disk on a white background and the other a black ring on a white background. The figures were placed so as to be concentric when presented simultaneously. Since it took less time for the disk to disappear for the brain-injured than the non-brain-injured group, it was concluded that the interaction of neural effects produced by the two patterns was reduced in the brain-injured child. The studies illustrate Goldstein's principle of the isolation of function following damage to the nervous system.

Werner, H., and Weir, A.: The figure-ground syndrome in the brain-injured child, *Int. Record of Med. Gener. Pract. Clinics, 169*:362–367, 1956. The authors review nine studies of normal and exogenous and endogenous children matched for MA which demonstrate that brain-injured children are much more susceptible to interference from background stimuli than the other groups. Figure-ground disturbances are demonstrated in perception, memory, and conceptual thought. Examples from the different studies are cited to support this. The "figure-ground syndrome does not imply impairment of a unitary function." It is concerned as a "psychobiologically fundamental performance that may be impaired because of a number of disturbing factors." These factors may even appear antagonistic to each other (*e.g.,* rigidity and lability) and yet be manifestations of the same syndrome.

Wood, N. E.: Comparison of right hemiplegics with left hemiplegics in visual perception, *J. Clin. Psychol., 4*:378–380, 1955. Fifty right and 36 left hemiplegics (CA 10–30) were equated for socioeconomic background, race, sex, seizures, and intelligence. They were further subdivided into two groups each of good and poor vision. There were no significant differences between groups on the Werner-Strauss embedded-figure test, the Street perceptual closure test, and the ambiguous face profile test, which was scored for perseveration.

Wood, N. E.: Comparison of right hemiplegics with left hemiplegics in motor skills and intelligence, *Percept. Motor Skills, 9*: 103–106, 1959. Twenty-five right and 25 left spastic cerebral-palsied hemiplegics (CA 10–16) were compared on the Wechsler-Bellevue Intelligence Scales and a battery of eight motor tasks. No differences were found between the groups.

Wortis, H. Z., and Margolies, J. A.: Parents of children with cerebral palsy, *Med. Social Work, 4*:110–120, 1955. Reality problems, which include not only the difficulties in the physical care of a severely handicapped child but also the financial, housing, personal, and familial problems, are the major source of personality problems and anxieties in parents of cerebral-palsied children. This is based on a study of parents of 37 children in the special class at Public School 135, New York City.

Zuk, G. H.: Autistic distortions in parents of retarded children, *J. Consult. Psychol.*, *23*:171–176, 1959. A comparison of Vineland Social Maturity Scores, which are based on the parents' observations of the child's behavior, with the intelligence test scores based on actual behavior showed that for two samples of nonhandicapped retarded children ($N = 95$ and 50; CA 1–8; MA 2–9) the Vineland score was higher than the intelligence test score ($p = .001$). However, this discrepancy did not exist for 22 retarded handicapped children, more than half of whom had a diagnosis of cerebral palsy. The tendency of parents of nonhandicapped children to overestimate their children's abilities may be seen by the fact that the discrepancy melted away when teachers were required to fill out the VSMS.

Zuk, G. H.: Clinical differentiation of patterns of distractibility in young retarded children, *J. Clin. Psychol.*, *18*:280–282, 1962. Distractibility was observed in 36 of 133 mental retardates (CA 2–8, MA 1–2). Sex ratio (31 males) was similar to Laufer and Denhoff's description of hyperkinetic behavior syndrome. As in brain-injured children, it was assumed to be due to overattention to moving as opposed to stationary stimuli. Two types may be distinguished: Type I (MA 12–18 mos.) precipitates movement in the environment, *e.g.*, push-pull activities for their own sake, and utilizes gross body parts. Type II (MA 18–24 mos.) shows more investigative motor activity involving refined body parts, *e.g.*, finger more than hand, hand more than shoulder. These are illustrated by case presentations rather than quantitative data. The distinction may be useful in examining the "untestable" child.

Zuk, G. H.: Overattention to moving stimuli as a factor in the distractibility of retarded and brain injured children, *Train. Sch. Bull.*, *59*:150–160, 1963. Distractible behavior in retarded and brain-injured children, often regarded as random or undirected, actually has goal direction and is purposeful. It serves to focus and sustain overattention to moving stimuli, a developmental characteristic common to younger children. Of 133 retarded children seen, 36 proved to be distractible. Two types of distractibility may be distinguished. The notion of overresponsiveness to moving stimuli is in contrast to the Strauss-Lehtinen view of distractibility as an overresponse to an intruding background. Hyperactive children, for example, grow less distractible while riding in a moving automobile or watching a television program. This would appear to contradict the Strauss-Lehtinen theory. According to Zuk's theory, the teacher should mobilize attention by exposing briefly moving stimuli, not by neutralizing the background.

4. ETIOLOGY—CLINICAL, EXPERIMENTAL, EPIDEMIOLOGIC

Adler, E.: Familial cerebral palsy, *Cereb. Palsy Rev.*, *22*:4–7, 1962. (Also in *J. Chronic Dis.*, *13*:207–214, 1961.) Prenatal causes are increasingly being invoked to account for cerebral palsy. Among 120 cases, there were 16 (8 families) with near relatives affected. In 5 of the families, consanguinity of parents was found. Some genetic factor seems to be present in some instances of cerebral palsy. Familial cases tend to have poorer prognosis than nonfamilial.

Apgar, V., Girdany, B. R., McIntosh, R., and Taylor, H. C.: Neonatal anoxia: I. A study of the relation of oxygenation at birth to intellectual development, *Pediatrics*, *15*:653–661, 1955. Capillary blood oxygen content, or saturation, was measured at various intervals in the first three hours after birth. Stanford-Binet test scores were available on 243 randomly selected subjects who were submitted to this procedure. By the second hour, most infants had stabilized at average adult levels of blood oxygen content. No significant correlations were obtained between the blood oxygen content measures and the Stanford-Binet scores. An incidental finding is the meager value of the Gesell developmental rating of adaptive behavior ($N = 65$) obtained at 2 years of age and the Stanford-Binet score obtained at 5 years of age.

Baumann, M. C., Ludwig, F. A., Alexander, R. H., Bergin, T. C., and Rauch, A. E.: *A Five-year Study of Brain Damaged Children,* Springfield Mental Health Center, 1962. This report is a follow-up of 40 children (CA 5–12) who had been previously diagnosed as brain damaged and evaluated on psychologic, physical, psychiatric, and neurologic examinations and on the EEG. Of this group, 19 were available for intensive re-evaluation. Symptom check lists were derived from the original evaluations of the social worker, the psychologist, and the psychiatrist and were matched against later behavior. (The accuracy of the clinic team appears established.) A behavioral symptom inventory designed for parents proved helpful. Although intelligence test results appeared reliable on retest, critical analysis of the Bender Gestalt and Pointwavering (a special test designed for this study) indicated a tendency to integrate conceptual abilities with age. Academic attainments remained a problem, although perceptual functioning improved. Short attention span and inconsistency interfere with schooling. The over-all hypothesis, confirmed in part by the data, is that acute symptomatology decreases with age.

Benaron, H. B. W., Tucker, B. E., Andrews, J. P., Boshes, B., Cohen, J., Fromm, E., and Yacorzynski, G. K.: Effect of anoxia during labor and immediately after birth on the subsequent development of the child, *Amer. J. Obstet. Gynec., 80*:1129–1142, 1960. From a group of 40,000 births in a predominantly Negro neighborhood in Chicago, 43 of the most profoundly anoxic were compared with two control groups, one drawn from siblings and the other from an *n* of 40 divided equally by sex and race. Examinations were carried out 3 to 19 years later. The incidence of retardation was greater in the anoxic group (20%) than in the controls (2%). EEG abnormalities (36%) and infantile habits (63%) persisted in this group. However, most of the children in the anoxic group did not show signs of general dysfunction. Anoxia appears to lower the functioning of a few people sharply rather than impair the functioning of the group as a whole.

Benton, A. H.: Mental development of prematurely born children, *Amer. J. Orthopsychiat., 10*:719–746, 1940. In this critical review of the literature, seventy studies are examined. After presenting the problem and its implications (*e.g.,* if mental retardation ensues, then premature birth should not be induced), the concept, and correlates of prematurity, the author suggests a number of conclusions: (1) Prematurely born children show developmental lag during the first two years. (2) Rate of development is not significantly affected by prematurity. (3) Most studies show that prematures are not inferior to normal children in intelligence. It is unclear, however, whether the evidence of frank mental defect is greater. (4) There is no solid evidence that birth weight is related to intelligence. (5) Although many studies report a higher incidence of "nervous traits" in prematures than in controls, there are no definitive studies on this point.

Byers, R. K., and McLean, W. T.: Etiology and course of certain hemiplegias with aphasia in childhood, *Pediatrics, 29*:376–383, 1962. The histories of 12 children who suffered acquired hemiplegia with aphasia are reviewed. Although in 4 the onset was prolonged, it was usually not sufficiently characteristic to allow diagnosis and treatment prior to the development of the complete syndrome. The dominant hemisphere, as demonstrated by the lesion, did not correspond accurately with handedness. Arteriograms were successful in demonstrating vascular malformation or thrombosis in 6 of 7 children on whom they were attempted. Recovery was followed in 10 children over a period of years. All had regained speech spontaneously and 4 appeared intact, or virtually so. All others showed psychologic and neurologic residue. Psychologic stages during recovery are briefly indicated and a philosophy of conservative therapeutic intervention is suggested.

Campbell, W. A. B., Cheeseman, E. A., and Kilpatrick, A. W.: The effects of neonatal asphyxia on physical and mental development, *Arch. Dis. Child., 25*:351–359, 1950. An examination of all health records at the Royal Maternity Hospital, Belfast (1938), disclosed the presence of 89 "asphyxiated" infants. They were matched with 178 controls. Of this total of 267, 73 percent were ultimately examined. No significant differences were found between the groups on physical measurements (height, weight, and chest measurements), hemoglobin levels, and intelligence (based on Raven's Progressive Matrices). All examinations took place at 8 to 11 years of age. The literature, which generally shows that asphyxia at birth causes later retardation, is critically examined. Most previous studies selected clinical samples on the basis of a deviant behavioral characteristic and looked for asphyxia at birth, in contrast to the present study.

Courville, C. B.: *Contributions to the Study of Cerebral Anoxia.* San Lucas Press, 1950. This book presents the history of cerebral anoxia, its pathogenesis and structural characteristics, its importance in evaluating brain damage in children, and the significance of the circulatory component. Cerebral palsy, epilepsy, and mental retardation are considered. Asphyxia in folklore and legend is also presented.

Courville, C. B.: *Cerebral Palsy: A Brief Introduction to Its History, Etiology, and Pathology, With Some Notes on the Resultant Clinical Syndromes and Their Treatment.* San Lucas Press, 1954. This book, written for the general practitioner, contains essays on the causes, diagnoses, prognoses, and principles of various therapies.

Crothers, B., and Paine, R. S.: *The Natural History of Cerebral Palsy.* Howard University Press, 1959. This book is a report of a reappraisal of a large number (1821) of persons with cerebral palsy who had been known to the Children's Hospital, Boston, between 1930 and 1957. Reexamination of 561 cases who spent a full day at the hospital emphasizes the effect of the disability on growth and development. Growth and development, in turn, may change motor patterns. Failure to recognize this leads to overstandardization of therapy. Overemphasis on physical care may foster docility, not independence. Results of treatment could not be evaluated because of poor records. It does appear, however, that physical treatment improves function in the group with pyramidal damage (spastics) but not in the group with extrapyramidal damage. The pyramidal group showed signs of emotional disturbance, the extrapyramidal group did not. Parents and adolescents have been neglected. Children should be encouraged to experiment. On the basis of retrospective data, comments about the classification, etiology and pathology, seizures, intelligence, employability, education, treatment, and family attitudes are offered. Motion pictures of earlier performance helped in the retrospective analysis of a number of cases.

Deaver, G. G.: Etiological factors in cerebral palsy, *Bull. N.Y. Acad. Med., 28*:532–536, 1952. One out of every 200 births shows the clinical signs of cerebral palsy. The prenatal causes include heredity, anoxia, maternal infectious disease, maternal metabolic disease, and erythroblastosis fetalis. The natal causes include anoxia, blockage, analgesia, trauma, sudden changes in pressure, prematurity, vitamin K deficiency. Postnatal factors also are listed.

DeHaas, D. J., Quinn, K. V., and Pryles, C. V.: Enforced delay at delivery and its relationship to brain damage and mental deficiency, *Amer. J. Ment. Defic., 65*:610–615, 1961. Results of a questionnaire survey of 83 institutions caring for mental retardates are presented. The questionnaire dealt with the effect of artificial delay during the second stage of labor. Of 64 (73%) replying institutions, 50 could offer no data, 5 positively stated that they had no children in their institutions with a history of holding back at delivery, and 9 reported that of a total of 130 children, 78 were thought by the staff members to be retarded because of brain damage sustained during enforced delay at the time of delivery. Although limitations of a retrospective survey are acknowledged, "the data suggest a causal relationship may exist between artificial delay and brain damage with mental deficiency."

Denhoff, E., and Holden, R.: Significance of delayed development in the diagnosis of cerebral palsied, *J. Pediat., 38*:452–456, 1951. "(1) The developmental histories of 100 cerebral palsied children were analyzed. Of the developmental items investigated, important deviations from normal were found in a majority of cases as early as three months of age. Deviations continued to be large in a majority of the cases until three years of age. (2) A chart which portrays normal, late normal, and abnormal stages of achieving developmental maturity has been found helpful in the early diagnosis of cerebral palsy. (3) A possible correlation between age of onset in speaking two- or three-word sentences and intellectual function is suggested by the data."

Denhoff, E., and Holden, R. H.: Etiology of cerebral palsy: an experimental approach, *Amer. J. Obstet. Gynec., 70*:274–281, 1955. A study of possible causative factors in cerebral palsy was made with 15 children who had "suspicious" findings of brain damage at birth and neonatally as evidenced by obstetrical or neonatal difficulties, *e.g.*, prematurity, hypertonicity, oxygen deficiency, etc. They were matched with 17 healthy baby controls drawn from a random sample of 504 consecutive births in the same hospital. Matching factors were age, sex, and parents' socioeconomic status. Only 4 (27%) of the "suspicious" group had abnormalities in physical, psychological, and/or social development when studied 2½ years later. Three (18%) of the control group had similar findings. The only factor common to the deviant children in both groups was a history of previous abortions in the mother. Investigations of reproductive physiology would, therefore, be helpful in uncovering the etiology of cerebral palsy.

Denhoff, E., Holden, R. H., and Silver, M. L.: Prognostic studies in children with cerebral palsy, *J.A.M.A., 161*:781–784, 1956. A sample of 50 cerebral-palsied children (CA 3½, IQ 60) was studied. Psychological tests and pneumoencephalograms to predict a child's progress as judged by a pediatrician over a two-year period were administered. There was 81 percent agreement between test predictions and clinical progress and 72 percent agreement between pneumoencephalogram and clinical progress. Prognosis is "good" for children in the normal or unilateral cerebral atrophy pneumoencephalogram classification if intelligence is borderline normal or better, whereas outcome seems "poor" for children in the bilateral cerebral atrophy and unilateral cortical atrophy classifications. Prognosis is guarded and depends on intellectual potential in the remaining categories. It would seem that those who will make adequate adjustments in later life are children with spastic hemiplegia, with unilateral brain damage and dull normal intelligence or better, or with a mild handicap of any category and a relatively good pneumoencephalogram and good IQ. The child with spastic quadriplegia with bilateral brain damage and mental deficiency appears destined for home or custodial care.

Drillen, L. M.: A longitudinal study of the growth and development of prematurely and maturely born children: Part VII. Mental development, 2–5 years, *Arch. Dis. Child., 36*:233–240, 1961. In a study of more than 500 singletons and twins of different birth weight in Edinburgh, intelligence test scores at 3, 4, and 5 years were correlated with birth weight. Twins showed consistently lower scores than singletons of like birth weight at 4 and 5 years. There was a striking excess in the smaller premature group (*i.e.*, 4½ lb. or less) of children who are ineducable in normal school or will need special educational treatment within normal school. Mental development was related to the apparent intelligence of the mother and to the type of home. Differences between social classes appeared to be greater between 4 and 5 years than at 2 years. In average and poor working-class homes there was little difference in mental ability between those prematures who were over 4½ lb. at birth and mature controls. In superior working-class and middle-class homes, the child between 4½ and 5½ lb. at birth was still at a disadvantage. Predictive value of early developmental testing is discussed. Response to preschool developmental tests is affected by birth weight, environment, and opportunity. Early developmental testing is of most value in the detection of children who later prove to be dull, retarded, or defective. (Previous studies in this series: *Arch. Dis. Child., 33*:417, 1958; *34*:37, 1959.)

Ernhart, C. A., Graham, F. K., and Thurston, D. L.: The relationship of perinatal anoxia to intelligence and to neurological deviations in the preschool child, *Amer. Psychol., 13*:324, 1958. In a comparison of a group of 76 children who had histories of anoxia at birth (48 mild and 28 moderate-severe) with a control group ($N = 88$) equated for sex, race, and socioeconomic status, the anoxic children did less well on the Stanford-Binet (IQ 95) than the controls (IQ 102). Anoxic children also did less well on a specially devised vocabulary test and neurological examination (anoxic = 17% normal, controls = 58% normal). These findings indicate an association between anoxia and deficit but not necessarily a causal relationship.

Freedman, A. M., Braine, M., Heimer, C. B., Kowlessar, M., O'Connor, W. J., Wortis, H., and Goodman, B.: The influence of hyperbilirubinemia on the early development of the premature, *Psychiatric Research Reports,* No. 13, pp. 108–123, 1960. Following a review of the literature, it is hypothesized that increasing amounts of bilirubin in the bloodstream of prematures are associated with increasing manifestations of cerebral injury. Correlating bilirubin levels at birth with developmental data obtained at one year, it was found that such a relationship exists for both the Gesell Gross Motor Schedules and the Cattell Infant Scales for males but not for females. Females ($N = 94$, low social class Negroes) exceeded males ($N = 68$, low social class Negroes) on both the Gesell and the Cattell, suggesting the greater vulnerability of males to the effects of prematurity. The findings confirm those previously reported on data obtained at four months of age (A. M. Freedman *et al.:* "The Effect of Neonatal Hyperbilirubinemia on the Premature Infant," in *IX International Congress of Pediatrics,* Montreal, 1959).

Goldstein, R.: Hearing and speech in follow-up of left hemispherectomy, *J. Speech Hearing Dis., 26*:126–128, 1961. Speech and hearing in a 42-year-old man who had undergone hemispherectomy for right infantile hemiplegia were normal 5 years later.

Goldstein, R., Goodman, A. C., and King, R. B.: Hearing and speech in infantile hemiplegia before and after left hemispherectomy, *Neurology, 6*:869–875, 1956. Four adults who had right infantile cerebral palsy received auditory tests before and after left cerebral hemispherectomy. Although auditory thresholds were normal for both ears preoperatively, there was difficulty in identifying 45 percent of the words presented to the right ear at intensities above normal thresholds. This pattern remained the same following removal of the abnormal hemisphere. Speech was not affected by the surgery. The findings are interpreted to confirm a previous hypothesis that abnormal activity in the pathologic hemisphere may disrupt the intact one.

Graham, F. K.: A longitudinal study of the effects of perinatal anoxia, *Amer. Psychol., 13*:334, 1958. This is a preliminary report of a re-examination of 3-year-olds ($N =$ approximately 400) who were seen at birth. Half had been exposed to cerebral anoxia or other trauma at birth. Half served as controls. Re-examination showed controls to be superior on personality traits. Only a handful of children showed gross motor defects. A general inferiority of the anoxic children as a whole rather than a few extreme cases seems to account for small group differences.

Graham, F. K., Matarazzo, R., and Caldwell, B.: Behavioral differences between normal and traumatized newborns, *Psychol. Monogr., 70*: Nos. 20 and 21, 1956. In the first monograph, five test procedures capable of differentiating normal newborns from those who have been traumatized and possibly brain injured are described. The tests consist of a pain threshold test, a maturation test, a vision scale, an irritability rating, and a muscle tension rating. The second monograph describes how they were administered to 265 infants who had a normal birth and 81 who had a traumatic birth at the St. Louis Maternity Hospital during a two-year period. Reliability data appear to be satisfactory. Norms for each test, with separate norms for each of the first five days of life and for social factors, are included. Normal and traumatized groups differed on all tests. When a cut-off point at the poorer end of the normal distribution was selected, all tests identified some traumatized infants as abnormal, whereas false positives ranged only from 1 to 3 percent. The percentage identified as abnormal increased with the seriousness of the traumas rated by pediatric judges. The problem of making predictions from test results is discussed.

Greenbaum, J. V., and Lurie, L. A.: Encephalitis as a causative factor in behavior disorders of children, *J.A.M.A., 136*:923–930, 1948. This is the third report (*Ohio Med. J., 41*:1018, 1945; *Amer. J. Psychiat., 104*:71, 1947) of 78 children who presented behavior disturbances following an attack of encephalitis. The group represents 3 percent of the children admitted to a child guidance home over a 28-year period. It is a follow-up four to ten years later. In 60 of the cases, onset was below age 10. The younger the patient at the time of illness, the greater the psychiatric disability. Behavioral changes were noted soon after the attack. Behavior patterns could be grouped into (1) simple disturbances, (2) psychopathic behavior, and (3) psychotic behavior. At intake, intelligence was normal or better in 57 cases. On retest, it remained the same in 9 cases, improved in 1 case, and deteriorated in 37 cases. Neurological abnormalities were noted in 56 cases. 61 children had a uniform personality pattern marked by impulsiveness, distractibility, etc. Only 12 had made a fair social adjustment. Prognosis is poor. The classic psychobiologic approach, which relates structure to function, is urged.

Greenspan, L., and Deaver, G. G.: Clinical approaches to the etiology of cerebral palsy, *Arch. Phys. Med. Rehab.*, *34*:478–485, 1953. A complete history including obstetrical data was obtained from 100 mothers of children attending a preschool cerebral palsy clinic in New York City. Each attending obstetrician and hospital was required to fill out retrospective forms pertaining to natal events. The responses from the 94 who complied led to the following conclusions: Age of mother at child's birth, the fact of the child's being the first born, and his birth weight do not play any role. Prematurity, multiple pregnancies associated with prematurity, prenatal anoxia (15%), and Rh (7%) seem to be potent factors. For the most part, it is difficult to point to a single etiologic factor as the "cause" in most cases.

Harper, P. A., Fischer, L. K., and Rider, R. V.: Neurological and intellectual status of prematures at three to five years of age, *J. Pediat.*, *55*:679–690, 1959. 460 prematurely born children were examined at ages 3 to 5 years and were compared with 440 full-term controls. Findings were related to similar data gathered at 40 weeks of age. In both examinations, the premature group were less intelligent and gave more signs of neurological disturbance. The prematures were subdivided by birth weight; those who weighed more than 2000 grams were impaired. A comparison of the data with those gathered at 40 weeks of age showed that a child's prognosis for improving or maintaining an average or better rating increased as birth weight increased. Although the premature group performed less well than the full-term group, the great majority of prematures fell within the normal range of intelligence. (This paper is part of a series of studies carried out in Baltimore by H. Knobloch *et al.*, *J.A.M.A.*, *161*:581–587, 1956.)

Hawke, W. A.: Current etiological concepts of cerebral palsy, *Cereb. Palsy Rev.*, *22*:7–9, 1961. In a survey of 377 records of cerebral palsied studied in Toronto, Canada, 10 percent showed a postnatal origin. The syndromes of postconvulsive pareses and kernicterus, as well as their frequency, etiology, and treatment, are described.

Johnson, E. M.: A study of psychological findings of one hundred children recovering from purulent meningitis, *J. Clin. Psychol.*, *16*:55–58, 1960. Of a total of 110 patients ranging in age from one month to 12 years who developed purulent meningitis, 10 died within the first week of hospital admission. For the remaining 100 children who survived, the pre-illness mental status was determined and compared with post-recovery status. 4 were not testable after illness because of severe mental and physical retardation. The Vineland Social Maturity Scale was used as the pre-illness measure, and the Cattell Infant Scales and the Stanford-Binet were used at one- and three-month intervals after illness. For the group as a whole, no significant loss in mental status was noted at three months, although impairment was noted at one month (data not cited). However, young children (under 2 years) showed the most significant differences and complications. Study of a limited number of cases suggests that subdural effusion probably has a detrimental effect upon mental status, especially in the very young. Causal organism, number of cells in cerebrospinal fluid, chemotherapy after hospitalization, duration of illness prior to hospitalization, sex, and race are noncontributory factors.

Kawi, A. A., and Pasamanick, B.: Prenatal and paranatal factors in the development of childhood reading disorders, *Monogr. Soc. Res. Child Develop.*, *24*:14, Serial No. 73, 1959. Following an extensive survey of the literature on theories of the origins of fetal abnormalities and theories of the etiology of reading disability, it was hypothesized that there exists an association between maternal and fetal factors and the development of reading disabilities. The hypothesis was confirmed by a study comparing the prenatal and paranatal records of 372 white male children with reading disorders, born in Baltimore to lower-class families between 1935 and 1945, with the records of a similar number of matched controls. The reading disability cases had a significantly larger number of premature cases with more toxemias and bleeding during pregnancy than did the controls. The findings support the more general hypothesis of a "continuum of reproductive casualty with lethal component consisting of abortions, stillbirths, and neonatal deaths and a sublethal component consisting of cerebral palsy, epilepsy, mental deficiency, behavior disorders, and reading disability." An excellent bibliography is included.

Kephart, N. C., and Strauss, A. A.: A clinical factor influencing variations in IQ, *Amer. J. Orthopsychiat.*, *10*:343–350, 1940. Fifty-one endogenous retardates (CA 11, IQ 67) were found to drop in IQ when they were in the community but to rise after institutionalization. Fifty matched exogenous retardates were found to drop in IQ in the community and to continue this trend after institutionalization. These data, based on a retrospective study of repeated tests, suggest that in some cases where there is a trend toward a falling IQ a modification of this trend may indicate a definitely favorable result. A theory for the differential effects of different etiologies on intellectual growth is offered along the lines that the endogenous group is retarded because of lack of stimulation. Increasing stimulation will, therefore, raise the IQ. This is not the case for the exogenous group.

Kidron, D. P.: The natural history of cerebral palsy: history and neurological analysis of cerebral palsy patients in Israel, *Cereb. Palsy Rev.*, *22*:13–15, 1962. This survey of the first 100 patients 14 years of age and over details family and obstetrical histories. Various etiological factors are discussed. Spasticity is the most common type of abnormality. Common disturbances noted in cerebral palsy, including mental deficiency, emotional problems, and dysarthria, occur in more than half of the group. Normal school achievement was obtained by only 15 of the patients. Most presented vocational problems at the time.

Knobloch, H., and Pasamanick, B.: Seasonal variations in the births of the mentally deficient, *Amer. J. Public Health*, *48*:1201–1208, 1958. A study of admissions to the Columbus (Ohio) State School of mentally defective children, born over a 35-year period, revealed that significantly more had been born in the winter months (Jan., Feb., and March). Decreased food intake in pregnant women during the hot summer months could result in damage to the baby. Hotter summer months were associated with a significant increase in the number of mental defectives born in the winter months in comparison with cooler summer months preceding winter birth. Possibilities of dietary control in prevention of disability are considered. Findings do not invalidate the hypothesis of infection as a cause of prenatal damage to babies.

Knobloch, H., and Pasamanick, B.: The syndrome of minimal cerebral damage in infancy, *J.A.M.A.*, *70*:1384–1387, 1959. Examination by means of the neuropsychiatric developmental schedule of Gesell and Amatruda of 500 premature and 492 full-term control infants (in Baltimore) at 40 weeks of age indicates that the amount of neurological damage increases as the birth weight of the child decreases. Reports of behavior from the first month to the time of the examination showed a correlation between the degree of abnormality diagnosed at the examination and certain historical material obtained from the mother. Analysis of 46 individual neurological records demonstrated a correlation between the amount of abnormality noted and the clinical diagnosis of neurological status and delineated those patterns most useful in discriminating between normal and damaged infants. Particular emphasis is placed on those symptoms that comprise the syndrome of minimal cerebral damage, which was found in 100 infants. Findings emphasize the importance of the physician's taking a good developmental history and illustrate the theory that there is a continuum of cerebral damage ranging from severe abnormalities to minimal damage.

Knobloch, H., and Pasamanick, B.: The developmental behavioral approach to the neurologic examination in infancy, *Child Develop., 33*:181–198, 1960. In this evaluation of deviation from normal neuropsychologic functioning in infancy, several points are stressed: (1) Damage to the brain is usually diffuse and leads to a variety of disabilities. (2) There is a continuum of damage which ranges from minimal to severe, and there is a quantitative difference in the abnormal patterns over this range. (3) There is a close relation between neurologic integrity and maturational level. The diagnosis that is made on the basis of observed abnormal behavior is dependent on the age and maturity of the infant. Development is orderly, so that early deviation can predict future deviation. Data on the reliability and validity (*i.e.,* predictive value) of the Gesell Developmental and Neurologic Examination are presented to indicate that deviant patterns are significant indicators of cerebral involvement. Using a rating scale for degree of deviation, it was found that more of the children found to be abnormal at the 10-month examination showed abnormal behavior during their first month, presented more behavior problems at the time of testing, had more anxious mothers, and had histories of more illnesses than normal children examined at 10 months of age. The abnormalities predict intellectual function, toilet control, and integrative behavior at 3 years of age.

Knobloch, H., Pasamanick, B., Harper, P., and Rider, R.: The effect of prematurity on health and growth, *Amer. J. Public Health, 49*:1164–1173, 1959. Incidence of illness, physical defects, and subsequent growth patterns in relation to weight at birth were studied in a group of 500 premature and 692 full-term babies comparable in respect to various socioeconomic variables. At 40 weeks of age, premature infants are, in general, lighter and shorter than mature infants and have more physical defects and/or higher incidence of illness. Neurologic status, physical growth, physical defect, and illness seem to be interrelated. Thus, factors responsible for prematurity and cerebral damage have a generalized deleterious effect. Socioeconomic factors that have a role in the production of prematurity, the complications of pregnancy, and the development of neuropsychiatric disability apparently operate in relation to physical disabilities as well.

Laufer, M. W.: Cerebral dysfunction and behavior disorders in adolescents, *Amer. J. Orthopsychiat., 32*:501–507, 1962. Abnormal functioning of the central nervous system, associated with a variety of causes, functional and structural, and present before birth or in the first five years of life, may result in behavioral and perceptual distortions and specific learning disabilities. By adolescence these distortions have often become further encrusted with all sorts of emotional difficulties. They appear as a composite of the underlying, organically determined behavior pattern and the special defensive and adaptational mechanisms of the particular adolescent to the people and situations that surround him. Proper diagnosis and treatment call for a manifold approach, including drugs, special educational help, and psychotherapy.

Lilienfeld, A. M., and Pasamanick, B.: The association of maternal and fetal factors with the development of mental deficiency, *Amer. J. Ment. Defic., 60*:557–569, 1960. Birth certificates and hospital records of mentally defective children born in Baltimore between 1935 and 1952 showed significantly more abnormalities during pregnancy, delivery, and in the neonatal period than similar records showed for a group of matched controls. Incidence of mental deficiency was related also to increasing birth order and maternal age at birth. The findings are similar to those observed in stillbirths, neonatal deaths, cerebral palsy, epilepsy, and certain behavior disorders in children. It is hypothesized that there is a continuum of reproductive casualty composed of a sublethal component causing cerebral palsy, epilepsy, mental deficiency, etc., and a lethal component causing stillbirth and neonatal death. Specific conditions represent varying degrees of brain damage. Implications for prevention and management are discussed.

Lurie, L. A., and Levy, S.: Personality and behavior disorders of children following pertussis, *J.A.M.A., 120*:890–894, 1942. This report is based on a study of 58 children who suffered whooping cough before 2 years of age. They represent 6.8 percent of an unselected group of 500 problem children. 34 showed definite behavioral, intellectual, and personality changes in later life, apparently as a result of neurologic sequelae. These types of behavior problems did not differ from the general problems presented by the larger sample.

Meyer, E., and Crothers, B.: Psychological and physical evaluation of patients with cerebral palsy studied for periods of ten years or more: 1. Psychological evaluation, by Edith Meyer; 2. Physical evaluation with motion pictures, by Bronson Crothers, *Amer. J. Phys. Med.*, *32*:153–158, 1953. The validity of forecasts based on psychological evaluations of 80 patients carried out at Boston's Children's Hospital have proved to be reasonably accurate, although complete data are not cited. A few instances of inaccurate prediction occurred. They had been (1) overpessimistic in early evaluation of extrapyramidal disorders, (2) overoptimistic in estimating recovery in cases of acute infections.

Findings among a large group of patients with acquired hemiplegia and among a smaller mixed group are discussed. Family attitudes, social life of the cerebral palsied, and the attitude of patients toward their handicaps were explored. Dr. Crothers reports general impressions of methods of physical evaluation in some 200 cases. Physiological changes in the patient may, in general, be responsible for failure of a prediction to hold up. Sensory evaluations have not received sufficient consideration.

Norris, A. S.: Prenatal factors in intellectual and emotional development, *J.A.M.A.*, *172*:413–417, 1960. This is a review of recent literature dealing with the pertinence of prenatal environmental factors to mental development. The well-known epidemiological investigations of Pasamanick and his co-workers are quoted, together with the work of Ingalls which is especially concerned with mongolism. The study of Stott in England—little known in this country—on the importance of maternal emotional stress during pregnancy in the causation of mental defect is also reviewed. No attempt is made to evaluate critically the data collected from various sources.

Paine, R. S.: On the treatment of cerebral palsy: the outcome of 177 patients, 74 totally untreated, *Pediatrics*, *24*:606–616, 1962. A comparison was made of 103 cerebral-palsied patients who had undergone physical therapy with or without bracing and orthopedic surgery with 74 untreated patients. The following results were obtained: (1) In patients with spastic hemiparesis, mild cases developed good gaits with or without treatment; treatment resulted in better gait and fewer contractures in moderate and severe cases. (2) Treating the hemiparetic arm did not induce stuttering or fits. (3) Patients with spastic tetraparesis did less well but were helped by physical therapy and functional training. (4) Gait and hand function of extrapyramidal types of cerebral palsy were not influenced by treatment. The types of therapy used were those fashionable between 1950 and 1960. Many specific findings are presented in this retrospective study of case material.

Pasamanick, B., and Knobloch, H.: Brain damage and reproductive casuality, *Amer. J. Orthopsychiat.*, *30*:299–305, 1960. In this survey of 22 papers in a series of studies extending over 15 years, it is suggested that there is a continuum of reproductive insult, partially socioeconomic in cause, resulting in a continuum of reproductive casuality extending from death through varying degrees of neuropsychiatric disability. Thus far, more than 4000 children, mostly in the Baltimore area, have been studied both retrospectively—*i.e.*, through examination of birth records of children with disturbances and their controls, and prospectively—*i.e.*, through repeated examination on Gesell-type scales of children followed from birth on. Preventive programs during the prenatal period would reduce the incidence of brain damage.

Russel, E. M.: Cerebral palsied twins, *Arch. Dis. Child.*, *36*:328–336, 1961. Forty-four pairs of twins in which one member of each pair suffered from cerebral palsy were matched with 44 control twin pairs without cerebral palsy in Edinburgh. The incidence of twins among cerebral palsy cases is 9 percent. In less than half, the twins of cerebral-palsied patients are surviving and normal. The cerebral-palsied twins differed from control twins in sex distribution (*i.e.*, like-sexed pairs were greater in cerebral palsy group), birth order, weight maturity, pregnancy and parturition, and neonatal course. The incidence of mental impairment, visual, auditory, and speech defects, was higher among the cerebral-palsied twins than among the controls. The most important factor in cerebral-palsied twins appears to be low birth weight due either to multiple pregnancy alone or to a combination of multiple pregnancy and preexisting fetal abnormality.

Schachter, M.: Observations on the prognosis of children born following trauma at birth, *Amer. J. Ment. Defic., 54*:456–463, 1950. 353 children who had suffered trauma at birth were compared with 100 normal controls. Developmental data on teething, walking, speech, and toilet training are presented. Alcoholism occurred in nearly one-third of the parents and seemed to be correlated with later, more severe neuropsychiatric disorders. Retardation was present in 47 percent of the cases and neurologic manifestations in 42 percent. Statistics on incidence of seizures, mongolism, encephalopathy, Little's disease, hydrocephalus, speech and visual problems are presented. The study showed that asphyxia does cause some retardation in comparison with a control group. Interpretation of the developmental data must be tempered by the fact that 93 percent of the traumatized group came from "poor homes" (control data not cited).

Thelander, H. E.: Observations on the development of brain damaged children, *Cereb. Palsy Rev., 20*:3;8–9, 1959. This is a report of a 6-year follow-up study of children seen between 1952 and 1958 at the Cerebral Palsy Unit of Children's Hospital, San Francisco. Its purpose was to determine the present status and future prognosis of 107 children from the original group of 122. Basic organization of the preschool program for such children is outlined. Much emphasis is placed on work with families of the children. Implications of the study for further research in certain areas are discussed.

Thurston, D. L., Middelkamp, J. N., and Mason, E.: The late effects of lead poisoning, *J. Pediat., 47*:413–423, 1955. Eleven cases of lead intoxication were followed for a period of five to ten years. Physical sequelae consisted of blindness and cerebral dysrhythmia. Sodium citrate was the specific therapy in all cases. There was no evidence of mental arrest or deterioration in contrast to previous reports. However, visual-motor problems persisted. These may have placed a child at a disadvantage in primary-grade instruction. As the child matured, there was a gradual loss of hyperactive behavior. There was no correlation between severity of illness and residual effect. Pediatric counseling was helpful.

Wagenheim, L.: The effect of childhood diseases on IQ variability, *J. Consult. Psychol., 18*:354, 1954. To substantiate previous findings that early contraction of measles, chicken pox, mumps, or German measles was related to later school achievement, the records of 493 boys were studied. Boys who contracted diseases at very early ages (under 3) were significantly more variable in IQ than those who contracted diseases at a later age. Whether this was caused by encephalomyelitis following childhood diseases or to trauma to the nervous system interfering with the developing ego is hard to say. There appears to be a hierarchy of ages at which diseases are most deleterious. The hierarchy seems to coincide with the emergence of language ideation.

Wortis, H.: The patient with childhood spastic hemiplegia, *Amer. J. Phys. Med., 36*:90–94, 1957. Twelve cases of childhood hemiplegia who were followed at a cerebral palsy clinic for more than five years are presented. In each case the presenting problem at the last visit is described. These problems had been in evidence from the patients' early visits to the clinic and were still unresolved. The main need is for vocational, social, and psychological help.

Wortis, H., and Cooper, W.: The life experiences of persons with cerebral palsy, *Amer. J. Phys. Med., 36*:328–345, 1957. Life histories of 63 cerebral-palsied persons over 15 years of age who lived in the New York City area were studied. The group was representative of a large clinic population. Major problems were social in nature, *e.g.*, average family income was $46 a week. Two-thirds of the families were disorganized. Medical treatment had been inconsistent, in part because of family disorganization. Inadequate community resources and overly medically oriented social service programs also contributed. Problems increased as the child grew older. Older patients lacked social integration. Hypothesis: The cerebral-palsied person may be generally vulnerable to emotional problems because of his brain injury. The chronically handicapping state further disorganizes family patterns.

Yacorzynski, G. K., and Tucker, B. E.: What price intelligence? *Amer. Psychol.*, *15*:201–204, 1960. A comparison of children who suffered anoxia or precipitate labor at birth with a control group of siblings drawn from 40,000 birth records in Chicago showed that the group with birth trauma were either significantly inferior or significantly superior to the controls. The reasons for this are unknown.

Yue, S. J.: Multiple births in cerebral palsy, *Amer. J. Phys. Med.*, *34*:335–341, 1955. At the Pediatric Cerebral Palsy Clinic of the Columbia-Presbyterian Medical Center, 301 cases, 27 of which were members of sets of twins or triplets, were reviewed. Analysis of data was made in terms of diagnostic classification, duration of gestation, birth weight, birth history, speech evaluation, ophthalmologic complications, and psychometric evaluation. Almost all members of the twins or triplets were of the spastic type.

5. TREATMENT, EDUCATION, AND MANAGEMENT

Anderson, C. M., and Plymate, H. B.: Management of the brain-damaged adolescent, *Amer. J. Orthopsychiat.*, *32*:492–501, 1962. The characteristic symptom picture of minimal, essentially life-long brain damage is presented. A sketch of typical behaviors in childhood, adolescence, and adulthood is presented along with criteria for the presence of "association deficit pathology." These criteria are: (1) Does the history suggest possible etiology? (2) Is perseveration present? (3) Do figure-ground disturbances and a tendency to deal with partials rather than wholes appear? (4) Are there difficulties in unstructured situations? (5) Are there problems in spatial relationships? (6) Is there poor capacity for empathy? Many of these can be detected through clinical observation and psychological tests. The EEG is also useful. Education of parents and teachers, rather than psychotherapy, is the treatment of choice. A new title or diagnostic label is suggested along with the rationale behind it. The article is based on general description rather than specific data.

Barger, W. C.: An experimental approach to aphasic and non-reading children, *Amer. J. Orthopsychiat.*, *23*:158–170, 1953. In this experiment, the mirror technique to improve reading ability and speech of aphasic and nonreading children was helpful, not only in regard to learning but also in regard to emotional status. High incidence of mixed cerebral dominance among children with verbal or reading aphasias seemed significant. Presence of mixed laterality and verticality was less important than the fact that, through intermediations of the mirror, the nonreader made an adjustment to reversals and inversions, often in as few as two lessons. Handedness should be encouraged to correspond to the dominant eye in the child of confused dominance. Psychogenic difficulties are beyond the scope of this paper.

Barger, W. C.: Late reading in children: a review of its origins with a discussion of a correcting device for the aphasic type, *Cereb. Palsy Bull.*, *7*:20–26, 1959. In hard-core reading problems, a physiological element manifested in a tendency to twist symbols (*e.g.*, "b" and "d") was noted in 59 percent of 1000 cases. Techniques for evaluating the deficits that determine laterality are stressed. Tutoring with the assistance of a "Mirroreading Board" is described. This technique has succeeded where others have failed. Special modifications, including an elaborately equipped room, have been found necessary for cerebral-palsied children. About 400 to 500 children have been helped in this way.

Bender, L.: The psychological treatment of the brain damaged child, *Quart. J. Child Behav.*, *3*:323–333, 1951. The largest portion of this article deals with principles and theories in understanding the brain-injured child. Two chief recommendations are (1) to evaluate the total problem and separate the effects of the brain damage from secondary disturbances, and (2) to understand the psychological needs of the child as exemplified in Schilder's work on motility problems. Clinical examples of motility problems are cited, with emphasis on the accompanying anxiety. Therapy should include a warm, mothering relationship with an extended period of dependency. Parent substitutes, sibling equivalents, and organized recreation programs are suggested. Families should be involved in the treatment as early as possible. The drives toward normality should be utilized.

Bryce, T. E.: Suggestions for teaching cooking to the cerebral palsied, *Cereb. Palsy Rev., 23*:15–18, 1962. Safe clothing, appropriate tools and working surfaces, and a plan of work are needed to overcome fear, messiness, slowness, and lack of organization. General techniques of measuring, scraping a bowl, and carrying are offered along with specific cooking procedures.

Clement, M.: Morse Code method of communication for the severely handicapped cerebral palsied child, *Cereb. Palsy Rev., 22*:5, 1961. This describes a technique for communicating with a severely impaired athetoid girl, 13 years of age. The speech therapist printed the Morse Code on a card and mounted it on the tray of her wheelchair. The girl and her therapist worked out a series of movements—raising her eyes quickly, a smile, and a slight vocal sound—to indicate dot, dash, and the completion of a letter.

Clements, S. D., and Peters, J. E.: Minimal brain dysfunctions in the school age child, *Arch. Gen. Psychiat., 6*:185–197, 1960. A diagnostic plan for detecting minimal brain dysfunctions in children of school age is outlined. This involves careful history-taking, a specialized neurological examination, a rigorously defined psychological evaluation, and an EEG. Omission of any one of these procedures may lead to improper diagnosis and an invalid treatment plan. A treatment plan involving medication, periodic checkups, occasional parental counseling sessions in which an "organic" interpretation of the symptoms is given, and guidance to teachers and principals proves to be an effective approach in a child guidance clinic. The article is typical of more recent approaches to the brain-injured child.

Cruickshank, W. M., Bontzen, F. A., Ratzeburg, F. H., and Tannhauser, M. T.: *A Teaching Method for Brain Injured and Hyperactive Children.* Syracuse University Press, 1961. Forty hyperactive, aggressive children (CA 7–12) were divided into two experimental and two control groups. Five children in each were classified as brain injured and five as learning and behavior disorders without brain injury. Experimental classes had environmental changes to reduce extraneous stimuli and a highly structured program that utilized auditory, kinesthetic, and tactile senses in learning. Thorough testing was done before the study, 10 months later, and again at the end of the next 12 months. Combining the experimental groups for the first retest period, gains were noted in ability to withstand distractions, visual-perceptual performance, and emotional maturity, but not the other variables. At the time of the second retest 12 months later, when the experimental groups had received a year of normal instruction in addition to special instruction, all 40 children had progressed smoothly. It is thought that the study confirms the Strauss-Lehtinen ideology.

Cruickshank, W. M., and Dolphin, J. E.: The educational implications of psychological studies of cerebral palsied children, *Except. Child., 18*:1–8, 1951. Psychological characteristics of cerebral-palsied children are used to show how educational methods and equipment must be adapted for effective teaching. Suggestions are made for the building and equipping of classrooms to eliminate the distracting stimuli of background detail.

Deaver, G. G.: Cerebral palsy: methods of treating the neuromuscular disabilities, *Arch. Phys. Med. Rehab., 37*:363–367, 1956. Various theories of treatment according to Phelps, Fay, Kabat, Pohl, Swartz, and the Bobaths are briefly outlined. A philosophy of treatment in which all but two movements of an extremity are restricted by a prosthetic appliance is found helpful where others fail. The two movements are then used to perform functional activities, including ambulation, hand activities, and bed and wheelchair activities. Various practical techniques to aid in increasing self-care activities are presented, *e.g.*, use of axillary crutches, having a bed at a given height, etc. There is no standard method of predicting which child will benefit from this treatment. Although intelligence is important, it is not always an accurate guide.

Doman, R. J., Spitz, E. B., Zucman, E., Delcato, C. H., and Doman, G.: Children with severe brain injuries: neurological organization in terms of mobility, *J.A.M.A.*,

174:257–262, 1960. A new system for the treatment of the child with severe brain injury is proposed. It is aimed at the injured central nervous system rather than the resultant peripheral symptoms. A developmental mobility scale describing 13 levels of normal development as the criteria of progress during a two-year study of 76 children was devised. The program (1) permitted the child normal developmental opportunities in areas where the "responsible brain level" was undamaged, (2) imposed externally body patterns of activity which are normally the responsibility of the "damaged brain levels," (3) permitted the establishment of hemispheric dominance and early unilaterality, (4) brought respiratory improvement as measured by vital capacity, and (5) provided sensory stimulation to improve body awareness and position sense. The results of the study are said to indicate the superiority of this method over the traditional ones, with an average gain of 4.2 levels in mobility. Changes in language and affect are suggested. The data and the theory appear promising but await cross validation.

Dudley, J. G., and Lennon, E. J.: Reciprocal innervation in the treatment of respiratory dysfunction, *Cereb. Palsy Rev., 22*:3–4, 1962. A technique for improving respiratory rhythm and depth, by Margaret Rood, emphasizes Sherrington's principle of compensatory reflex stimulation. Utilizing brush strokings and applications of cold, the technique encourages temporary changes in spontaneous respiration as a basis for establishing and retaining more adequate rhythm and control of breathing. Favorable results in clinical work suggest a need for adequate experimental investigation.

Epps, H. O., McCammon, A. B., and Simmons, Q. D.: *Teaching Devices for Children with Impaired Learning; A Study of the Brain-Injured Child from Research Project 50 at the Columbus State School,* ed. R. M. Patterson. The Columbus State School, 1958. A manual for teachers dealing with children who are mentally deficient as a result of brain injury, this booklet represents five years of experience in applying and expanding ideas gained from Dr. Lise Gellner. The three authors, who are teachers, discuss in detail practical teaching methods and materials for educating brain-injured children. Methods are adapted to the particular type of handicap. Children are classified into four major groups according to performance and behavior patterns. Chapters discuss materials for developing sensory perception, discrimination and recognition, techniques for observing and developing motor coordination, class methods for encouraging social perception and emotional development, and the use of constructive tools and musical activity as teaching tools. Ways of teaching number concepts, reading readiness, and writing are also included. A discussion of classroom equipment and sources for obtaining class scheduling, a glossary of terms used in the book, and an index add to the practical value of the book.

Foster, R. E.: A survey of 300 case histories of cerebral palsied patients at Sonoma State Hospital as to their need for continuous care, *Cereb. Palsy Rev., 23*:5–7, 1960. Reviewing 300 out of 800 records of a state hospital in California, the author examined admissions in terms of age and reasons for hospitalization. He concludes that the functionally dependent cerebral-palsied individual may need some agency outside of the family to help with continuous care. There are many different reasons for institutionalization, some of which are determined by the age of the patient. Continuous care planning is important.

Fouracre, M. H., and Thiel, E. A.: Education of children with mental retardation accompanying cerebral palsy, *Amer. J. Ment. Defic., 57*:401–411, 1953. Four recent studies of cerebral-palsied children ($N = 1741$) independently concluded that 75 percent have IQ's below 90. Educational planning must be realistic. Suggestions for countering segregation and its harmful effects are proposed. A school placement system of four levels, which requires a minimum MA of 3 years, is proposed. The scheduling must allow for adequate therapies, which should be worked out with the cooperation of other disciplines. A preacademic program to nurture readiness for skills is helpful. A diagram of a proposed school progress chart for ages 4 to 16 is offered with suggestions as to promotional policies and content.

Gallagher, J. J.: *The Tutoring of Brain Injured Mentally Retarded Children.* Charles C. Thomas, 1960. Forty-two institutionalized, brain-injured, retarded children (CA 7–13, IQ 33–63) were given individual tutoring during a three-year experimental period. The 21 members of Group E were given two years of tutoring and one year of no tutoring. The 21 members of Group C (individually matched on Binet MA with Group E) received no tutoring for the first two years and tutoring for the final year. Test findings show that, for Group E, there were verbal and nonverbal intelligence gains (4 and 2.4 points respectively) following tutoring but a loss of half the gains when tutoring was removed. Both groups showed improvement in (1) language development (verbal labeling and simple association but not sequential language), (2) copying and memory for designs (rotations were reduced), (3) quantitative skills (writing and recognizing numbers and grouping principles), and (4) Vineland Social Maturity Scale (regression in independent behavior). Gains in one area of abilities are related to gains in other areas. Younger children (8 to 10) profited more than older children (10 to 12). Other variables—particular tutor, length of institutionalization, etiology, medication, number of days tutored—were not related to results. Detailed review of the literature on the tests used, case studies, and implications are included. Tutoring in an institutional setting can offer modest gains, which dissipate when the tutoring ceases. It is suggested that brain injury is secondary, from an educational standpoint, to intellectual behavior patterns.

Gallagher, J. J.: Changes in verbal and non-verbal ability of brain-injured mentally retarded children following removal of stimulation, *Amer. J. Ment. Defic.*, *66*:774–781, 1962. Forty-two brain-injured retardates (CA 7–13, IQ 33–63) were divided in half. Group A received two years of tutoring and two years of no tutoring. Group B received two years of no tutoring, one year of tutoring, and one year of no tutoring. On the Stanford-Binet for Group A, there was a gain of four points which vanished when tutoring was removed, whereas for Group B the tutoring had the effect of halting the downward trend in verbal intelligence commonly observed in institutionalized populations. On the Leiter Scale (a performance test) the gains made under tutoring conditions for Group A were maintained when tutoring was removed; Group B showed no changes following tutoring. It is unclear whether the gains shown resulted from actual improvement of mental functioning or from educational stimulation of a culturally deprived child. Early educational crash programs are urged.

Gottschalk, L. A.: Effects of intensive psychotherapy on epileptic children: report on three cases with idiopathic epilepsy, *Arch. Neurol. Psychiat.*, *70*:361–384, 1953. The seizure frequencies of 3 epileptic children decreased notably during and after psychotherapy. The seizures of 2 of the children had not recurred in two years. The form of the ictal manifestations was modified, as was the frequency of seizure. These findings constitute evidence that psychological as well as other factors can contribute to the form and frequency of seizures and associated clinical manifestations. Evidence is given which supports the hypothesis that interpersonal events, as well as intrapersonal conflicts, can activate epileptic behavior. The detailed account of the treatment is of interest.

Jolles, I.: A teaching sequence for the training of visual and motor perception, *Amer. J. Ment. Defic.*, *63*:252–255, 1958. An actual teaching sequence, developed in the Quincy, Illinois, school system, is presented. It features a progression of pegboard and block designs, with a graduated schedule of the amount of time to be allotted to each unit, based on levels of increasing complexity. Basic objectives for training visual and motor perception are discussed.

Kaliski, L.: Educational therapy for brain-injured retarded children, *Amer. J. Ment. Defic.*, *60*:71–77, 1955. Experience with non-motor-handicapped, brain-injured children (CA 5–14) reveals that perceptual, conceptual, and emotional problems interfere with education. Specific techniques and suggestions are offered for perceptual training, *e.g.*, space perception. Tactile and kinesthetic stimulation are useful, along with copying activities. The "total child must be considered."

Kamin, S. H., Llewellyn, C. J., and Sledge, W. L.: Group dynamics in the treatment of epilepsy, *J. Pediat.*, *53*:410–412, 1958. This article describes methods used in parent education in a pediatric seizure clinic which may be applied in group office practice. Purely medical questions are to be answered by physicians; all other questions are to be discussed by parents as a group.

The clinic team should include a social worker.

Katz, A.: Therapeutic aspects of parent associations for the handicapped, *Cereb. Palsy Rev. 22*:6–7, 1961. Interviews with 50 parents who were members of parents' associations and whose children were variously handicapped indicated that the greatest benefit derived from membership in a self-organized group is a therapeutic value. Many were anxious and hypersensitive, feeling rejected by professionals. Therapeutic value is achieved through (1) group participation and (2) actual, concrete help with daily life experiences.

Lennard, H. M.: Vocational implications for the cerebral palsied, *Cereb. Palsy Rev., 23*:13–17, 1962. A half-day work program for one month during the summer was designed and tried out at a United Cerebral Palsy Work Evaluation and Classification Unit. Seventeen (CA 15; IQ 80; 13 boys, 4 girls) individuals participated. Prior to the experience, counselors attempted to obtain the vocational aspiration level of the parent and the child. This was repeated at the end of the month. The work activity consisted in a work-sample approach with graphs to help the client judge his productivity. At the end of the project, "before and after" interviews were rated blindly by two judges. There was a change from an extreme rating (*i.e.*, very high or very low aspirations) to a middle rating in 71 percent of the parents and 86 percent of the clients. Parents from low social and economic groups tended to change less than parents from high groups. A case illustrates this: A boy who had initially wanted to be a lawyer spoke of becoming a law clerk at the end.

Levy, S.: Post-encephalitic behavior disorder —a forgotten entity: a report of 100 cases, *Amer. J. Psychiat., 115*:1062–1067, 1959. Postencephalitic behavior disorder as a clinical syndrome has been neglected recently in favor of psychogenic theories, particularly in regard to delinquency. The author claims that treatment by drugs for this condition in 100 cases has yielded "uniformly excellent results." Several cases are cited to illustrate his point.

McCartney, L. D.: A differential program for mentally retarded children of the exogenous group, *Train. Sch. Bull., 51*:27–33, 1954. This outlines a program for 6- to 10-year-olds, with IQ's from 50 to 70, whose retardation is from noninherited causes. Methods, techniques, and content found useful in the communicative arts, *e.g.*, speech, writing, and reading, are suggested.

McCartney, L. D.: A technique for developing social competency with a group of exogenous children classified as mentally retarded, *Amer. J. Ment. Defic., 59*:1–5, 1954. A group of parents of exogenous children (IQ 50–79) was invited to see a class demonstration each month. Taking Doll's Social Maturity Scale, the teacher explained the items and their rationale and how the school attempted to teach the items. Discussion involved the role the parent can play. The parents responded and "seemed happy."

McCartney, L. D.: Helping mentally deficient children of the exogenous type showing central nervous system impairment to make better social adjustment, *Amer. J. Ment. Defic., 61*:121–126, 1956. On the basis of experience with 12 children (CA 6–9; IQ 50–70; MA 3–6), the author proposes a method to enhance social adjustment, *e.g.*, playing card games to overcome apathy, structuring assignments with repetition to train for following through, alternating activities to adapt to change, and exchanging toys to prevent perseveration. Methods of applying the learned procedures in social situations are presented.

Messner, S. A.: Attempts to meet the problem of long-term care for patients with cerebral palsy, *Cereb. Palsy Rev., 22*:14–23, 1961. The diagnostic category of cerebral palsy gives little indication of problems related to long-term care. Families should be encouraged and assisted to keep their child home rather than to institutionalize him. Many supportive services can be organized in every community. Residential facilities for cerebral palsied are not indicated. The paper is discussed by A. Ghiora, M. O'Donnell, J. T. Mitchell, G. Tardieu, and O. Roberts. Roberts presents recent data on survivorship in cerebral palsy for different ages. These data contradict the assumption that survivorship rates are the same as for normal people. The mortality rate rises with severity of disability and age.

Pollack, C.: Sleep-learning as an aid in teaching reading to a brain-injured boy, *J. Ment. Defic. Res.*, *6*:101–107, 1962. After presenting a review of 10 studies demonstrating some positive effects of sleep-learning, including one partially successful attempt to teach speech to an aphasic child, a case study of a 17-year-old boy is cited. The boy, a nonreader (IQ 71) with "an organic brain syndrome of a developmental character," was tested on two sets of words to assure equal difficulty. Both tests were consciously learned; the experimental list was sleep-learned in addition. Errors and number of attempts were scored. A significant gain was found in the accuracy of synthesizing words as well as in the number of attempts with which words were attached. Auditory material is learned during sleep. A Pavlovian theory is offered.

Posniak, A. O., Saturia, P., Tobis, J. S., and Wallace, H. M.: Evaluation of rehabilitation of the severely handicapped cerebral palsied child, *Arch. Phys. Med.*, *39*:482–487, 1958. A 40-bed children's unit was opened in 1954 at Bird S. Coler Hospital, New York City, for severely disabled cerebral-palsied youngsters. A review of the functional accomplishments of 53 consecutive patients (average length of treatment: 11 months) shows that ambulation training as well as self-care skills can be taught successfully to even the most severely retarded. Type of motor disturbance, number of extremities involved, and intelligence quotients are intercorrelated. Progress by IQ groupings is recorded for feeding, dressing, ambulation, wheelchair activities, toileting, and speech. Criteria for speech improvement are most difficult to quantify.

Sarvis, M. A.: "Psychiatric Implications of Temporal Lobe Damage," in *Psychoanalytic Study of the Child*, eds. R. S. Eissler, A. Freud, H. Hartmann, and M. Kris, Vol. 15. International Universities Press, 1960. A six-year-old boy who had had temper tantrums since the age of nine months was referred for an EEG because of the intensity of his mother's anxiety and because his behavior did not fit the neurotic interactions of the family. Extensive focal and degenerative lesions in the right temporal lobe were discovered. The case history is presented in detail to demonstrate how psychogenic theories may be prematurely invoked and to illustrate the strategies for management. These included anticonvulsive medication, encouragement for the parents to trust their own judgment, reducing school pressure, and psychotherapy for the boy. The various psychodynamic themes that recurred in the course of therapy, including doll play, form the major part of the paper.

Simar, A.: About the re-education of cerebal palsy, *Cereb. Palsy Rev.*, *22*:7–8, 1961. On the basis of a 10-point scale developed for each of a number of activities, including ambulation, occupational therapy, speech therapy, intelligence, and education, the author plotted the progress of 27 children seen at cerebral palsy centers in Brussels, Belgium. A number of conclusions are suggested: (1) motor progress is not related to intelligence; (2) progress is greatest at the beginning of treatment; (3) the earlier treatment begins, the better the results; (4) improvement for all groups on the scales described ranges from 20 to 30 percent.

Sortini, A. J.: Rehabilitation of brain-damaged children, *Volta Rev.*, *63*:101–105, 1961. Speechreading and auditory training are useful for the child who is hearing-handicapped as well as brain-damaged. Clinicians should try to establish relationships with such a child. Lauretta Bender's designation of difficulties in patterned motor behavior, severe anxiety, and the need for human support are useful. Problems in teaching speechreading stem from short retention span in addition to the neuromuscular impairment. Suggestions on how to deal with practical problems in working with the cerebral-palsied child are offered. A wholistic approach, which emphasizes using what works, is offered.

Spankus, W. H., and Freeman, L. G.: Hypnosis in cerebral palsy, *Int. J. Clin. Exp. Hypnosis*, *10*:135–139, 1962. Hypnosis was used with 19 cerebral-palsied patients. Four definitely benefited but, in general, the results were not remarkable. In the 4 cases, improvement was noted in speech, ambulation, decreased pain, and increased extroversion. Librium, trancopal, and nembutal did not facilitate the trance. The interpersonal relationship during therapy probably helped as much as the hypnosis. In view of the occasional benefits with this treatment, further study is warranted.

Ward, M. M.: Group therapy for eleven preschool cerebral palsied children, *Except. Child., 21*:207, 1955. A detailed account of the purposes and content of weekly group sessions of one-and-a-half hours. The mothers conducted physiotherapy and speech therapy in a group, under professional supervision. They also received informal talks on health needs, general care, and community resources.

Watkins, H. A.: Visual perception training for the moderately retarded child, *Amer. J. Ment. Defic., 61*:455–460, 1957. Principles, theories, and methods described by Strauss are applicable to the field of mental deficiency. The qualifications for using the method, the design of the classroom, and methods and materials are illustrated in the program at the Polk State School. Beneficial effects have been achieved in children with IQ's as low as 15.

Whitehouse, F.: When does vocational preparation start? *Cereb. Palsy Rev., 12*:7–8;14, 1951. Preparation of a child for a vocation begins at an early age—almost from the time he is born. Parents of cerebral-palsied children should be made to realize this even more than other parents. A child must be taught to live and assume those responsibilities which will make him vocationally acceptable. Very often the "C.P. personality" includes traits that present problems in vocational guidance and placement.

Young, E. H.: The moto-kinesthetic method as applied to the cerebral palsied, *Cereb. Palsy Rev., 23*:7–8, 1962. The mother or teacher may set the pattern for the child to follow by using her own fingers to move the lip to the desired position and then uttering the sound. The child then imitates this. The mother must try to locate the source of the sound and move the mouth as a pattern. Muscular habit training of speech is a difficult and dynamic process.

6. REVIEWS, OVERVIEWS, AND THEORIES

Allen, R.: "Cerebral Palsy," in *Psychological Practices with the Physically Handicapped,* eds. J. F. Garrett and E. S. Levine. Columbia University Press, 1962. This is a review elucidating the incidence, etiological factors, definitions and classifications, medical aspects, and psychological aspects and implications. Half of the 32 pages of text are devoted to the special considerations in psychological appraisal. A brief section on rehabilitation and research needs concludes the text. It is a good introduction for beginning psychologists.

Asher, P., and Schonell, F. E.: A survey of 400 cases of cerebral palsy in childhood, *Arch. Dis. Child., 25*:360–369, 1950. Statistics on a survey of children in the Midlands (England) are given. The sample is thought to be representative. Incidence is one case per 1000. Data on types of cerebral palsy and etiology are presented. Approximately 50 percent achieved IQ's below 70, for both athetoids and spastics. Mean IQ correlated negatively with severity of disability. School attainments of the normally intelligent children showed considerable retardation. Special education is needed. A great deal of data are presented.

Baer, P. E.: Problems in the differential diagnosis of brain damage and childhood schizophrenia, *Amer. J. Orthopsychiat., 31*:728–738, 1961. Problems exist not only in distinguishing between the conditions; there is disagreement and uncertainty even within each condition. A review of the symptoms ascribed to childhood schizophrenia illustrates this. Likewise, the assertion that hyperkinesia is the only, or even major, response to brain damage is an oversimplification. A variety of descriptions in recent studies of brain-damaged children are reviewed. The organic components in childhood schizophrenia and the psychogenic factors in brain damage suggest that parallel sources of etiology in specific cases be acknowledged.

Beck, H. S.: Detecting psychological symptoms of brain injury, *Except. Child., 27*:59–63, 1961. This paper is a summary of the incidence of brain injury. A list of 43 symptoms commonly ascribed to the non-motor-handicapped child is presented with the stress on the "disturbance of integrative behavior." A discussion of some findings on general intelligence tests (*e.g.,* scatter) indicates their helpfulness. Tests designed to measure specific functions have not withstood replication when applied to children, although the Ellis Visual Designs and the marble board appear promising. The major problem seems to be in discriminating the brain-injured child from the emotionally disturbed one. One possible reason for this state of affairs is that the emotionally disturbed child may develop changes in body chemistry. In practice, the presence of brain injury may make no difference in how the child is managed.

Bender, L.: The brain and child behavior, *Arch. Gen. Psychiat.*, *4*:531–547, 1961. In summarizing the intellectual forces which contributed to her thinking, Bender pays tribute to Percival Bailey, in whose honor this paper was presented. She propounds the thesis that "disordered maturation, mentation and behavior, autistic and neurotic defenses and the ongoing development, behavior and mentality of brain-injured and schizophrenic children can be understood from what we know of the evolution and development of the brain as the organ of biological homeostasis, mentality, and behavior of the organism as a whole."

Benton, A. L.: Behavioral indices of brain injury in school children, *Child Develop.*, *33*:199–208, 1962. The use of behavioral indices as a criterion for brain damage is complicated by the fact that not all brain-damaged children show signs of behavior impairment. Furthermore, the indices vary. The most common is gross mental retardation (which in itself is not always a sign). The brain-damaged child of adequate intelligence may show motor, intellectual, and personality aberrations. Hyperactivity is the primary symptom. Clinical tests are merely refined methods of observation and do not bear directly on the question of brain damage. Clinical studies of nonretarded, non-motor-handicapped brain-injured children reveal the presence of (1) variability of behavior, (2) sensorimotor disturbances, and (3) a variety of other problems including school difficulties. Other approaches, *e.g.*, linguistic behavior, may prove useful in picking up subtle changes in higher level functions. A review of animal studies and the work of the Boston group on the postencephalitic child constitute the data for the article.

Block, W. E.: Some experimentally based implications for personality habilitation of children with cerebral palsy, *Cereb. Palsy Rev.*, *17*:4–7;12, 1956. Drawing on the findings of a previously reported study comparing 20 spastic with 18 athetoid children (CA 9–14), the author concludes that the emotional problems in cerebral palsy have been underestimated. Sources of frustration arise within the family setting, but they seem to be related ultimately to the broader social setting. The child shows an inordinate need for affection and acceptance by adults. The carry-over of these attitudes to rehabilitation personnel is examined.

Bucklew, J., and Hafner, A. J.: Organismic versus cerebral localization of biological defects in feeblemindedness, *J. Psychol.*, *32*:60–78, 1951. This paper reviews literature on feeblemindedness as it is associated with brain defects, especially defects of cortical tissue, to determine the factual basis for localizing feeblemindedness in cerebral defect. Many feebleminded persons, especially the less severe cases, have no discernible organic deficiency or anomaly, indicating the necessity for considering concrete circumstances of personal development to account for the beginnings of retardation.

Cardwell, V. E.: *Cerebral Palsy: Advances in Understanding and Care,* Association for the Aid of Crippled Children, 1955. This book is addressed to students and professionals specializing in this field. "It will be valuable for teachers who are interested in well-organized scientific material . . ." and for "parents who desire something more than run-of-the-mill information." Prepared with the advice of more than 30 consultants, topics range from detailed consideration of the medical background and diagnosis through the community aspects of cerebral palsy. More than half of the book is concerned with the cerebral-palsied individual and his habilitation. The level of the content ranges from lay discussions for parents and teachers to considerably technical discussions for neurologists and other professionals. Its 26 chapters encompass just about all facets of the problem and include good introductory bibliographies.

Cerebral palsy: parent views on diagnosis and treatment, *Nervous Child, 8*:107–261, 1949. This entire issue of *The Nervous Child* is devoted to cerebral palsy. There are 15 articles covering medical, social, psychological, speech, recreational, and vocational areas in addition to a review of the problem in Britain. The authors are: Phelps, Perlstein, Josephy, Putnam, Burgmeister and Blum, Little, Bice, Palmer, Kinov, Oderoff, Deaver, Brunner, Gilden, Dowd, and Creak.

Cromwell, R. L.: Theory and research in activity level, *Train. Sch. Bull.*, *4*:134–141, 1963. Using the ballistograph as the major, but not exclusive, index of activity level, the author tries to pull together different theoretical approaches which may lead to an integrated conception of activity level. Implications from the following theories are deduced and applied to some recent research in activity level: (1) Strauss-Lehtinen-Kephart theory, (2) Arousal theory, (3) Drive theory, (4) Gellner's theory, (5) Zaporozhet's theory, (6) Bindra's Formulation, and (6) McKinney's Factor Analysis. It is best not to view theories as totally correct or incorrect but as working tools for developing hypotheses. Activity level must be regarded as a complex construct that can be subdivided into poorly understood components.

Cruickshank, W. M., and Raus, G. M.: *Cerebral Palsy; Its Individual and Community Problems*. Syracuse University Press, 1955. This book is a text prepared by a variety of authorities. Contents include: (1) "Size and Scope of the Problem," by W. M. Cruickshank and G. M. Raus. (2) "Medical Aspects," by E. Denhoff. (3) "Evaluation of Intelligence," by H. V. Bice and W. M. Cruickshank. (4) "Personality Characteristics," by W. M. Cruickshank and H. V. Bice. (5) "Hearing and Speech Problems among Cerebral Palsied Children," by L. M. DeCarlo and W. W. Amster. (6) "Physical Therapy," by E. C. Snell. (7) "Occupational Therapy," by R. Hadra. (8) "Educational Planning," by W. M. Cruickshank. (9) "Mental Retardation and Cerebral Palsy," by G. O. Johnson. (10) "Parent Education and Counseling," by H. V. Bice. (11) "Realistic Vocational Guidance and Placement," by J. G. Garrett. (12) "Social Casework in Relation to Cerebral Palsy," by G. White. (13) "Total Community Planning for the Cerebral Palsied," by M. Abbott. (14) "The Rehabilitation Process," by G. M. Raus.

Daley, W. T.: *Speech and Language Therapy with the Brain-Damaged Child.* Catholic University Press, 1962. This is the proceedings of the seventh Special Education Workshop at Catholic University. It contains 10 papers and an introduction by Richard Masland, which consists of an overview of the research approaches to the problems of language disabilities in children. The topics include: neurological and psychological approaches, differential diagnosis, clinical evaluation, and evaluation of the preschool child. Reports of special programs, such as the study of the aphasic child at the Central Institute for the Deaf and the educational procedures used in the Syracuse study of brain-injured children, appear along with a chapter on psychotherapy. The audience was drawn mainly from the fields of speech therapy and special education.

DeHirsch, K.: Gestalt psychology as applied to language disturbances, *J. Nerv. Ment. Dis.*, *120*:257–261, 1954. Clinical observation indicates that it is possible to predict future dyslexias in a fairly large percentage of 3-, 4-, and 5-year-olds who were originally referred on account of motor-speech delay, developmental word-deafness, and severe dyslalia. A generalized language disability is postulated to account for this. There are basic and underlying dysfunctions in motor, perceptual, and emotional performance. A defect in the ability to experience and respond in terms of Gestalten is thought to account for the general lack of integration.

Denhoff, E., Laufer, M. W., and Holden, R. H.: The syndromes of cerebral dysfunction, *J. Okla. Med. Ass.*, *52*:360–366, 1959. The term "brain-injured child" or "brain-damaged child" might well be replaced by the phrase "Syndromes of Cerebral Dysfunction." The following syndromes are included: (1) cerebral palsy, (2) mental retardation (organic), (3) convulsive disorders, (4) sensory disorders, (5) hyperkinetic disorders, and (6) perceptual disorders. These syndromes correspond to the primary area of dysfunction, including the neuromotor, intellectual, consciousness, neurosensory, behavioral, and perceptual, although more than one category of dysfunction may be present in a single syndrome. Newer methods of diagnosis, including psychological tests that are sensitive to visuo-motor deficit, EEG advances such as the Gestalt photo-Metrazol test, sensory tests, tests of tactual discrimination, formboard perception, and visual perceptual tests such as the Archimedes Spiral are very useful. Some of the findings on a small number of a variety of cases which represent different subsyndromes are presented to illustrate the tests. Many of the clinical disturbances are due to diencephalic dysfunction.

Denhoff, E., and Robinault, I. *Cerebral Palsy and Related Disorders: A Developmental Approach to Dysfunction.* McGraw-Hill, 1961. This book is based on the notion that growth and development are an ever-changing aspect in the lives of children with a variety of central nervous system disturbances. After a definition and description of these disturbances, including an historical overview of the field, a detailed analysis of sensory and perceptual motor dysfunctions is presented. This is followed by a comprehensive medical approach to diagnosis, prognosis, and treatment, which include the findings and uses of the team approach. Chapters on neuromuscular education, psychological functioning, education and community care, and illustrative cases round out the book. The materials present an integration of research literature and practical clinical experience at the Meeting Street School and Emma Pendleton Bradley Home, both located in Providence. An appendix of pertinent films for professional use and a good bibliography at the end of each chapter are provided. The information presented ranges from the technical to the nontechnical.

Denhoff, E., Smirnoff, V. N., and Holden, R. H.: Cerebral palsy, *New Eng. J. Med.* *245*:728–735;770–777, 1951. Cerebral palsy is a brain-damage syndrome rather than a disease entity. Its definition, causes, and treatment are surveyed. Special consideration is given to psychiatric and psychologic factors, and a rationale based on physiopathology, neuropathology, and neurophysiology is offered. The authors discuss early clinical diagnosis and suggest some clinical practices, with emphasis on a wholistic rehabilitation program. The nonmedical components, such as parental attitudes and vocational guidance, which influence rehabilitation are discussed.

Doll, E. A.: Mental deficiency vs. neurophrenia, *Amer. J. Ment. Defic.*, *57*:477–480, 1953. Differences between mental deficiency and neurophrenia are pointed out. The prognosis for neurophrenia is more favorable. The concept of neurophrenia is still at the exploratory clinical level. Methods of treatment and management are also at the speculative, experimental stage. Although difficult to define precisely, the flavor of the term "neurophrenia" may be gleaned from the following: ". . . in place of specific areas of impairment such as is apparent in cerebral palsy, aphasia, etc., the neurophrenic has a more generalized involvement. . . . It is impossible, here, to reproduce the total behavior complex of neurophrenia except to emphasize that, in addition to such areas as perception, laterality, language, rhythm, and so on, the over-all consequences are apparent in generalized incoordination not amounting to cerebral palsy, generalized expressive retardation not amounting to mental deficiency, personality disorders not amounting to schizophrenia, intermittency of behavior not indicative of epilepsy, and withdrawn behavior not resembling autism."

Doll, E. A.: *Behavior Syndromes of CNS Impairment: Neurophrenia, Cerebral Palsy, and Mental Deficiency*. Devereux Schools, 1954. This publication consists of two previous papers by Doll, "Distinction between Neurophrenia and Cerebral Palsy" and "Mental Deficiency vs. Neurophrenia."

Edgerton, R. B., and Sabagh, G.: From mortification to aggrandizement: changing self concepts in the careers of the mentally retarded, *Psychiatry, 25*:263–272, 1962. The process by which the high-level retarded is stripped of his self-esteem in his daily competition in the world is examined. The usual mortification following placement in a total institution is often turned into a vehicle for enhancing self-esteem by denial and the use of the following rationalizations: (1) he makes invidious comparisons with lower IQ-level retardates, (2) peer-group relationships support an acceptable, "nonretarded" conception of self, (3) employees encourage a more acceptable self-image, and (4) unrealistic avenues of self-aggrandizement are sought. Those patients who eventually adjust following discharge have been helped by the hospital to have a nonretarded view of themselves.

Eidinova, M. B.: Principles of compensatory work in cerebral palsy of children, *Cereb. Palsy Rev., 22*:27–28, 1961. The lability of motor functions can be explained by the presence of neurodynamic functional cerebral disorders, as a result of which the correlations and interchange of the inhibitory and excitatory processes in the motor-functional system become deranged. Therapy is guided by the attempt to readjust functions in the central nervous system. Experience indicates that during the whole period of growth, galanthanism and other preparations of a normalizing action in combination with pathogenetically determined corrective gymnastics and other medical measures are advisable.

Freidman, A., and Levinson, A.: Neurologic disorders in children, *Arch. Pediat.*, *72*:51–69, 1955. A survey of in-patient admissions to the Children's Division of the Cook County General Hospital, one of the largest pediatric neurology clinics in the country, during a 12-month period in 1953, yielded 282 relevant cases. Of these, there were 65 cases of meningitis, 50 with convulsions and mental disorder, 37 with birth injury (mostly cerebral palsy), and 37 with encephalitis. Acute infections seemed to be the largest problem, with birth injuries next. Whereas antibiotics helped with the former, there were no great gains in preventing or treating the latter. A variety of less frequently occurring disorders (*e.g.*, congenital malformations, subdural hematoma, sickle-cell anemia, lead encephalopathy) are discussed. Comments on treatment and outcome are offered.

Garmezy, N.: Some problems for psychological research in cerebral palsy, *Amer. J. Phys. Med.*, *32*:348–355, 1953. Many initial questions may be asked: Is intelligence the sole determiner of effective learning and retraining? What techniques and procedures should we use to secure optimal learning of motor skills? How can we predict successful adjustment? Examples of studies being carried out are: (1) In a learning study on 25 children, verbal reward did not influence learning; but the mere presence of material incentives, whether for reward or punishment, improved learning; (2) A picture choice test was used in an attempt to measure dependency behavior; (3) Personality ratings of fear, love, and anger by the hospital staff did not distinguish athetoids from spastics in accordance with Phelps's theory.

Gauger, A. B.: Statistical survey of a group of institutionalized cerebral palsy patients, *Amer. J. Ment. Defic.*, *55*:90–96, 1950. 149 (18%) institutionalized mental defectives were diagnosed as having cerebral palsy. Ages ranged from 3 to 64, intelligence from low idiot to high moron, and physical disability from monoplegia to total disability. Causes included trauma (50%), infection (21%), and developmental defects (29%). Most significant of the birth factors was that in 45 percent of the cases the child was first-born or born after a ten-year interval. Incidence of spasticity (93%) exceeded athetosis (10%). The nonambulatory group (56%) were in the lower IQ categories. The average case was diagnosed by the age of one but was not filed for admission until the age of seven. The lower the intelligence and the greater the physical handicap, the earlier the child should have institutional placement. Epilepsy is an important factor. "We must realize that a major problem exists in convincing families of these children that early placement is advisable."

Gellner, L.: *Various Sources Contributing to the Clinical Picture of Abnormal Behavior in a Retarded Child,* Julian D. Levinson Foundation for Mentally Retarded Children, 1959. A neurophysiological theory on mental retardation is presented in this series of five lectures. A theory of perceptual disturbance is offered to account for aberrant productions. The implications of the theory for diagnosis and education are presented.

Goldstein, M., ed.: *Psychological Services for the Cerebral Palsied,* United Cerebral Palsy Associations of New York State, 1956. This book comprises four papers presented at a symposium in 1955. (1) "Critical Analysis of Psychological Tests in Use with the Cerebral Palsied," by H. Michal-Smith. Michal-Smith's paper is a general review of the many problems and criticisms of existing psychological tests, with the conclusion that tests are valid despite the criticisms and that we err in the direction of overestimation rather than underestimation. (2) "The Role of the Psychologist in Habilitation of the Cerebral Palsied," by G. R. Stephenson. Stephenson describes the role of the psychologist in evaluation and treatment. He presents data to indicate that IQ and personality predict progress less well than severity of physical handicap in occupational and physical therapy. (3) "Theoretical Aspects of Psychological Behavior in the Brain Damaged," by H. G. Birch. Birch attempts to re-individualize the problem of central nervous system damage by examining the mechanisms which mediate the varieties of brain damage and behavioral dysfunction; *e.g.*, we must distinguish a variety of parameters, including the place, extent and type of injury, when it occurred, whether it disorganizes the capacity to inhibit stimuli, and whether it interferes with the hierarchy of sensory relationships. (4) "Psychological Research Needs in Cerebral Palsy," by E. Miller. Miller points out that we are ignorant of the basic interplay of the organic and the functional. She raises a number of unanswered empirical questions, including what child benefits from which treatment, and urges that we construct tests which will not penalize the child for his handicap.

Graham, F. K., and Berman, P. W.: Current status of behavior tests for brain damage in infants and preschool children, *Amer. J. Orthopsychiat.*, *31*:713–728, 1961. The authors indicate that few conclusions can be drawn from this extensive, sophisticated survey of tests for brain damage in young children. It is only in the last decade that interest has extended to preschool children. In this review, an attempt has been made to relate measurement problems to other unsolved research problems and to show that both must be considered in studying the nature of a preschool group. Measurement difficulties lie less in the ability of investigators to devise ingenious techniques than in the stubborn problems of defining a brain-injured group. Longitudinal studies should help clarify some of the controversial questions, *e.g.*, does undetected brain injury at birth contribute to later defects? There is no definitive evidence that test patterns can distinguish brain-injured from non-brain-injured children. A review of the literature is followed by an extensive bibliography.

Haring, N. G.: Cerebral palsy and emotional adjustment; a review of research, *Except. Child.*, *25*:191–193, 1959. Studies dealing with the emotional adjustment of cerebral-palsied children reveal no evidence for personality differences between spastic and athetoid types, although brain injury can lead to specific behavioral problems. Twin studies show that the cerebral-palsied twin is less adjusted than his co-twin control. This is thought to be a function of the adverse effects of parental over-protection. Parental consistency, evaluating the child on the basis of his own rate of development rather than external norms, and a structured environment are most helpful.

Herlitz, G., and Redin, B.: The prevalence of cerebral palsy, *Acta Paediat.*, *44*:146–154, 1955. To account for the differences in estimates of prevalence in different countries, methods of estimating prevalence are examined. A report is made of a survey of incidence in Sweden in a group of 2- to 11-year-olds in a population of 265,000. Data are presented and findings are compared with previous literature. Mother's health and baby's birth weight are recorded. 57 percent had IQ's below 70.

Hill, A. S.: Cerebral palsy, mental deficiency, and terminology, *Amer. J. Ment. Defic.*, *59*:587–595, 1955. This is a review of the relationship between cerebral palsy and mental deficiency, with a discussion of recent findings in the psychological and educational literature. Educators should view cerebral palsy not in terms of orthopedic parameters but in terms of educational parameters. If most cerebral-palsied are retarded, what are the implications of these findings for education? We must redefine educability and trainability in terms of multiple handicapping conditions.

Holden, R. H.: A review of psychological studies in cerebral palsy: 1947 to 1952, *Amer. J. Ment. Defic.*, *57*:92–98, 1952. A review of research shows 91 articles in *Psychological Abstracts* from 1947 to 1952 in contrast with 17 from 1931 to 1946. During the five-year period, most attention was paid to the problem of intellectual evaluation. Most studies indicate 45 to 50 percent incidence of retardation when flexible test procedures are used. Test results seem fairly stable, including data from several cerebral palsy clinics in this country and one from England. Newer test instruments (Raven's Progressive Matrices and Ammon's Full Range Vocabulary Test) are briefly presented. Absence of empirical study of personality, parent-child relations, and research on basic psychological processes such as distractibility is noted. Absence of an adequate theory is noted.

Hughes, J. G.: *Symposium on Brain Damage in Children, Pediatric Clinics of North America.* W. B. Saunders Co., 1957, pp. 981–1093. This symposium "for newer practical and useful information" includes: (1) "Experimental Teratology," by J. Washing, H. Kalter, and J. Geiger. (2) "The Causes and Prevention of Cerebral Palsy," by N. Eastman. (3) "The Early Diagnosis of Cerebral Palsy," by L. P. Britt. (4) "The Physician's Responsibility," by R. K. Byles. (5) "Psychological Aspects of the Management of Children with Defects or Damage of the Central Nervous System," by S. D. Garrard and J. B. Richmond. (6) "Characteristics and Management of Children with Behavior Problems Associated with Brain Damage," by C. Bradley. (7) "The Study of the Epileptic Child," by J. G. Hughes. (8) "The Drug Therapy of Epilepsy, with Special Reference to Newer Drugs," by M. A. Perlstein.

Illingworth, R. S.: *Recent Advances in Cerebral Palsy.* Little, Brown & Co., 1958. This is a collection of essays designed to present an up-to-date account of cerebral palsy. The contributors, most of whom are British, present information on the classification problem, brain changes, diagnosis, survey of the handicaps, deafness in cerebral palsy, psychological and educational practices, community services, and therapeutic procedures including equipment, drugs, speech, surgery, and physiotherapy. The ten British contributors for the most part cite references and studies reported in British journals, whereas the four American authors cite more references in United States journals. In addition to the survey, there is a useful bibliography for each section.

Katz, A. H.: *Parents of the Handicapped: Self Organized Parents' and Relatives' Groups for Treatment of Ill and Handicapped Children.* Charles C. Thomas, 1961. Four self-organized parents' groups (children were cerebral palsied, had muscular dystrophy, were emotionally disturbed, or retarded) were studied in terms of motivations of the founders, their origins, relations to community agencies, attitudes of leaders and members, and development of professional services. The nature of parental participation was examined in the light of sociological theory. The relationships of the groups to community agencies and professional workers were surveyed. Data were based on interviews with 53 leaders and members, 25 professional workers who had contact with the groups, and a review of written documents. The similarities and differences between the groups are reviewed. A hypothesis about the nature of self-organized groups is formulated.

Kempf, E. J.: Abraham Lincoln's organic and emotional neurosis, *Arch. Neurol. Psychiat.*, *67*:419–433, 1952. Genetic inferences are made from photographs of Lincoln's face. At the age of ten he was kicked by a horse, probably resulting in a fractured skull. Evidence from photographs shows a sharp depression in the forehead above the left eye and asymmetry in facial expression. Visual discoordination was noted by many observers. He complained of diplopia and consulted several physicians for his nervousness, drowsiness, and melancholia. There is evidence of how he attempted to adapt to neurovisual difficulties. A theory of where the damage occurred and the interplay with emotional forces in the background is presented.

Klebanoff, S. G., Singer, J. L., Wilensky, H.: Psychological consequences of brain lesions and ablations, *Psychol. Bull.*, *51*:1–42, 1951. A review of 307 studies on brain injury is presented, covering work done during the previous decade. The early '40's witnessed a concern with relating mental functions to localized areas of the brain, the determination of brain pathology on the basis of test data, and the definition of the organic mental syndrome. Later work showed a reliance on more sophisticated, specialized test techniques, more interest in developmental aspects of brain injury, emphasis on patterns of functioning, and "overly hasty concentration of effort upon the psychological consequences of psychosurgery." There was less optimism about the possibility of psychological test technique contributing toward pinpointing brain pathology. Laboratory methods, it was felt, hold greater promise than omnibus assessment techniques. Impairment in brain-injured children parallels that in brain-injured adults; however, children manifest unevenness suggesting more generalized effects of cerebral damage. Distinction between exogenous and endogenous retardation appears promising.

Mills, M. A.: Facilities and programs for the mildly retarded, severely involved cerebral palsied in the city and county of San Francisco, *Cereb. Palsy Rev., 22*:5–9, 1961. This survey of facilities for mildly involved cerebral palsied (CA 12–20, IQ 50–80) reveals the existence of a variety of uncoordinated programs with gaps and overlaps. Need for additional facilities and a single coordinating agency is pointed out.

Mitchell, R. G.: The growth and motor development of children with cerebral palsy, *Cereb. Palsy Rev., 22*:3–7, 1961. A survey in eastern Scotland (1955–1957) showed the incidence of cerebral palsy to be 2.0 per thousand, or 240 cases. The findings are similar to those in other surveys in the United Kingdom. 78 percent were spastics. None of the other types exceeded 10 percent. The children were below normal standards in all body measurements except body weight. Deviations were greatest in spastic tetraplegia. Right-sided hemiplegics were retarded in growth to a greater degree than left-sided hemiplegics. Developmental data on the achievement of motor skills were untrustworthy. Reliable data on sitting and standing unaided are presented.

Mitchell, R. G.: Mixed types of cerebral palsy, *Cereb. Palsy Rev., 23*:3–6;13–15, 1962. In a survey of 240 cases of cerebral palsy in Scotland, 23 (9.6%) had mixed types of cerebral palsy. The main clinical features of these cases and the difficulties in making their diagnoses are presented. A table of the findings of 15 previous investigators who surveyed more than 5000 cases of cerebral palsy indicates that estimates of mixed diagnoses range from 1 to 13 percent.

Money, J., ed.: *Reading Disability; Progress and Research Needs in Dyslexia.* The Johns Hopkins Press, 1962. This is a report of a conference on dyslexia and related aphasic disorders. The introduction is by L. Eisenberg and the contents, listed by chapter titles, is as follows: (1) "Dyslexia, a Post-Conference Review," by J. Money. (2) "Dyslexia, its Phenomenology," by R. E. Saunders. (3) "Dyslexia as an Educational Phenomenon; its Recognition and Treatment," by G. Schoffman. (4) "A Study of Reading Achievement in a Population of School Children," by J. R. Newbraugh and J. G. Kelly. (5) "Dyslexia–Psychiatric Considerations," by R. D. Rabinovitch. (6) "Dyslexia in Relation to Form Perception and Directional Sense," by A. L. Benton. (7) "Dyslexia in Relation to Cerebral Dominance," by O. L. Zangwell. (8) "The Anatomy of Acquired Reading Disorders," by N. Gerschwind. (9) "An Approach to the Quantitative Analysis of Word Blindness," by D. Howes. (10) "Dyslexia and the Maturation of Visual Function," by H. G. Birch. (11) "Dyslexia in Relation to Diagnostic Methodology in Hearing and Speech Disorders," by W. G. Hardy. (12) "Dyslexia–its Relation to Language Acquisition and Concept Formation," by J. M. Wepman. (13) "Reading Difficulties as a Neurological Problem," by H. R. Prechtl. A glossary and consolidated bibliography are included.

Newland, T. E.: Psycho-social aspects of the adjustment of the brain injured, *Except. Child., 23*:149–153, 1957. A general discussion of the adjustment of brain-injured children is presented. The implications of perceptual and conceptual disturbances for social relationships and self-concept are discussed. Psychological phenomena of the brain-injured must be understood in terms of more generic facts and principles of learning, perception, etc.

Perlstein, M. A.: The child with cerebral palsy, *Nat. Educ. Ass. J., 41*:215–216, 1952. (Reprinted in *The Exceptional Child,* eds. J. F. Magary and J. R. Eichorn. Holt, Rinehart & Winston, 1961.) Cerebral palsy is a disturbance in motor function due to brain injury. It occurs once in 200 births. There are three major types: athetoid, spastic, and ataxic. Visual, auditory, speech, and intellectual impairment occurs. Nutrition and dental care are important. The goals of rehabilitation are to improve locomotion, self-care, communication, appearance, and vocational and avocational self-fulfillment. Clinical characteristics and suggestions for teachers are mentioned.

Pollock, M.: Brain damage, mental retardation, and childhood schizophrenia, *Amer. J. Psychiat., 115*:422–428, 1958. Intellectual functioning of children diagnosed as schizophrenic is reviewed. More than 50 percent can be classified as borderline or retarded. On perceptual-motor tests, the performance of the intellectually retarded schizophrenic children is similar to that observed in younger normal children, adult retardates, and adults with brain damage. Neither childhood schizophrenia nor mental retardation is a distinct clinical entity. Where severe behavior disorder coexists with intellectual defect in childhood, the altered behavior may reflect cerebral dysfunction. Which aspect is stressed—the retardation or the behavior disorder—is, in part, a function of the observer; it is not dictated by the child's behavior. A number of the studies reviewed utilized brain-damaged subjects as controls.

Psychological Problems of Cerebral Palsy, National Society for Crippled Children and Adults, 1952. This is a collection of papers that were presented at a symposium held by the American Psychological Association in 1951. The symposium is alleged to have been the first ever devoted to psychological problems of the cerebral palsied. The papers, which are followed by discussants' comments, include: (1) "Some Anatomical Facts Related to Spasticity," by Douglas Buchanan; (2) "The Psychological Appraisal of Children with Cerebral Palsy," by Charles R. Strother; (3) "Group Counseling with Parents of Cerebral Palsied," by Harry V. Bice; (4) "Distinction between Neurophrenia and Cerebral Palsy," by Edgar A. Doll; and (5) "Educational and Vocational Planning for the Cerebral Palsied Child," by T. Ernest Newland.

Sato, C.: Survey on vocal pitch range of cerebral palsied children, *Cereb. Palsy Rev., 21*:4–5;8, 1960. Motivated by "an ardent desire to have cerebral palsied children sing in unison," the writer conducted an informal test of pitch range on 103 cerebral-palsied children in Tokyo. It was extremely difficult to find a sufficient number of songs to fit the narrow vocal pitch range of the students. Most had difficulty in firmly keeping their respective parts. No definite solution was obtained.

Schlitt, R., and Hopper, G. R.: A survey of scheduling practices of cerebral palsy centers, *Cereb. Palsy Rev., 23*:3–13, 1962. A questionnaire was distributed to 100 cerebral palsy centers throughout the country to survey scheduling practices. Of the 28 that responded, only 6 had full-time medical personnel and only 4 had a full-time psychologist. There was wide disagreement concerning the physical plant and its importance in the establishment of a treatment schedule, although the number of weekly treatments seemed uniform. Further study is needed to establish a causal relationship between a given condition and its degree of involvement and the number of treatments per week which are indicated.

Skatvedt, M.: *Cerebral Palsy*. Oslo University Press, 1958. This clinical study of 370 cases received the King's Gold Medal at the University of Oslo. On the basis of a brief survey of the literature and an intensive examination of etiologic factors, it appears that perinatal brain injury is of major importance. The role of hereditary genetic factors, external fetal injuries, and kernicterus are examined. "The same cerebral injuries which cause perinatal mortality, when of sublethal degree, are also responsible for cerebral palsy." Results of pneumoencephalography, intelligence tests, and EEG's are evaluated by type of cerebral palsy. It is suggested that organic epilepsy, cerebral palsy, and mental impairment due to cerebral lesions should be considered a pathologic entity, with the same etiology and the same pathologic-anatomical basis. Prophylaxis, rather than treatment, is the answer for cerebral palsy as a condition.

Small, J. G.: A psychiatric survey of brain-injured children, *Arch. Gen. Psychiat., 7*:120–124, 1962. These findings were based on examinations of 131 patients seen during a nine-month period in a multidisciplinary clinic for children with cerebral palsy and language disorders. About one-third had emotional problems. Problems appeared more frequently in the older groups and were more common in boys than girls. Factors associated with emotional problems were perceptual defects and emotional difficulties in the parents.

Stevens, G. A., and Birch, J. W.: A proposal for classification of the terminology used to describe brain-injured children, *Except. Child., 23*:346–349, 1957. (Reprinted in *The Exceptional Child,* eds. J. F. Magary and J. R. Eichorn. Holt, Rinehart & Winston, 1961.) In view of the confusion growing out of the inappropriate use of the term "brain injured" to describe a group of children with mild-to-severe perceptual disturbances and disorganized behavior, it is suggested that the term "Strauss syndrome" may be a useful, delimiting name. The term "brain injured" is open to at least four objections: (1) it is an etiological concept and does not describe the symptom complex; (2) it is associated with other conditions, some of which have no relation to the symptom complex commonly referred to as "brain injury"; (3) it does not help in the development of sound therapeutic approaches; (4) it is not suited to a descriptive purpose, since it is essentially a generic expression, the use of which results in oversimplification.

Strauss, A. A.: The education of the brain-injured child, *Amer. J. Ment. Defic., 56*: 712–718, 1951. (Reprinted in *The Exceptional Child,* eds. J. F. Magary and J. R. Eichorn. Holt, Rinehart & Winston, 1961.) Although the term "exogenous child" was used first, the term "brain-injured child" is preferable in describing any child who comes from a normal family, has a history of brain injury, and who shows characteristic behavioral deviations. In contrast to cerebral palsy, which emphasizes the neurophysiological (sensori-motor) processes, the term refers to the neuropsychological (mental) processes. Among the higher level mental processes affected in the brain-injured child is perception. The author gives a description of figure-ground disturbances in perception and states principles of education for this condition: (1) readjusting normal growth patterns by regressing to lower genetic levels, then progressing to higher ones; (2) directing the organization and integration of mental processes by cueing the stimulus.

Strauss, A. A.: Aphasia in children, *Amer. J. Phys. Med., 33*:93–99, 1954. Aphasia in children is identified as "oligophasia" to signify a deficit in language development, thus distinguishing it from aphasia in adults. A definition and description of types of oligophasia are given, with a brief discussion of tests and treatment.

Strauss, A. A., and McCarus, E. N.: A linguist looks at aphasia in children, *J. Speech Hearing Dis., 23*:54–58, 1958. This is a review of theoretical constructs of the contributions of linguistics to the rehabilitation of aphasic children. It may be necessary to view faulty enunciation of aphasic children as a motor inadequacy. If echolalia is merely an advanced form of babbling, there is little to be gained in using it to train a 10-year-old aphasic child. Linguists can assist speech therapists in the selection of materials, the choice of nouns and verbs, and the use of echolalia or gestures.

Taft, L., Delagi, E. F., Wilkie, O. L., and Abramson, A. S.: Critique of rehabilitative techniques in the treatment of cerebral palsy, *Arch. Phys. Med. Rehab., 43*:238–245, 1962. The rehabilitative techniques used in treatment of patients with cerebral palsy are reviewed from the standpoint of neurophysiologic theory. Two basic concepts—that changes in the nature of movement demonstrate phylogenetic and ontogenetic components and the dependence of movement on sensori-motor integration—are applied to current theories of therapy. The subject is controversial, with scanty experimental evidence and impressionistic evaluations, yet favorable results seem to occur on occasion. All methods of treatment may have value at one time or another. None can service all patients. More attention should be paid to sensory and motor interdependence rather than to the motor disability alone.

Tenney, J. W., and Lennox, M. A.: Children with epilepsy, *Nat. Educ. Ass. J., 40*:327–328, 1951. (Reprinted in *The Exceptional Child,* eds. J. F. Magary and J. R. Eichorn. Holt, Rinehart & Winston, 1961.) Various types of seizures, the electroencephalogram, and various medications are described. Some facts about epilepsy are stated: (1) it occurs in one of every 100 children, (2) seizures can be completely controlled in more than half of the cases and reduced in an additional 30 percent, (3) intelligence is normal, and (4) epileptic children should attend regular school. A variety of school plans in effect in some cities (New York, Detroit, Baltimore, etc.) in this country are described.

Tizard, B.: The personality of epileptics, *Psychol. Bull., 59*:196–211, 1962. In this review of the literature, five basic theories about the personality of epileptics are outlined, and the extent to which they are confirmed or rejected by clinical and psychological investigations is considered. Findings of studies that have used the Rorschach have been shown to be contradictory, and the inadequacies of this test are pointed out. Progress depends on the recognition of the complex environmental and pathophysiological factors involved.

Winfield, D. L.: Emotional disturbances of the brain damaged child with reference to the electroencephalogram, *Memphis Mid-South Med. J.*, *36*:403–406, 1961. After presenting a brief description of how the EEG works, the author points out that it is sensitive to disturbed brain neurophysiology but not to dead tissue. He discusses some of the factors correlated with disturbed EEG's, including age, source of referrals, completeness of studies, competence of the electroencephalographer, nature of the brain-wave activity, and conditions of examination. More extensive use of the EEG, even in cases without significant history of damage, is urged. Particular characteristics of temporal lobe seizures are outlined. A majority of patients referred for acting-out behavior, convulsions, or headaches show the "6 and 14 per second positive spike pattern" described by Gibbs. The finding is important from a medico-legal standpoint and requires a persistent regime of medication. "An EEG is never contraindicated."

Wortis, J.: A note on the concept of the "brain-injured child," *Amer. J. Ment. Defic.*, *64*:204–206, 1956. Strauss and Lehtinen's concept of the brain-injured child is accurate but oversimplified. There is a variety of brain-injured children having a variety of causes and a variety of behavioral consequences. Experience in a retardation clinic demonstrates this. Behavior is a function of anatomy and configuration of the brain, personality, the momentary situation, and "the condition of the organism."

Wepman, J.: *A Selected Bibliography on Brain Impairment, Aphasia and Organic Psychodiagnosis*, Language Research Association, Chicago, 1962. This list of references contains a bibliography of 267 items on language development and language impairment in children plus an extensive bibliography on brain-injured adults.